The Celtic Poets

Songs and Tales from Early Ireland and Wales

The Celtic Poets

Songs and Tales from Early Ireland and Wales

Translated and Introduced
by
Patrick K. Ford

Ford & Bailie, Publishers
Belmont, Massachusetts
1999

Published by
Ford & Bailie, Publishers
P. O. Box 138
Belmont, MA 02478-0002

Graphics by Fine Line Design
Cover photograph © 1995 Photography by Marcheterre

Library of Congress Cataloging-in-Publication Data

Ford, Patrick K.
    The Celtic poets : songs and tales from early Ireland and Wales /
translated, with introduction and notes by Patrick K. Ford.
    p. cm.
    English translations of early Irish and Welsh texts.
    Includes bibliographical references (p.).
    ISBN 0-926689-05-3 (pbk. : alk. paper)
    1. Celtic poetry—Translations into English. 2. Ireland—
Poetry. 3. Wales—Poetry. I. Title.
PB1100.F67 1999
891.6'21208—dc21   98-53069
                                                              CIP

Printed on acid-free paper and bound in the United States of America.

This book is dedicated to my students,

who have also been my teachers.

Atlantic Ocean

Creeve

ULSTER

Enniskillen

ORIEL

Emain
Macha

BRÉIFNE

CONNAUGHT

Boyne R.

Roscommon

Tara

Howth

MEATH

Dublin

Durlas

Shannon R.

Allen

LEINSTER

Cashel

Irish Sea

MUNSTER

Cork

0   60 km

60 mi

IRELAND

BRITAIN

0   75 km   150 km

    75 mi   150 mi

North Sea

• Din Eidin (Edinburgh)

GODODDIN

BERNICIA

RHEGED

• Catraeth (Catterick)

ISLE
OF MAN

DEIRA

MÔN
(ANGLESEY)

Aberffraw • • Conway

GWYNEDD

Brogynin •   POWYS

DYFED   *Severn R.*

Thames R.

English Channel

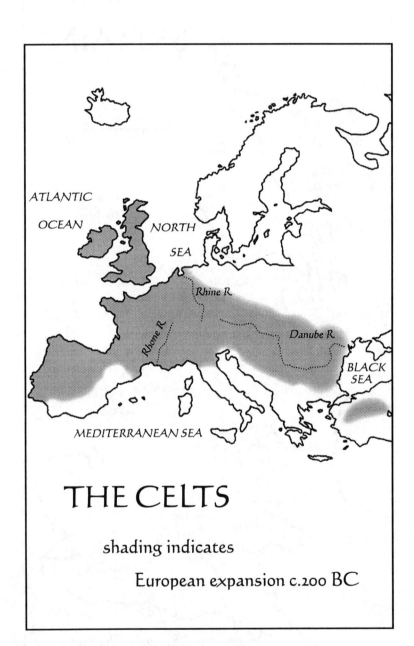

THE CELTS

shading indicates

European expansion c.200 BC

Table of Contents

Preface

This collection of translations of early Irish and Welsh texts grew out of materials I had gathered for my Harvard undergraduate Core course on "Poets and Poetry in the Celtic Literary Tradition." The course focuses on the function of the poet, as far as that can be determined, from earliest times through the Middle Ages. The materials I assembled for the 'coursepack' were translations of narratives about poets and samples of their poetry. Some of the translations were old, such as Owen Connellan's 1860 translation of "The Proceedings of the Great Bardic Institution," or Kuno Meyer's 1892 "The Vision of Mac Con Glinne." More recent translations, in particular those of the poetry, are often the work of scholars seeking to guide beginning students of those languages through the Irish and Welsh texts. Most of them are concerned with word for word rendering, and are thus of little value to readers who will never have access to the originals. What the reader will find here, then, are my own translations, aimed at such an audience.

The selection of texts was determined by the syllabus, and will, no doubt, disappoint those who would have preferred a broader representation of the tradition. It is clear that there are many more narratives about poets in Ireland than there are about poets in Wales, and I have compensated for that by presenting more poetry from Wales. Early Irish 'nature' or 'hermit' poetry is ignored, as is poetry from Irish sagas. There exist some splendid translations of that material, readily available to those interested.

While some will feel that my translations take unlicensed liberties with the originals, I have attempted to the best of my ability to insure that they represent the spirit and vigor of those works, elements that display the merits of this literary tradition independent of more formal characteristics. Exceptionally, I have attempted to imitate the meters of the originals, but that, I believe, is a dangerous path to follow too rigidly. Usually, I have been content to introduce a degree of alliteration, internal and end rhyme, assonance, and other ornamentation that characterize the native meters. I am deeply indebted to all earlier translations of these texts, as well as to the notes provided by editors of the texts; the final product, however, is my own responsibility. I discuss my views on translation in the Introduction.

I would like to express my thanks to Professor Joseph Falaky Nagy and to Dr. Gene Haley, who read drafts of the work and offered many helpful suggestions. Needless to say, I accept full responsibility for the final shape of the book. Thanks, too, to the masterful storyteller, John McGahern, for permission to quote from his short story, "Bank Holiday." Marcheterre Fluet's graphics and cover photography have enhanced the work considerably.

I have had the privilege of working with some very talented teaching fellows in this course over the past few years, and I would like to acknowledge their contributions to its continuing development. They are too numerous to name in this space, but I would like to recognize head teaching fellows (in the order in which they served) Anne Lea, Jerry Hunter, now lecturer in the Department of Welsh at University of Wales Cardiff, Kathryn Chadbourne, and Laura Radiker – who also assisted in the research for this book and read an early draft of it. To these and to the numerous fellows who have been my co-teachers in the Core course, I offer my deep gratitude. I am grateful for the support of my colleagues Tomás Ó Cathasaigh and Kaarina Hollo, and for Chadine's unfailing encouragement. Lastly, I thank my students, whose questions, interventions, and other promptings have, over the years, helped to shape my own thinking about the Celtic poets.

Belmont, Autumn of 1998

Introduction

Poseidonius of Apameia says, in the twenty-third book of his *Histories*: 'The Celts, even when they go to war, carry round with them living-companions whom they call parasites. These persons recite their praises before men when they are gathered in large companies as well as before any individual who listens to them in private. And their entertainments are furnished by the so-called Bards; these are poets, as it happens, who recite praises in song.' (from *Athenaeus: The Deipnosophists;* Gulick 1927, p. 109)

✳   ✳   ✳

'Are there…poets…still?'

'Are there poets?' he laughed out loud. 'They say the standing army of poets never falls below ten thousand in this unfortunate country.'

'Why unfortunate?' she said quickly.

'They create no wealth. They are greedy and demanding. They hold themselves in very high opinion. Ten centuries ago there was a national convocation, an attempt to limit their powers and numbers.' (from "Bank Holiday"; McGahern 1993, p. 356).

✳   ✳   ✳

The authors of these two observations are separated by a span of 2,000 years. But they are motivated by a single, incontrovertible cultural phenomenon: the relentless presence of poets and poetry among the Celts. Poseidonius lived from about 135 BC to 51 BC, and is one of our most important sources of information about the Celtic poets in antiquity. Though the works of this Greek historian are now lost, later Greek and Roman writers quoted extensively from them, and it is through these writers that his observations have been preserved and passed on to us. And it is through them, too, that we find early attestations of the native nomenclature of the poetic orders. The Greeks refer to *bárdoi* 'bards,' *drouídai* 'druids,' *Ouáteis* 'vates' (whence Irish *fáithi* 'seers; poets' and Welsh *gwawd* 'song,' later 'mockery').

What Poseidonius says about the bards is equally applicable to the poets of early Ireland and Wales, right through the Middle Ages. The poet functioned at the core of society. He was genealogist, historian, singer of praise, satirist. His presence at the courts of princes and chieftains was essential to the maintenance of social order, and so he was an honored guest at feasts (the meaning of Greek *parasitos*). I say 'he' because most of our evidence shows that poets were men, though there are exceptions. As keeper of genealogies, he alone could determine whether this individual or that had the right pedigree to be eligible for the kingship, for example. As historian, he knew the histories of battles, where they were fought, who killed whom, where heroes were buried, why places were named as they were, and so on. As singer of praise, the poet instilled those virtues in his patron that were the most highly regarded in the society. One might as well say 'created,' for, consistent with many other oral cultures, and certainly consistent with the ancient Indo-European cultural community, the poet created virtues in his patron by the very act of proclaiming those virtues. In the same way, by articulating negative qualities or statements about a person, that is, through satire, the poet was able to induce decay and even death for that person. So the poet wielded a great amount of power. He was often guilty of abusing that power, and John McGahern's character is correct in asserting that there was an attempt in the Middle Ages to rein in the power of the poets and to reduce their numbers.

Further information about Celtic poets in the period of Celtic habitation on the European continent from the writings of Poseidonius comes to us through the Greek writers Diodorus Siculus and Strabo. These two were approximate contemporaries (first century BC) of Poseidonius. Diodorus noted,

> Among them are also to be found lyric poets whom they call bards [*bárdoi*]. These men sing to the accompaniment of instruments which are like lyres, and their songs may be either of praise or of obloquy [satire]. Philosophers, as we may call them, and men learned in religious affairs are unusually honoured among them and are called by them druids [*drouídai*]. The Gauls likewise make use of diviners [*mánteis*], accounting them worthy of high approbation, and these men foretell the future by means of the flight or cries of birds and of the

slaughter of sacred animals, and they have all the multitude subservient to them (Oldfather 1939, pp. 177-9).

And Strabo construes Poseidonius this way:

> Among all the Gallic peoples, generally speaking, there are three sets of men who are held in exceptional honour; the Bards, the Vates and the Druids. The Bards are singers and poets; the Vates, diviners and natural philosophers; while the Druids, in addition to natural philosophy, study also moral philosophy (H. L. Jones 1939, p. 245).

In his account of the war against Gaul, Caesar reduced the social organization of the Celts to three groups: the *plebs*, whom he dismisses as of little account, the warrior aristocracy (*equites*), and a sacral, learned class of druids (*druides*). Of the last, he says,

> The Druids usually hold aloof from war, and do not pay war-taxes with the rest; they are excused from military service and exempt from all liabilities. Tempted by these great rewards, many young man assemble of their own motion to receive their training; many are sent by parents and relatives. Report says that in the schools of the Druids they learn by heart a great number of verses, and therefore some persons remain twenty years under training. And they do not think it proper to commit these utterances to writing, although in almost all other matters, and in their public and private accounts, they make use of Greek letters. I believe that they have adopted the practice for two reasons—that they do not wish the rule to become common property, nor those who learn the rule to rely on writing and so neglect the cultivation of the memory; and, in fact, it does usually happen that the assistance of writing tends to relax the diligence of the student and the action of the memory (H. J. Edwards 1968, pp. 335-9).

These commentaries, taken together, give us a picture of Celtic culture that situates the poet in a position of honor and respect—a functioning member of society whose learning made him a key player in the orderly conduct of society's business. Such learning was awesome in the eyes of those who depended upon it for the conduct of daily life. And so the poet was respected and feared.

THE CELTIC POETS

The migration of Celtic tribes in the prehistoric period affected the social hierarchy little. When we come to the Celts of Ireland and Britain – the lands for which we have the most information in the Middle Ages – we find the poets enjoying the kind of prestige and position afforded them in Gaul in earlier times. Irish law texts, among the earliest written documents in the Irish language, have a good deal to say about poets. In these texts, the poet is accorded the highest status among lay professional people. Two categories are recognized: the *fili* (plural *filid*) and his inferior in training and rank, the *bard*. There are seven grades of *fili*, according to training and accomplishment. The highest grade, *ollam*, had the same honor price as a tribal king. In addition to composing praise poems and satire, the *fili* was a storyteller, and the highest ranking poet, the *ollam* was expected to know 350 tales. The law apparently recognized women poets too, though they are exceptional and seem to have been especially connected with satire and other vituperative activities (Kelly 1988, pp. 43-9).

In Wales, the *bardd teulu* or 'household bard' was one of the twenty-four officers who belonged to the court of a king. The *pencerdd* 'chief of song,' the highest ranking in the Welsh bardic order, was one of those additional officers who by custom were members of a royal court. The *pencerdd* held his lands free of rents and duties and enjoyed special incomes stipulated by law (Jenkins 1990).

The power and status of poets in early Celtic society and in early Ireland and Wales is very different from that of poets in our contemporary society and requires some explanation.

THE SPOKEN WORD

The power of the spoken word in Celtic culture is dramatically illustrated by the Greek rhetorician Lucian (second century AD). Lucian was a kind of visiting professor in Gaul, and in a lecture on Heracles he provides insight into the almost hypnotic power of those who wield words, and how among the Celts power is associated not with physical strength or the sword but with the word. Lucian describes an occasion when he stood before a picture of Heracles, clearly the man because he was dressed in lion's skin, had the characteristic club in his right hand, carried a quiver at his side, held the bow in his left hand, and was Heracles from head to heel. However, this Heracles was also extremely old, bald except for a few gray hairs, wrinkled, with burnt skin. But the most surprising thing about this Gaulish Hercules was as follows:

> That old Heracles of theirs drags after him a great crowd of men who are all tethered by the ears! His leashes are delicate chains fashioned of gold and amber, resembling the prettiest of necklaces. Yet, though led by bonds so weak, the men do not think of escaping, as they easily could, and they do not pull back at all or brace their feet and lean in the opposite direction to that in which he is leading them. In fact, they follow cheerfully and joyously, applauding their leader and all pressing him close and keeping the leashes slack in their desire to overtake him; apparently they would be offended if they were let loose! But let me tell you without delay what seemed to me the strangest thing of all. Since the painter had no place to which he could attach the ends of the chains, as the god's right hand already held the club and his left the bow, he pierced the tip of his tongue and represented him drawing the men by that means! Moreover, he has his face turned toward his captives, and is smiling.
>
> I had stood for a long time, looking, wondering, puzzling and fuming, when a Celt at my elbow, not unversed in Greek lore, as he showed by his excellent use of our language, and who had, apparently, studied local traditions, said: 'I will read you the riddle of the picture, stranger, as you seem to be very much disturbed about it. We Celts do not agree with you Greeks in thinking that Hermes is Eloquence: we identify Heracles with it, because he is far more powerful than Hermes' (Harmon 1913).

The explanation given to Lucian by our Celtic docent is analogous to the time-worn adage that "the pen is mightier than the sword." In our version, the reference is to the power of literature to influence the course of human events. But consistent with Caesar's remark about the druids, learning was communicated orally among the Celts: it was spoken and it was heard. In primarily oral cultures – and they still exist – we might say that the *word* is mightier than the sword (Bloomfield 1989). Respect and awe before the spoken word is apparent everywhere in the literature that has survived from early Celtic cultures. Not just any word, but words spoken by certain persons and appropriated to special uses – as in poetry, charms, prayers, recitation of traditional narratives (see the parody of the virtues accruing from recitation of a narrative at the end of "The Vision of Mac Con Glinne"), recounting of genealogies, explanations of the names of well-known persons and places, and so on. Among the Celts, all of these categories of traditional knowledge were the responsibility of the class of learned persons we call 'poets', though there are other names that designate different aspects of their functions, as we shall see.

In the Christian tradition, which introduced and fostered literacy in early Ireland and Wales, we note the opening words of the gospel of John: *In principio erat verbum* 'in the beginning was the word.' And 'word' here translates *verbum*, in its turn a translation of the Greek *logos*: God is *logos*, God is the word. And through the word the world was created: "By the word of the Lord the heavens were made" (Psalms 33.6), referring to the opening verses of Genesis, where creation occurs as God says "let there be light," etc. and those things are created. We find the same thing in ancient Greek tradition in the Homeric Hymn to Hermes, where the god sings of the origin of things and by his song the gods themselves are brought into existence (Ford 1992a, p. 44). The power of the word as the tool of creation may well be universal in human experience; it is certainly a dynamic concept in Celtic culture.

The power of words to create can be seen in a variety of expressions in more or less everyday use in our own language. One notorious example may suffice. The words *hocus pocus* are used to consummate or create a magical transformation of some dimension. They had their origin in religious ritual: the words of the transubstantiation in the Catholic liturgy, the moment when, in Catholic theology, bread is turned into the body of Christ, as the priest intones the words *hoc est corpus* 'this is the body.' The phrase, for disbelievers, became a catch phrase for bogus acts of all kinds and eventually evolved into the form we have now, *hocus pocus*.

Other examples could easily be adduced that illustrate the fact that words uttered in particular contexts by persons endowed with special gifts through training, ordination, or some other form of initiation or rite of passage, are believed to have the power to create or transform. In Celtic society, poets were such persons, and their words had the power to destroy as well as to create--to create fame in a patron through poems of praise, to destroy a person through words of blame. This act of creation through words alone, is, as we have seen, explicit in the Judeo-Christian tradition. There, we see Adam, the first man, functioning as a poet, for as God shapes the beasts of the earth it is Adam who creates their identity (Genesis 2.18-20). In J. G. Herder's interpretation,

> In giving names to all, and ordering all from the impulse of his own inward feeling, and with reference to himself, he [Adam] becomes an imitator of the Divinity, a second Creator . . . a creative poet. (quoted in Ford 1992b, p. 13).

What the Celtic poets created with their spoken words was fame for their patrons or destruction for their enemies.

In these functions, the Celtic poets demonstrate their affinity with their Indo-European ancestry. "To speak of the imperishable fame of the hero was, above all, the job of the poet" (quoted in Schmitt 1967, p. 67). As Gregory Nagy has asserted with respect to Homeric poetry, fame is what a hero gets "*specifically by way of poetry*" (1990, p. 136). The Greek word that came to mean 'fame' is *kléos* which originally meant 'the act of hearing.' Fame, then, is that which is 'heard,' namely, the praise of an individual in a poet's song. The same semantic development is to be found in Irish and Welsh, in the words *clú* and *clod* respectively.

The importance of hearing emphasizes the fact that we are dealing with oral cultures. Latin *fama,* 'fame,' means 'the talk of the multitude'; the original and primary meaning of *rumor* is 'widespread report of a favorable nature'; similarly, our word 'acclaim' originally meant to extol or praise someone by the raising of voices, as in 'clamor.' Another way of extolling someone is through making a noise by hitting two things together, usually the hands; that is the original sense of our 'applaud.' In each case, fame, acclaim, applause, is the result of something heard.

Because of the significance of speaking and hearing for the building of reputation, repetition gains a special significance . In an oral culture, you cannot retrieve a word or phrase except by uttering it again. When you *read* a poem, if you didn't quite get the second line after you have read the stanza, you can glance back up the page and read it again. Not so in an oral tradition: once the word is spoken it is gone. If it is a word of more than one syllable, it disappears by bits, by syllables. Hence the frequent repetition of things that are important, that provide stability, that constitute the ethos of the culture. In the praise poems we find constant reiteration of the most esteemed virtues. In the poems of "The Gododdin," for example, the words mead, wine, vigilance, bravery, generosity, among others, recur with great frequency. The effect may seem tedious to us as we read the poems, but it reinforced the message for the original audiences, who only heard them.

The importance of repetition in oral cultures is succinctly put by Walter Ong in *Orality and Literacy* (1982): "you know what you can recall." And he goes on to say,

> Your thought must come into being in heavily rhythmic, balanced patterns, in repetitions or antitheses, in alliterations and assonances, in epithetic and other formulary expressions, in standard thematic settings (the assembly, the meal, the duel, the hero's 'helper', and so on), in proverbs which are constantly heard by everyone so that they come to mind readily and which themselves are patterned for retention and ready recall, or in other mnemonic form. (p. 34).

This concept helps us to understand metrical regularity and such 'decorative' features as rhyme, assonance, consonance, alliteration. These are all part of the aural effect of the poetry, and our readings of such poetry and appreciation of the status of the poets who composed it must always be informed by an understanding of the oral cultures in which they functioned. Because poets wielded such immense and seemingly magical power, a mystique developed about them, a mystique they surely cultivated. They stood apart, were not like ordinary people. And just as there is a specific biographical pattern attached to great heroes, poets too have their strange beginnings and early careers. These are recounted in the opening section of this book, "Origins of Poets." It is a pattern which, we might say, constitutes the mythology of poets.

INSIDER/OUTSIDER

The Celtic poet functioned within society as upholder of social order through poetry of praise and blame and through custody of tradition and tribal lore. As such he was a person of prestige, and as such we might view him as an 'insider,' in contradistinction to the poet as 'outsider,' to use Joseph Nagy's (1985) very useful paradigm. This latter designation shows us a darker side: the poet as one who communes freely with the natural world that lies outside of the ordered cosmos that society represents. The poet as outsider is well represented in Irish tradition in the person of Finn Mac Cumhaill. Finn is both poet and outsider (Nagy 1985). As poet, he is skilled in divination, and thus has access to hidden knowledge. As outsider, he lives on the fringe of civilized society, going about in the wilderness with his band of hunter/warriors. While poets of praise and blame are singing of the virtues and failings of people and courts, Finn and others like him are singing of the otherworld and of nature. In what Nagy calls "a fabulative metaphor of cultural truth" (Nagy 1985, p. 21), such poetry expresses the preference for (or at least an intimate familiarity with) nature and the wild as against society and the civilized. Such poets not only live in nature, they are a part of it.

In a poem claimed by Irish scholars in the Middle Ages to have been the first poem ever uttered in Ireland, the poet Amairgen proclaims,

> I am an estuary into the sea,
> I am a wave of the ocean,
> I am the sound of the sea,
> I am a powerful ox,
> I am a hawk on a cliff,
> I am a dewdrop in the sun,
> I am a plant of beauty,
> I am a boar of valour,
> I am a salmon in a pool,
> I am a lake in a plain,
> I am the strength of art. (Quoted in Ford 1992a, p. 32)

And Taliesin, the earliest Welsh poet, similarly claims an association with all of nature:

> I was rain drops in the air, I was stars' beam,
> I was a word in letters, I was a book in origin;
> I was lanterns of light…
> I was a bridge over estuaries,
> I was a path, I was an eagle, I was a coracle in seas;
> I was a bubble in beer…(Ford 1977, p. 184)

Unlike any other member of the society, the poet is one who transcends his world, who crosses the boundaries of both this world and the other, crosses gender borders, dissolves the boundaries between animal and human.

The matter of boundaries and the idea of division between the sacred and profane, between the otherworld and the world of ordinary human experience in early Irish narrative is the subject of an insightful discussion by Tom Sjöblom (1994). According to Sjöblom, cosmological thinking in early Ireland was built up around the the tribe as basic social unit. The cosmos was constructed from the communal reality of the tribe, from all the familiar and shared experiences and realities. At the center of this cosmos is the person of the king, a sacral figure, who is in fact the *axis mundi*. Everything outside the tribal experience, and indeed the tribal boundary itself, is chaos. Borders represent the threshold between the communal reality of the tribe, the cosmos, and the chaotic outer or other world. Thus, in early Irish tales we read that it is the function of the hero to stand guard at the border and to give battle to any who might attempt to penetrate, to cross the border, or to provide safe passage to poets seeking to enter the tribal precincts. Thus the hero is defender of cosmos, of communal reality against the chaos that lies beyond. The special treatment afforded to poets, heirs of the ancient druids of Gaul, reflects the sacred nature still accorded the class of poet/priest, equally at home in this world and the otherworld, and capable of negotiating between those worlds. It was expected that poets would be crossing borders, both terrestrial and ethereal.

It is thus not surprising that Finn, poet and outsider, composes a poem in celebration of summer upon completing his initiation into poetry (p. 8-10 below); that is, his poetic debut is in praise of nature not culture (man). Another Irish figure who epitomizes the outsider is Suibhne Geilt, 'Mad Sweeney,' the subject of Seamus Heaney's masterful *Sweeney Astray*. The Irish word *geilt* was translated by the medieval Irish with the Latin word *volatilis* i.e., 'flying' (whence our 'volatile'). The Irish word itself is used to refer to someone who goes mad from terror, a fugitive from battle, a crazy person living in the woods and supposed to have the power of levitation, a lunatic.

In the medieval Irish tale about him, Sweeney had epitomized the social and civilized life, having been king in his own territory. Cursed by a cleric, he lost all the marks of civilization: home, spouse, defined territory, clothing, humanity. His new life finds him living in treetops, unclothed, keeping company with other wild men like himself, a poet singing of the life he has left and the painful existence that is now his lot. Sweeney and Finn as denizens of the uncivilized world beyond the cosmos represent the darker side of poets and poetry, poet as outsider. They exemplify the magical as opposed to the mundane, quotidian aspect of the poet. It is by recognition of this aspect, the magical and dark aspect, that we can begin to appreciate the tremendous power wielded by the poets, and why the culture was willing to cede such power to them, why the words they uttered were unlike the words uttered by any lay person: potent, effective, affective. We understand why chieftains never went into battle without poets present; why kings were not inaugurated without poets at hand.

It is clear from a number of narratives about poets that have survived in early Ireland and Wales that society was very aware of the sacredness, the otherness of poets. These narratives provided a rationale, as it were, a means of understanding and accounting for the respect that was shown to poets and the fear and awe in which they were held, a reason why they were considered infallible and untouchable. These narratives give the impression that poets were born not made, that is, that destiny had preordained their careers. The truth is that in Ireland and Wales, as in ancient Gaul, poets went through long years of training to achieve their status. The training included the practice of rituals, such as the Irish *imbas forosnai*, which surely helped mystify them in the eyes of ordinary people, and reinforced the mystique the narratives promulgated.

DIVINATION

As we have seen, the Greek Strabo, writing in the first century BC and drawing on Poseidonius, wrote that the Vates (Irish *fáithi*) were diviners. His contemporary, Diodorus Siculus, uses the native Greek word *mánteis* for 'diviners,' from the root that gives us 'mania,' 'maniac,' and so on. Of these, he noted,

> They also observe a custom which is especially astonishing and incredible, in case they are taking thought with respect to matters of great concern; for in such cases they devote to death a human being and plunge a dagger into him in the region above the diaphragm, and when the stricken victim has fallen they read the future from the manner of

his fall and from the twitching of his limbs, as well as from the gushing of the blood, having learned to place confidence in an ancient and long-continued practice of observing such matters (Oldfather 1939, p. 178-9).

As far as we know, such bloody divination was not practiced in early Ireland and Wales. Nevertheless, divination and prophecy were mainstays of poetic practice in the historical period.

For the Irish, *imbas forosnai* 'illuminating inspiration' was one of the three things that characterized a fully-trained poet. It was a ritual involving raw animal flesh, and one in which the principal, who went into a sleep/trance, was assisted by other poets. Sleep of this sort is an integral part of other divination rituals in Ireland and in Scotland (Greene 1970), and elements of the rituals apparently survived down to modern times. In his *Memoirs*, published in 1722, the Marquis of Clanricarde described the Irish bardic schools of his time. He noted that the fledgling poets worked out their compositions while lying on their cots in small, windowless, unlit compartments. Of this practice of composing in the dark, Osborn Bergin said,

> It looks very like a relic of some rite or ceremony of divination handed down from pagan times, long after its original purpose had been forgotten. (Quoted in Greene 1970, p. 9)

We have a description of Welsh diviners recorded by Giraldus Cambrensis (Gerald of Wales) in his *Description of Wales* (late 12th century). In Book I, chap. 16 of that work, he says,

> There are certain men among the people of Wales that you will find nowhere else, called Awenyddion [*awennithion*], who are led by their innate understanding. When consulted about some uncertainty or another, they immediately roar out as if seized from without by some spirit [*spiritus*] and, as it were, taken over. They do not set forth coherently that which is requested, rather they speak through many evasions and riddles, and in meaningless and empty words, disjointed rather than cohering – but sounding splendid! The one who listens attentively will have an answer to the information that is sought. In the wake of this ecstasy, they are roused by others as if from a deep sleep, and are thus forced to come to themselves.

You will notice two remarkable things about this: after they
have given their reponse, they do not come to themselves again unless
they are violently shaken and thus restored; and once restored, they will
remember nothing of what they have poured forth. If they are
questioned on the same matter again, or by some other person, they
respond in an entirely different way. It is as if spirits [*spiritus*] speak
through the frenzied [*fanaticus*] and those possessed by the devil
[*energumenus*], however unaware they may be. For the most part, this
gift [*donum*] is infused in them in their sleep through visions they
receive. (Dimock 1868)

In this account, we have no evidence of ritual behavior of the sort we see
in the Irish account, such as ingesting or chewing certain foods, but we
do see frenzied behavior and trance; notice the references to heavy sleep,
visions, and dreams. Giraldus's word for these folk is *awenyddion*,
plural of *awenydd*, which means someone who has *awen* 'poetic
inspiration.' Giraldus's account is far from a sympathetic one, but the
details he provides dovetail neatly with the profile of the Celtic poet that
emerges from our other texts.

In *awen* we have yet another remnant of the Celtic poetic
lexicon. The word is cognate with Irish *ái* (older **aui*), and the basic
meaning is 'blowing, breath, wind,' in a word, 'in-spiration.' The same
meaning underlies Irish *fáith* and its Welsh cognate *gwawd*, in what
Calvert Watkins has called "a metaphor of Indo-European date linking
'poetic art' with 'blowing, breath, wind'...ultimately of pagan religious
and cultic origin..." (Watkins 1963, p. 216). In "The story of Gwion
Bach," Ceridwen concocts in her caldron a brew which is intended to
make her ungainly son full of the '*spirit* of prophecy.' As we see, the
essence is stolen by Gwion Bach, later reborn as Taliesin. Although
there is no mention of *awen* in this section, Taliesin later claims in the
court of Maelgwn Gwynedd that, "I got poetic inspiration [*awen*] from
the caldron of Ceridwen." The notion that the source of *awen* is a
caldron is echoed in an early Irish text which claims, "My fine caldron...
pours forth the oral language of poetry [*ai*]" (Henry 1979-80, p. 123).
Thus we see the tenacity of a basic concept of poetry among the Celts.

THE CELTIC POETS

SATIRE

Diodorus says that the Celts have lyric poets called bards who sing songs of praise or of obloquy. Diodorus uses the word *blásphemos* for the latter, 'evil-speaking, slanderous.' The Irish lexicographer Cormac mac Cuillennáin, writing about the year 900 AD, says that *fili*, the most frequent word for a poet, is comprised of two elements: *fí* 'poison' and *lí* 'praise.' This primary concern with praise and satire reflects the overriding concern the early Irish had with fame and honor. The Irish word for honor, *enech*, is also the word meaning 'face'; the same is true of its Welsh cognate *wyneb*. Thus, a satire brings about loss of face, metaphorically speaking, i.e., loss of honor, but it also causes disfigurement in that satire produced blisters or blotches on the face of the person against whom it was pronounced.

The Celtic poets, then, were doubly indemnified: they were valued for their ability to bestow praise and create reputation, and they were feared for the potency of their invective. But just as the law tracts set forth the rewards to which they were entitled for their poems of praise, so too was their use of satire rigidly controlled. Satirizing without just cause was a serious offence and punishable by fine or by loss of station. And in the narratives about poets, an unjust satire could often result in the death of the poet who pronounced it. That is, the 'poison' was turned inward.

Not many examples of satire have survived, for obvious reasons. The first satire ever pronounced in Ireland, it is said, was that of the poet Cairpre against Bres mac Elatha, and occurs in the tale known as "The Second Battle of Mag Tuired" (Gray 1982). Cairpre was the poet of the mythical Túatha Dé Danann. He paid a visit to Bres, the king, who was already getting a reputation for stinginess, lack of military leadership, and ill-treatment of poets and musicians. After being treated to a miserable night and left hungry, Cairpre awoke and chanted the following:

> Without food speedily on a platter,
> Without a cow's milk whereon a calf thrives,
> Without a man's habitation after the staying of darkness –
> Be that the luck of Bres mac Eladain.

And the text says that there was only decay on Bres from that moment. In other words, the satire is designed to bring about the conditions that reflect the reign of an evil king, and, therefore, make that king unfit to reign. Taliesin's satire of Maelgwn Gwynedd in "The Story of Gwion Bach" is similar in tone.

That satire was believed to have real and not metaphorical potency is demonstrated in the story of Nede and Caier. Caier was king of Connaught, and he adopted the poet Nede. Caier's wife loved Nede and conspired with him to kill her husband. The plan was that Nede should ask Caier for a gift, something a poet was legally entitled to do. But he was to ask for something which he knew beforehand Caier was forbidden by taboo to part with. When Caier refused the gift, as Nede knew he would do, Nede pronounced the following satire:

> Evil death, short life to Caier!
> Let spears of battle wound him, Caier!
> May Caier die, May Caier depart, Caier under earth,
> Under ramparts, under stones be Caier!

The next morning Caier discovered he had blisters on his face, the three blisters caused by satire: stain, blemish, and defect, a red blemish, a green one, a white one. Caier ran away in disgrace, and Nede took the kingship. Later, when in remorse Nede went to find Caier, Caier died of shame upon seeing him.

Now the satires against Bres, Maelgwn, and Caier function like curses – the poet expects that the words will bring the subject down and destroy him (Ó Cathasaigh 1986). The satires on Dafydd ap Gwilym and Rhys Meigen are of a different variety. They are extremely personal and meant to insult. Nevertheless, the end result is the same, if we can believe the tradition, in that the verses are lethal.

In his seminal article on "Satirists and Enchanters in Early Irish Literature," F. N. Robinson (1912) demonstrates how well known the lethal power of Irish satire was in Elizabethan England. Among others, he cites Shakespeare's *As You Like It*, where Rosalind says of Orlando's verse, "I was never so berhymed since Pythagoras' time, that I was an Irish rat, which I can hardly remember." In the Epilogue to Ben Jonson's "Poetaster," the author says he will "rhyme them to death, as they do Irish rats." Whatever the Elizabethans' source of information about killing rats with satires might have been, surely the most outrageous instance of it in Irish literature is in "Guaire's Greedy Guests" (see below).

POETS AND CLERICS

We have spoken of the oral tradition that lay behind the practice of poetry and the custody of traditional learning among the Celts. Obviously, the songs and tales have come down to us not by way of an oral tradition but through writing. Whatever of their provenance, the materials we have before us are literary texts, not oral texts, and it is to the scribes and the ecclesiastical establishment that we owe their survival. When Christianity came to the islands, a tension developed between the old Celtic religion and its culture and the new religion. There are some obvious points in this relationship, which can be seen most clearly in the surviving literature of early Ireland. The native culture was oral, passed on through a privileged class that was essentially hereditary. The culture that Christianity brought with it was a written one and its adherents were the Church and its representatives. Both groups required the patronage of the aristocracy in order to succeed, and so were in competition with one another for that support. But however fiercely they might have struggled against each other in the beginning, in the end they collaborated rather well. Both were scholars and went through long periods of training. The clerics studied Latin, the Bible and its commentaries, and had some familiarity with Classical learning; the poets studied the Irish language in detail and mastered the materials of traditional, native learning. In some instances the two groups were drawn from the same noble families: the saintly Colum Cille, who saved the poetic orders from being driven out of Ireland by the high king, was a trained *fili* as well as a cleric. Over time, the native lore was recorded in writing and preserved in the scriptoria and libraries of the clerical establishment.

Still, surviving texts speak clearly of tension between cleric and poet. Surely, two of the finest tales from early Ireland are *Tromdámh Guaire* and *Aislinge Meic Con Glinne*. The first of these is also known as *Imtheacht na Tromdháimhe*, usually called in English 'The Proceedings of the Great Bardic Institution'; here it is called "Guaire's Greedy Guests." It paints the poets in a very bad light, showing their willingness to use satire unjustly for the sake of personal reward, their arrogance, and their exorbitant demands upon their patrons. Guaire, a seventh-century king of Connaught, is the unfortunate recipient of a visit by the chief poet Senchán Torpéist and his huge entourage. Not a single day went by without them making the most outrageous demands of their host. As he did not wish to refuse them and so risk being satirized by them, he enlists the support of his saintly brother, Marbán, who overcomes the poets and puts them to shame. Here are the clerics, having some fun at the expense of the poets.

"The Vision of Mac Con Glinne" may be seen as a diatribe on the clerical establishment, with the poet as hero. Here the focus is on the meanness and inhospitality of the monasteries, with the author parodying ecclesiastical rituals, holy relics, even the crucifixion of Christ. Mac Con Glinne starts out as a clerical student but gives it up for poetry, from which he expects to enjoy a far better life. His cleverness enables him to get the best of the monks, and gives us one of the most brilliantly creative compositions of the Middle Ages.

ON TRANSLATION

The present work was undertaken primarily to provide access to these early Irish and Welsh songs and tales by audiences unfamiliar with the Celtic literary tradition and unable to read them in their original languages. Many of these texts have been translated before; some quite recently, others more than a hundred years ago. That means that those wishing to become familiar with the range of texts through those translations must accommodate the biases and abilities of disparate generations of scholars and literateurs. The present collection represents the work of a *single* bias and ability. Such a project requires some justification, both of its methods and its rationales.

A general discussion of translation requires answers to some questions, the most basic of which is, perhaps, *why* do we translate? One obvious answer is that we translate to bring a work of literature to a wider audience, an audience that cannot access the work in the source language. Sometimes translations come to supplant the original work. It's a fact that far more people have read the Bible in translation than have read it in the original Hebrew, Aramaic, or Koine Greek – it is estimated to have been translated into over 1100 languages (Eoyang 1993, p. 7). And it's likely that more people have read Homer, Dante, and even Chaucer in translation than have read them in the original source langauge. Another reason for translating is to provide an aid for students and others who are learning to access the originals in the source language. This requires a different approach by the translator, as we shall see.

Of primary importance is the question of audience: for whom is the translation intended? There are different approaches to this question, but I like the classification of Eoyang (1993), who distinguishes three discrete types of translation, each aimed at a distinct audience. The first he identifies as contingent translation. This is intended as an introduction to the original text. It is not intended to take the place of the original, so its value is entirely conditional, it constantly refers to the original, so that its meaning does not reside in its own text but is addressed to the original text. Its audience is a bilingual one or at least potentially so. Contingent translations, in his words, "create a void which can only be filled by reading the original" (p. 199).

The second type is surrogate translation. This is intended to be a literary work in its own right: its meaning is not referred outside the text, it does not merely point to the original. Its audience is not likely to have access to the original and will depend fully on the translation as an index to the concepts and aesthetics of the original.

The third type is coeval translation. This is conceived neither as a replacement for the original, as is a surrogate translation, nor as an aid for the potentially bilingual who want to access the original, as is a contingent translation. The coeval translation exists alongside the original, is perhaps even its rival. Eoyang gives as examples Pope's versions of Juvenal and Homer, and Dryden's versions of Ovid and Virgil (p. 192).

With respect to early Irish and Welsh poetry, we are most familiar, perhaps, with contingent translations. This is evidenced by the large number of facing-page translation editions of our poetry, especially the early poetry. Contingent translation is what is frequently called 'literal' translation. In his monograph on *Translating Poetry*, André Lefevere (1975, p. 27) begins the section on "Literal translation" with these words: "Ever since the rise of philology in the nineteenth century, literal translations emphasizing 'fidelity' to the sense of the source text have enjoyed an enormous prestige in the field." He goes on to describe what he calls the 'myth' of literal translation, a myth because, as he emphasizes, the semantic mapping of the universe by any one language is essentially arbitrary and no two languages map it the same way. Thus there is virtually no such thing as one to one correspondence between languages. Those who insist on literal translation are often reduced to various strategies, such as resorting to outdated meanings for words, compelling the reader to have, say, the OED at hand in order to understand the translation. According to Lefevere (p. 96),

> It is therefore absolutely essential not only to expose the idea of a 'literal' translation for the myth it really is, but also prove that translation of literature is indeed possible, once it has been freed from the obligation to render only sense for sense. It follows that...the translation of literature is mainly concerned with matching communicative value with communicative value.

Or, as another scholar put it: "In discussing translations, one must look at two kinds of authenticity: faithfulness to the original...and faithfulness to the audience" (Eoyang 1993, p. 23).

But regardless of the degree or kind of literalness that motivates the translator, he will probably claim that he has attempted to remain faithful to the 'original.' This too is a problematic notion. Our editions of medieval texts sometimes draw upon a number of manuscripts, with the editor choosing which variants are worthy of inclusion and often creating texts from the 'best' evidence of the various manuscripts (Ford 1996b) As Edgar Slotkin has argued (1978-79), this is of dubious value when dealing with texts that derive from an oral tradition. Even so, we do not know what surgeries were performed on the 'originals' before they were committed to manuscripts. So if there is no absolute original, then absolute faithfulness becomes a moot point. As Eoyang (1993, p. 19) says,

> the equivalence [that translation strives for] lies not in reproducing, however faithfully, the actual original...but in the approximate correspondence between the author's words to the audience in his lifetime and his words to each succeeding generation of readers.

The would-be translator is confronted with numerous choices. In the case of poetry, the choices would include: verse translation or prose? metrical? phonetic? 'literal'? paraphrase? Generally speaking, the choice of one of these or various other options will rule out the rest. A translation that attempts to imitate the meter of the original will likely sacrifice the sound, the syntax, or the lexical inventory of the original. But, in any case, it could be argued that meter is no more translatable than vocabulary: the rhythm of regularly stressed lines may have one meaning for one culture (i.e., the original poet and his audience) and another meaning for another culture (i.e., for the target audience). The same may be said of alliteration and other phonetic features of verse forms. As Conran points out with respect to trying to reproduce *cynghanedd*, "Full Welsh *cynghanedd* sounds too much like a tongue-twister in English – even Hopkins rarely made it sound natural" (1986, p. 339).

In his introduction to *Medieval Welsh Poems*, Dafydd Johnston (1992) offers reasons for translation that transcend the formal features of some of the poems:

> Since it is impossible to preserve the harmony of *cynghanedd* in translation, English renderings of these poems seem lamentably flat to anyone familiar with the rich music of the Welsh originals. However, the poems have so many merits independent of their versification that translations can retain at least some of their poetic effect. Warmth of feeling and sharpness of thought, drama and irony, rich and resonant imagery – these qualities alone are enough to make this poetry a significant part of the literature of medieval Europe. (p. 9).

I would agree wholeheartedly with those sentiments and say that what remains is to try to find ways of conveying those qualities that so appealed to a poem's contemporary audiences in language that will appeal in a similar way to our contemporary audiences. And that is what I have tried to do here. Eoyang offers a similar counsel:

> When the sense lies in sentences and in contexts, and not in the composites of meanings for individual words, the flavor of the work must be captured intuitively, not analytically. Poems in translation must not read like scholarly glosses, and common words in one language must not present themselves in uncommon guises in another...(p. 102).

I have tried to make these translations as fresh for modern audiences as they were for their original audiences. If I have succeeded at all, I have only succeeded partially. In many cases, the syntax, diction, and much else will seem strange to those familiar with the originals. I can only say that it is my own familiarity with and unde standing of those original texts that has driven the translations. Obviousıy, the prose texts present far fewer problems than the verse. The Welsh and Irish strict meters presented the early poets with both constraints and opportunities. It was poetry for the ear: measured, harmonious, tuneful. The content may have ordinarily been conventional, but the artistry was evident in the hearing of the poem.

In undertaking what Rachel Bromwich (1982, p. xxvi), in reference to her splendid translations of Dafydd ap Gwilym, called a "daunting task," I have high hopes that I have to a degree reenacted a relationship that will allow contemporary audiences to experience something of the richness and beauty of the original texts that are offered here in my translations.

Metrical Analysis

I offer only brief comments on the meters of the poems that are found in the last two sections of the book. It should be noted that those poems are arranged and printed according to the conventions for representing the several meters. The reader interested in pursuing this difficult subject will find sources for further study in the introductory notes and in the bibliography. It must always be borne in mind that virtually all of this poetry was orally and publicly recited or declaimed, probably to musical accompaniment. Whether the composition of lines of poetry was determined by syllable count or by number of accents, and whether those accents were tonic or stress, is still debated by scholars. Another point of contention is the degree of indebtedness to prosodic antecedents in Indo-European or in early medieval Latin poetry. These matters are not at issue in the present volume, though it is felt that some general guidelines, offered in the introductory notes to the poems, will be of use to readers.

THE ORIGINS OF POETS

THE BOYHOOD DEEDS OF FINN

Macgnímartha Finn, as this narrative is called in Irish, is a rather loose and somewhat chaotic account of the early years of Finn mac Cumaill. It is usually dated to the twelfth century, though it survives in a fifteenth-century manuscript known as Laud 610 (Bodleian Library, Oxford University). It is from about the twelfth century that stories about Finn begin to attract the interest of the compilers of manuscripts, with Finn eventually eclipsing Cú Chulainn, the great Ulster hero, in the popular imagination. In the eighteenth century, upon the publication of James Macpherson's 'Ossianic' (after Finn's son, Oisín) poems, the stories about Finn (Fingal) ignited the imagination of all of Europe. In Ireland, stories about Finn have survived right down to the present day.

The cycle of tales about Finn (as an adjective the word means 'white, bright, lustrous') is known as the Fenian Cycle. Finn himself is the leader of a band of warriors and hunters known in Irish as a *fían*, plural *fiana*. Their exploits bring them into contact with inhabitants of the *sídh* (pronounced 'shee'), the Irish otherworld, as well as with legendary and historical folk. For our purposes, the most significant thing about Finn is that he is a poet (*éces*) and seer (*fili*). Several episodes in "The Boyhood Deeds" tell how Finn acquired his gifts of poetry and divination. The first of these deals with a tradition that magically inspired wisdom and knowledge resided in hazelnuts from a tree that grew beside a well in the otherworld. When the nuts fell from the tree into the well, salmon consumed them, and they in turn were consumed by men destined to be poets. The second episode has to do with Finn's vengeance against a *sídh* for the death of a poet called Orcbél. The word *orc-bél* means, among other possiblities, 'pig-mouth,' and indeed a pig figures prominently in this episode. It will also be noticed that the instrument by which Finn subsequently invokes his special knowledge is his thumb, the 'thumb of knowledge.' Now *orc* may also mean 'salmon,' recalling the salmon on which Finn burned his thumb when he first acquired wisdom. Thus it will be seen that several different traditions have come together in this somewhat confused (to us, at any rate) text. Nonetheless, together they stress Finn's primordial role in the Irish concept of the acquisition and use of divinely inspired wisdom. The translation is based on the edition of Meyer 1882.

Bibliography: MacNeill 1908; Meyer 1882, 1896, 1904, 1910; Murphy 1933, 1953, 1955, 1971; Nagy 1985; Scott 1930; Tymoczko 1983

The Boyhood Deeds of Finn

There was war and feuding between Cumall son of Trénmór and Uirgriu son of Lugach Corr concerning the *fian* and the chief-stewardship of Ireland. Uirgriu was of the Luaigni and Cumall was of the Corco Óchae of Cúl Contuinn, for Cumall's tribe, the Uí Thairrsig, was part of that group. Cumall's wife was Torba daughter of Eochaman of the Érainn, until he married Muirne Fair-neck.

The battle of Cnucha was fought between them, between Cumall and Uirgriu. On Uirgriu's side was Daire the Red son of Eochu Finn son of Cairpre Galach son of Muiredach, and Daire's son Aedh. This Daire was also known as Morna Fair-neck. In the course of the battle, Luchet and Aedh clashed and Luchet blinded Aedh in one eye, hence Aedh became known as Goll 'One-eyed' from that time on. The man who kept Cumall's crane-bag of treasures wounded Cumall. Then Goll son of Morna killed Cumall and departed with his head and his battle-gear. And that was the cause of the family feud between Finn son of Cumall and the sons of Morna.

As the shanachie sang,

> Goll son of Daire, famous,
> Son of Eochu, fair and valorous,
> Son of valiant Cairpre Galach,
> Son of Muiredach of Findmag.

> 'Tis true: at the battle of Cnucha
> Goll slew mighty Luchet;
> Fair Luchet of bright weapons,
> Slain by Morna's son.

> Great Cumall, too, by the same hand,
> At the battle of Cnucha of the warbands;
> They waged bitter war for this reason:
> For control of Ireland's *fian*.

> The children of Morna were there,

And the Luaigni of Tara,
Theirs the *fian*-ship of the men of Erin,
Vigorously, in the service of every king.

Mighty Cumall had a son,
Valiant and dangerous Finn;
Of great renown were Finn and Goll,
And boldly did they do battle.

Afterwards they made their peace,
Finn and Goll of the hundred deeds,
Until fell Banb Sinna,
Concerning the pig of Tara Luachra.

The name of Daire's son was Aedh,
Until he was wounded by glorious Luchet:
When the spear had taken its toll,
He was thenceforth referred to as Goll.

Cumall left his wife, Muirne, pregnant, and she bore a son whom she called Demne. Fiacall son of Conchenn and Bodbmall the druidess and Gray of Luachar sought out Muirne, and they took the boy with them; his mother did not dare keep him with her. Later on, Muirne slept with Gleor Red-hand, king of Lamraige, and that's why Finn is also known as son of Gleor. Bodbmall and Gray took the boy into the forests of Slieve Bloom, and there the boy was raised secretly. A good thing, too, for there was any number of ruthless and reckless lads out after him and Tulcha son of Cumall, including the angry, hotheaded warriors of the Luaigni and the sons of Morna. The two woman-warriors raised him for a long time under those conditions.

Six years later his mother set out to see her son, for she had been told where he was, and anyway she feared the sons of Morna might get to him. So she went from one wilderness to another until she finally reached the forests of Slieve Bloom. She found the hut where the boy lay sleeping. She lifted him to her bosom and hugged him, she being pregnant at the time. And she sang this song, rocking her child:
Lullaby, and sleep in peace...etc.

Afterwards, she took leave of the woman-warriors and told them that they should look after the boy until he was capable of bearing arms. And so the lad grew till he was ready for the chase.

One day he went out by himself and spied some ducks on a lake. He made a cast at them, shaving all the feathers from one of them, which promptly fainted. The lad took the bird and brought it with him to the hut. That was Finn's first hunting expedition.

He went off with a group of poets who were fleeing from the sons of Morna, and was with them in Crotta. These are their names: Tuth, Ruth, Regna of Moy Fea, Temle, Olpe, and Rogein. In Crotta he got the scurvy and his hair fell out, and as a result they called him Demne the Bald. There was a robber in Leinster at that time named Fiacal son of Codna. He set upon the band of poets in Feegile and killed them all except Demne, whom he carried off to his house in Seiscenn Úairbeóil. The two woman-warriors came south to Fiacal's house seeking Demne, and he was given to them. They brought him back to the old place.

On another occasion he went out by himself as far as Moy Liffey, to a certain fort there, and he saw these young boys playing hurley on the green in front of the fort. He joined them in the sport. The next day, when he came again, the boys sent a fourth of their number against him. Then they sent a third. Finally, they all drove against him, but he won against them all.

"What's your name?" they asked.

"Demne," he replied. The boys went in and told that to the man of the fort.

"Kill him, if you can," he ordered.

"We can't do anything to him!" they answered.

"Did he tell you his name?" the man asked.

"Yes, he said his name was Demne," they answered.

"What's he like?"

"He's a handsome and fair (*finn*) lad," they said.

"Then this Demne shall be called Finn," the man declared. And so the boys called him Finn.

He returned on the following day and went up to them as they were playing. They threw their hurley sticks at him all at the same time. He attacked them and laid out seven of them, after which he returned to the forests of Slieve Bloom.

A week later he went back to that same fort. At the time, the boys were swimming in a lake beside the place. They dared him to try to dunk them. He jumped into the lake, held nine of them under water, then went back to Slieve Bloom.

"Who dunked the boys?" folks asked.

"Finn!" they cried. And so the name stuck.

One time he set out across Slieve Bloom, the two female warriors with him. They saw a herd of fierce red deer along the hillside.

"What a shame that none of us can grab hold of any of those!" exclaimed the old ones.

"I can!" says Finn, and he ran at them, laid hold of two deer, and took them back to the hut. After that, he did all their hunting for them.

"Go from us now, lad," the women told him, "for the sons of Morna are plotting your death."

So Finn set out by himself and travelled as far as Loch Leane in Luachair, where he offered his services to the king of Bantry. He didn't give his name there, but he was without peer as a hunter. This caused the king to say to him, "If Cumall had left a son, it seems to me that you'd be him. But we haven't heard that he left any son other than Tulcha, and he's away in the service of the king of Scotland."

Subsequently, Finn left the king and traveled on to Cairbrige – called Kerry these days. He took service with that king. One day the king was playing *fidchell*. He taught the game to the boy, who promptly won seven games in a row from him.

"Who are you?" asked the king.

"Son of a nobody of the Luaigni of Tara," the boy answered.

"No you're not," said the king, "you're the son that Muirne bore to Cumall. And don't stay here a minute longer lest you be killed in my presence!"

Off he went to Cullen of the Uí Chúanach, to the house of Lochan, a noble smith. The smith had a beautiful daughter named Cruithne. She fell in love with the lad.

"I'll give you my daughter," said the smith, "even though I don't know who you are." So he and the girl slept together.

"Make me a spear," he said to the smith. Lochan made him a spear, and the boy bade him farewell and set out.

"Don't follow the path the sow takes," advised Lochan. We call her 'The Live One,' and it's she who laid waste to all of central

Munster!" Of course, that's the path the lad followed. The sow attacked, and the lad cast his spear right through her, so that she fell dead. He brought her head back to the smith and gave it to him as bride-price for his daughter. That's where we get the name Slieve Mucc ('Sow Mountain').

Then the lad went forth into Connaught to seek Crimall son of Trénmór. As he was going along, he heard the cry of a lone woman. He approached until he could see the woman, who was alternately crying tears of blood and buckets of blood, so that her mouth was red.

"You're a red-mouthed one!" the lad said.

"And with good reason," she replied, "for my only son has been killed by some big, ugly warrior we met up with."

"What was your son's name?" the other asked.

"Glonda," she answered. And it's from that that we have Glonda Ford and Glonda Well in Moinmoy. And from 'red-mouth' (*bél-derg*) we have Bélderg Ford from that day to this. Well, Finn pursued the warrior, they fought, and Finn killed him. As it turned out, he had the crane-bag of treasures with him, Cumall's treasures. His name was Gray of Luachar, the one who gave Cumall his first wound in the battle of Cnucha.

Finn continued on into Connaught, then, and found the aged Crimall in a wooded retreat, surrounded by some of his old *fian*, who did his hunting for him. Finn gave him the crane-bag and related from start to finish how he had killed the man who had taken the treasures. Then he bade Crimall farewell and went to learn the art of poetry from Finnéces [*éces* 'poet'], who was at the Boyne River. Finn did not dare remain in Ireland unless he took up poetry, for fear of the sons of Morna.

This Finnéces had been on the banks of the Boyne for seven years, waiting for the salmon of Linn Féic, Féc's Pool, for it had been prophesied to him that he would consume the salmon of Féc and that thenceforth nothing would be concealed from him. The salmon was caught, and it was entrusted to Demne to cook. Finnéces told Demne not to eat any of the salmon. After it was cooked, the lad brought the salmon to him.

"Did you eat any of the salmon, boy?" asked the poet.

"No," he replied, "but I burned my thumb on it and then put my thumb into my mouth."

"What is your name, boy?" asked the poet.

"Demne," the lad answered.

"It's Finn now," declared the poet, "it was for you the salmon was intended, and 'tis you who are the true Finn." Finn ate the salmon then, and that's what gave him his wisdom: whenever he put his thumb into his mouth and chanted through *teinm laída* whatever he needed to know would be revealed to him.

He learned the three things that confer status on a poet, namely: *teinm laída*, *imbas forosnai*, and *díchetal di chennaib*. Then Finn made this lay to inaugurate his poetic gift:

> Summertime! season fair;
> most splendid of the year;
> blackbirds are full of song
> at the very first sign of dawn.
>
> The cuckoo sings, loud and clear;
> welcome to splendid summer:
> gone are the stormy blows
> that whip the naked boughs.
>
> Summer tames the river's flow;
> lively horses off to the pool;
> heather spreading far and wide,
> pale, fresh growth's alive.
>
> Hawthorns now burst forth;
> sea holds a steady course –
> it's as if the briny dozes;
> but earth is roofed in blossoms.
>
> Tiny, busy bees bear
> their cargo of flowery nectar;
> hillside sates the hungry herds,
> offering up its rich rewards.
>
> The trees murmur a lullaby,
> bringing peace and harmony;
> from the hillside haze is chased,

fog, too, from brimful lakes.

The raucous rail sings out,
and the crystal clear falls spout
a welcome of warm water;
rushes have begun to stir.

Swallows dart about aloft;
music in the hills circles softly;
trees bear rich, plump fruit;
a spongy lay from marsh's roots.

The swale's a sight to admire;
keen cuckoo sings clear;
trout rising up for a fly –
heroes, too, leap on high.

Men's exuberance on the rise;
the young bold and full of themselves;
lovely every stretch of forest land,
and lush is every open plain.

Delightful is this season!
winter's harsh winds have gone;
woods stand tall, the wave is full:
joyous summer – so peaceful!

A flock of birds settles down
alighting gently on the meadow ground;
a field of green rustles and roars
as a brook hurries through its borders.

Champions raging, horses prancing,
hosts close-formed and brawling;
throughout the land flowering trees,
ennobled, like golden iris.

The timorous fellow insists,

cheeps at the top of his tiny voice,
announcing tidings clear:
'Summertime – O season fair!'

Finn went to Cethern son of Fintan to learn the art of poetry with
him too. At that time there was a beautiful girl in Brí Éle, that is, in the
sídh, the fairy-mound of Brí Éle – Éle was the name of that girl. The
men of Ireland fought over her, and each of them in turn would go to
court her. The courting was done on *Samain*, November Eve, each year,
for the fairy-mounds of Ireland always lay open on *Samain*, a day when
they could not be hidden. Now this is what happened to every man who
used to go a-courting there: one of his company would be killed. This
served as proof of the attempted courtship, and it was never discovered
who did it.

Like all the others, Cethern went to win the maiden. Finn didn't
like Cethern going off on that business (actually, Finnéces was the name
of Cumall's son at that time). Three companies of them went along on
that courtship, nine men in each company. As they approached the *sídh*,
one of them was killed and no one knew who did it. Orcbél Éces was the
name of one who was killed, and that's where we get the name Fert
Orcbéil ('the grave of Orcbél') in Clonfad. After that, they abandoned
the business, and Finn left them and did not return. He felt sorry about
what had happened and was much aggrieved.

He traveled on until he reached the house of the warrior Fiacail
son of Conchenn in Slievemargue, where Fiacail lived at the time. Finn
poured out his troubles to Fiacail and told him how the fellow had been
killed at the fairy-mound. Fiacail told him to go and station himself at
The Paps of Anu beyond Luachair. Finn did so and took up a position
between the two forts which are between the two Paps of Anu.

As he stood there on the eve of *Samain*, he saw the two fairy-
mounds opening about him, their veils of invisibility having fallen away.
He could see a blazing fire inside each of the two forts, and he heard a
voice from one of them call out to the other, "Are you well disposed?"

"We are indeed," answered a voice from the other fort.

"A question: shall we bring something over to you?" asked the
first voice.

"If you do, you shall get something in return." Finn saw a man,
then, coming out of the one fairy-mound. He held a large tray with a live

11

pig, a cooked calf, and a bunch of wild garlic; it was now *Samain*. The man went past Finn, on his way to the other fairy-mound. Finn made a cast with Fiacail's spear, which he had brought with him from Slievemargue.

"If that spear strikes someone, it'll take his life and I will have avenged my friend," Finn said. He drew back then, and immediately heard loud wailing and lamentation, and a voice that said,

> From the sharp spear, on the river Barrow,
> Aedh son of Fidga has fallen;
> Finn killed him in the night,
> with the spear of Fiacail, Codna's son!

Fiacail came then and joined Finn at The Paps of Anu. He asked Finn whom he had killed.

"I don't know," replied Finn.

"Even though you don't know the name," said Fiacail, "I am sure you killed someone with that cast. And I am also certain that if you didn't succeed this night, you will have to wait a year to try again." Finn answered that he had indeed made a cast and that he was certain that it had found its target. Then he heard loud wailing from within the fairy-mound, and a voice that said,

> This spear, it's poison;
> Poison whoever owns it;
> Poison the one who throws it;
> Whoever it hits is poison.

Finn seized a woman outside the fairy-mound of Cruachan Brig Ele and held her hostage to get his spear back. The woman promised on her life to return the spear, so Finn let her go back into the *sidh*. After she was inside, the woman sang these words:

> The spear is poison;
> Thrown from a poison hand;
> If it's not tossed out of the *sidh*,
> A plague will grip the land.

Thereupon the spear was tossed out and Finn took it to where Fiacail was.

"Well," said Fiacail, "you must keep the spear with which you did such an incredible deed." And he said that the hour in which Finn had killed the man who killed his friend was a propitious one. "The man who killed him," he said, "was the same man who has killed everyone who has ever come to court the maiden, for it was he himself who loved her."

Finn and Fiacail set forth then. Fiacail had to meet his *fian* in Inber Colptha, so he told Finn that they should each go their own way since their business was finished.

"Let me go with you," Finn said.

"I don't want you to go with me," replied Fiacail, "for your strength is sapped."

"We'll see about that," Finn said. Fiacail wore twelve balls of lead around his neck to keep his speed in check. As they raced along, he dropped the balls one by one. Finn collected them and carried them along with him and still Fiacail ran no swifter than Finn.

When they reached Inber Colptha, Finn gave the lead balls back to Fiacail, and this pleased him. They spend the night there, and Finn was delegated to stand guard during the night. He was told to wake the warrior if he should sense trouble. At a certain hour of the night, as he stood watch, Finn heard a cry from the north, but he didn't wake the warrior. Rather he went alone in the direction of the sound toward Slieve Slanga. There, in the evening and amongst the Ulstermen, he saw three women with banshees' combs, lying upon a green mound. They were keening there, and as they did so they would all place their hands upon the mound. Then the women flee from Finn into the mound. He overtook one of the women as she was going into the fairy-mound of Slang and snatched the brooch from her cloak. The woman went after him and begged Finn to return her brooch to her, and said that it was not proper for her to go into the fairy-mound thus blemished. She promised him a reward. [The story breaks off here.]

THE STORY OF GWION BACH, WHO BECAME TALIESIN

There are actually two separate tales here, though they form a continuous whole. Like "The Boyhood Deeds of Finn," they tell of the acquisition of divinely inspired wisdom and knowledge by a figure on the horizon of the literary tradition, here that of Wales. Indeed, the Irish and Welsh narratives connect in interesting ways. Taliesin is found by the spendthrift courtier, Elphin, in a salmon weir, a dam or barrier constructed to catch fish. Thus he is, in a sense, a catch of salmon. His name, explained as *tal-* 'brow' *iesin* 'fair,' could also be explained as from *tal* 'catch (e.g., of fish).' He is, of course, Gwion Bach renamed – just as Finn 'fair' is Demne renamed. Water and salmon figure prominently in this transformation, just as they do in the Finn episode. The caldron in which Ceridwen brews the magical three drops is reminiscent of the Caldron of Poesy of Irish tradition (Breatnach 1981 and Henry 1979-80). And of course the idea of poetry, divine wisdom, coming from a caldron is one that is shared by Scandinavian tradition as well (Frank 1981).

The relationship between the Taliesin whose poetry is found in the thirteenth-century Book of Taliesin (some of which is included in this volume) and the poet/trickster of our narrative is unclear. Sir Ifor Williams (1957) distinguished between a Taliesin of legend and myth and the historical, sixth-century poet named in the *Historia Brittonum* (see the introductory note to "The Gododdin," below). Whatever of the relationship between the two, it is interesting to note that none of the poems recited by Taliesin in the present narrative are to be found in The Book of Taliesin. It is also clear that our Taliesin claims to have been in existence from the beginning of time, to have traveled the world over, and to be capable of existence in a multitude of forms. He is, in short, wisdom personified.

The earliest known version of the stories of Gwion Bach and Taliesin is that in National Library of Wales MS. 5276, a sixteenth-century manuscript containing a history of the six ages of the world written by Elis Gruffudd. Elis drew on a variety of sources, written and oral, in compiling his history. He introduces the Gwion Bach story in the section dealing with the legendary British king Arthur, noting that the story was 'widely known' in Wales in his, Elis's, own time. He continues with the Taliesin part of the story a bit further on, when he reaches the time of the reign of the historical king Maelgwn of Gwynedd (North Wales). This disjuncture of our story may be significant, in that the Gwion Bach/Arthurian material deals with witches, shape-shifting, and other marvels, whereas the Taliesin/Maelgwn material has a more historical or real 'feel' to it, treating of heralds, courtiers, and other realities of courtly life. But Elis is a constant element in both stories. He can't resist commenting on the characters and the action. His intrusions give the narrative a rather odd flavor, but they also keep us in touch with this most industrious sixteenth-century scholar. The translation is based on the edition of Ford 1992b.

Bibliography: Breatnach 1981; Ford 1975, 1976, 1979, 1987, 1990, 1992b; Frank 1981; Hamp 1978; Haycock 1983-84; Henry 1979-80; Morris-Jones 1918; Williams 1957; Wood 1982, 1983

The Story of Gwion Bach, Who Became Taliesin

This is the story of Gwion Bach, a tale widely known in Wales.

In the early days of King Arthur, there was a nobleman named Tegid Foel living in the area now called Penllyn. His patrimony, as the story says, was the body of water now known as Llyn Tegid. The story also says that he had a wife called Ceridwen who, according to the text, was expert and learned in the three arts: magic, witchcraft, and sorcery. The text says that Ceridwen bore Tegid a son, who was extremely ugly, misshapen, and ungainly. His name was Morfran, but because of his gloomy appearance they called him Afagddu 'utter gloom.'

His mother grieved because of his grim looks, for she knew that there was no manner or means for him to gain acceptance among noble people unless he had something of value other than his appearance. To achieve this goal, she focused her thinking on her arts to discover the best way to make him full of the spirit of prophecy and a great prophet of the world's future. After long contemplation of her arts, she discovered a way to achieve that sort of knowledge through herbs, hard work, and cunning. She was to select and gather a large amount of certain herbs on just the right day and hour, put them into a caldron full of water, and cook them. The caldron would have to be kept simmering night and day for a year and a day, after which time she would see three drops containing the essence of all those herbs spring forth unerringly. Whomever those drops landed on would then be expert in various arts and full of the spirit of prophecy. She would also see that the juice of those herbs, except for the three drops, would be the most powerful poison in the world and would burst the caldron and overrun the land.

Now really, this story is irrational and contrary to faith and piety. But anyway, the story states clearly that she gathered a large number of herbs, put them into a caldron of water, and set it on the fire. And it says that she hired an old, blind man to watch the caldron and stir it. But the story makes no mention of the name of this fellow, any more than it says who the author of this story was. However, it does say that the name of the lad who was leading the blind man was Gwion Bach, and Ceridwen set him to keeping the fire going. So each kept to his task: tending the fire, watching and stirring the caldron, while Ceridwen kept it full of herbs and water till the end of a year and a day.

At the appointed time, Ceridwen took her son Morfran and stood him next to the caldron so as to receive the three drops when they sprung from the caldron. She herself lay down to rest, and was asleep when the magical drops sprung forth. When they did, they landed on Gwion Bach, who had pushed Morfran out of the way! Immediately, the caldron screamed out and broke apart from the potency of the poison. Ceridwen woke with a start, like a madwoman, and saw Gwion. Gwion was now so full of knowledge that he could see clearly that she was crazy enough to kill him as soon as she discovered that he had robbed her son of the magical drops. So he took to his heels and fled. As soon as Ceridwen gathered her wits and questioned her son, he told her how Gwion had driven him from the place where she had positioned him. When she heard that, she ran out of the house in frantic pursuit of Gwion Bach. As the story says, she saw him fleeing in the shape of a hare, so she turned herself into a greyhound and pursued him from place to place. Finally, after long pursuit in various shapes, she was so dogged in pursuit that he had to seek refuge in a barn, where there was a huge pile of winnowed wheat. Quickly, he turned himself into a grain of wheat. Ceridwen turned herself into a black, tailless hen, scratched about till she found him, and in that form, so the story says, she swallowed Gwion. She carried him within her for nine months, after which time she gave birth to him.

When she looked at him, having thus come into the world, she couldn't bring herself either to do him bodily harm with her own hand or to allow anyone else to harm him in her presence. In the end, she had him put into a coracle, or skin bag, in which she covered him up and made him snug. She cast him into the lake like that, as some of the books say, although others say that he was set afloat on a river, and still

16

others that he was cast into the sea, where he was found long afterwards, as this book will explain in due course.

How Taliesin was discovered

In the days when Maelgwn Gwynedd kept court at Castle Degannwy, a holy man named Cybi dwelt in Môn. And also at that time, says the story, there was a wealthy man named Gwyddno Garanhir living near Caer Degannwy. The text says that he had a weir on the banks of the Conway, near the sea, in which he caught ten pounds worth of salmon every Halloween. The story goes on to say that this Gwyddno had a son, Elphin, who was in service at the court of King Maelgwn. It says that he was a generous and noble youth, much admired by his companions, but that he was an incorrigible spendthrift – as are the majority of courtiers! While Gwyddno's wealth lasted, Elphin never lacked for money to spend on his comrades. But as Gwyddno's riches began to dwindle, he stopped plying his son with money. Elphin complained to his friends that he was no longer able to keep company and fellowship with them as he had done before, because his father had fallen on hard times.

Nevertheless, he prevailed on some of the men of the court to go ask Gwyddno to give Elphin the salmon catch that next Halloween. Gwyddno granted the request. When the time came, Elphin and some of his fellow courtiers went to set up and observe the weir, which he watched over from high tide until the tide ebbed. Then he and his friends went into the weir enclosure, which was normally full of fish on that particular night, but they found neither head nor tail of a single young salmon. The story says that the only thing they found on that occasion was some dark object trapped there.

Elphin hung his head and began to bemoan his misfortune, saying, as he turned homeward, that his bad luck and misfortune were greater than that of any man alive. But something made him turn back to see just what the object was that was trapped there in the weir. What he found was a coracle, or skin bag, completely covered over. He took out his knife and cut through the hide, revealing a human forehead. Upon seeing it he exclaimed, "What a radiant brow!" Or, in Welsh, "Tal iesin!" At that, the young child in the coracle replied, "Taliesin it is!"

People say that this was the spirit of Gwion Bach, the one who had been in the womb of Ceridwen, who, having given birth to him, set him afloat on water or in the sea, as we have said above. There in the water, in his bag, he had been tossing about from the beginning of Arthur's reign till the time of Maelgwn, a period of about forty years.

Really, this is far from reason and sense, but nevertheless I'll continue with the story, which says that Elphin took the bag and loaded it onto one of his horses. From that position, Taliesin sang the stanzas that are called "Elphin's Consolation." It goes like this:

Fair Elphin, leave off weeping;
Despair will bring you nothing;
Never in Gwyddno's weir
Has a catch ever been better!
None should despise his lot,
For man sees not his support;
Gwyddno's prayer is not amiss –
God does not take back a promise.

Fair Elphin, dry your tears –
You need have no fears;
For though you think you've nothing here,
Excessive grief leads nowhere;
Doubt not the Lord's miracles,
Though I'm small, I'm skilful;
From sea and mount and rivers' depths,
God sends wealth to the wise.

Elphin of cheerful manner,
Timid is your behavior,
Don't be so dejected,
Better God than bleak prospect!
Though I seem small and weak,
I've sailed through Dylan's sea,
And I'll profit you more in days to come
Than three hundred young salmon!

Elphin of splendid habits,
Don't decry your catch;
Though here in my bag I seem feeble,

18

My tongue is indeed remarkable;
Don't be overly afraid:
As long as I'm on your side,
By invoking the name of the Trinity,
To you alone will come victory!

These and other verses he sang to console Elphin along the way. Once home, Elphin handed over his catch to his wife, who raised the boy well and lovingly. From then on, Elphin's fortunes increased from day to day, and he was well-received and loved by the king.

Some time after this, at Christmas time, the king was holding open court at Castle Degannwy, with his full complement of lords of both estates, secular and religious, and a great multitude of knights and squires. And they began to praise the king in terms such as these:

"Is there in the entire world a king as powerful as Maelgwn, or one to whom the Heavenly Father has given so many spiritual gifts? And above all – in addition to the properties of his soul – such shape and form, grace and strength?" And they said that, in addition to all that, the Father had given him one outstanding gift that surpassed all the rest: the shape and form, carriage, wisdom, and chastity of his queen. In these characteristics, she surpassed all the noble women and maidens in the entire realm. They went on in this vein, saying, "After all, whose men are braver than Maelgwn's? Whose horses faster? Whose horses and hunting dogs fairer and swifter? Whose poets better-informed and wiser than Maelgwn's?"

Now at this time, poets enjoyed great favor among the eminent ones of the realm. No one could hold this office, what we now call herald, unless he were learned not only in the service of kings and princes but knowledgeable and accomplished in the matter of genealogies, heraldic arms, and notable deeds of the kings and princes of foreign realms as well as of the leaders of this realm, in particular the histories of the chief nobles. They had to be ready to respond in several languages, such as Latin, French, Welsh, and English. They had to be excellent historians and chroniclers, skilled in the highest branch of poetic composition, and ready to compose metrical stanzas in each of these languages. On this particular feast day, there were as many as twenty four of these poets, and the chief of them was one Heinin Fardd, that is, Heinin Poet.

So after everyone had finished praising the king and all his blessings, Elphin said, "Indeed, no one can argue with a king except another king; but really, if he weren't a king, I'd say that my wife is as chaste as any noble woman in this kingdom. And I'd say, too, that I have a poet who's better informed than any of the king's poets!" A while later, some of the king's friends told him of Elphin's boast, whereupon the king ordered him put in prison until such time as he could get proof of his wife's chastity and his poet's intelligence. He was put in one of the castle towers, with a heavy chain around his feet; some folks say that it was a silver chain, on account of Elphin being related to the king.

The story says that the king sent his son Rhun to test the chastity of Elphin's wife. As the author explains, Rhun was the most libidinous and licentious person imaginable. The story says that no woman or maiden that he spent any time at all with came away with her virtue intact.

As Rhun was hurrying off to Elphin's residence, fully intent on despoiling his wife, Taliesin was explaining to his mistress how the king had imprisoned his master and how Rhun was coming there with the intention of ruining her chastity. And so Taliesin urged his mistress to dress up one of her scullery maids in her own clothing. The noble woman agreed readily and without hesitation to the plan, adorning the maid's hands with the finest rings she and her husband owned. Taliesin, having thus switched their identities, had his mistress seat the maid at supper at her own table and in her own chamber.

As they were sitting elegantly at their supper, in the manner described, Rhun arrived. He was given a warm welcome, for all the servants were well acquainted with him. They brought him straight to their mistress's chamber, where the maid disguised as the mistress rose from the table and greeted him cheerfully. Then she sat down to her supper again, and Rhun with her. Immediately he began a line of suggestive banter with her, she maintaining the whole while the bearing of her mistress.

Indeed, the story says that the girl got so tipsy that she eventually fell asleep, for it says that Rhun had put some kind of powder into her drink. It caused her to sleep so soundly that, if we can believe the story, she didn't even feel him cutting off her little finger, the one on which she wore a ring that Elphin had given his wife some time before. In this way, Rhun had his way with the girl. Afterwards, he brought the finger with the ring around it to the king, explaining that he had slept with the girl, and that he had cut off her finger before he left without her ever waking up.

All this made the king very happy. He sent for his council and told them the whole story, from beginning to end, and then had Elphin fetched from his cell to taunt him about his boast. He said to him, "Elphin, you can be sure that it's folly for any man to trust his wife any farther than he can see her when it comes to the matter of chastity. And so that you can be quite sure that your wife *did* break her marriage vows last night, look: here's her finger and your own ring on it, cut off by the person who slept with her, while she was asleep. So there's no way you can deny that she was unfaithful to you!"

To this Elphin replied, "By your leave, your royal highness, indeed I cannot deny that that is my ring, for a good many people will recognize it. But I can certainly deny that this finger, on which my ring sits, was ever on my wife's hand, for it has three peculiarities not one of which ever characterized a single finger of my wife's hands. The first, if it please your grace, is that wherever my wife is at this moment, be it sitting, standing, or lying down, this ring will not even fit her thumb! And you can see clearly for yourself that it was only with difficulty that this ring was forced over the very tip of the little finger of the hand from which it was cut. The second thing is that ever since I have known her my wife has never let a Saturday go by without trimming her nails before going to bed. And you can easily see for yourself that the nail of this finger has not been trimmed for a month! And the third thing is that the hand from which this finger was cut kneaded rye dough sometime within the three days prior to the cutting off of the finger, and I can assure your grace that my wife has not kneaded rye dough since she has become my wife!"

The story says that the king grew even angrier at Elphin for opposing him in the matter of his wife's fidelity, and so he sent him back to prison a second time until he could make good on his boast, both about his poet's wisdom and his wife's fidelity. These two, in the meantime, were back at Elphin's place resting comfortably. Taliesin was explaining to his mistress how Elphin was in prison on their account, but told her not to worry, because he was going to go to Maelgwn's court to free his master. She asked how he was going to accomplish this, and he replied, saying:

21

I'll take a walk
come to the gate,
enter the hall,
and sing a song.
The song I sing
will check that bunch –
I'll find their chief,
greet him well,
and overcome them all.

When the contention comes,
in front of the lords,
and minstrels are called
for good clean song,
there in the court of nobles,
at Gwion's banquet,
some will fall prey
to painful agonies.

Harsh words will silence them;
as if by great king Arthur,
his blades red
with the blood of nobles,
a king against his foes,
their blood will run
from the battleground
throughout the North.

Let neither grace nor shape
remain on Maelgwn;
the wrong will be avenged,
and the rape and rampage
wrought by Rhun;
let his lands abort,
his life fall short,
and vengeance long
remain on Maelgwn!

And then Taliesin bade his mistress farewell, and after a while arrived at the court of Maelgwn. The king had gone in royal state into his hall to supper, as kings and princes used to do on high holy days at that time. As soon as Taliesin came into the hall, he found an out of the way place for himself to sit, near where bards and minstrels had to pass to perform their service and functions before the king – proclaiming his generosity, as is still done in royal courts on major feast days, except that it is now done in French.

And so the time came for the bards or heralds to come forth and proclaim the generosity and wealth of the king, as well as his power. They passed by the corner where Taliesin was crouching, and as they went past he pursed his lips and made a silly sound by strumming his lips with his fingers. The poets paid no attention but proceeded on their way until they came before the king and bowed down, as they were obliged to do. But then, instead of declaiming their poems, they pursed their lips and made silly sounds at the king by strumming their lips with their fingers, as they had seen the lad doing before.

The king was amazed and stunned at the sight, supposing that they had had too much to drink. He asked one of the lords who was attending his table to go to them and ask them to compose themselves and remember where they were and what they were supposed to be doing. The lord did this readily, but still they did not leave off their foolishness. So the king sent word for them to leave the hall. Twice they were asked to leave, and finally the king told one of his squires to go to their leader, Heinin Fardd, and hit him over the head. The squire took a platter and hit Heinin over the head so that he fell on his arse. Heinin scrambled to his knees and begged leave from the king to explain that their problem was not lack of manners or excessive drink, but was caused by some spirit that was in the hall. "Your royal highness!" he pleaded, "let your grace be advised that it is not from the intoxicating effects of distilled spirits that we stand here like drunks, dumb and unable to entertain, but rather because of the spirit that sits in the corner over there in the guise of a little person."

The king ordered a squire to go and bring Taliesin from the corner where he was lurking and into his presence. He asked Taliesin what he was and where he had come from. Taliesin answered the king in verse, saying as follows:

23

> General chief-poet
>   am I to Elphin,
> And my place of abode
>   is the land of the Cherubim.

Then the king asked him what he was called, and he answered the king like this:

> John the divine
>   called me Merlin;
> But now kings
>   call me Taliesin.

So then the king asked him about his career, and he told his story to the king in the following manner:

> I was with my Lord
>   in the heavens
> When Lucifer fell
>   to the depths of hell.
> I held the banner
>   ahead of Alexander;
> I know the stars' names
>   from North to South.
> I have been in Caer Gwydion
>   and in the Tetragrammaton;
> I was in Canaan
>   when Absalom was slain;
> I brought seed down
>   to the vale of Hebron;
> I was in the noble courts
>   before Gwydion was born;
> I have been patriarch
>   to Elijah and Enoch;
> I was head keeper
>   on Nimrod's tower;
> I was atop the rood

of the merciful Son of God;
Three times have I been
  in Arianrhod's prison;
I was in the ark
  with Noah and the Lord;
I saw the destruction
  of Gomorrah and Sodom;
I was in Africa
  before Rome was built;
I came to these shores
  to Troy's survivors;
And I was with my Lord
  in a humble manger;
I nurtured Moses
  in the Jordan's waters;
I was there in the air
  with Mary Magdalen;
I got poetic inspiration
  from the caldron of Ceridwen;
I was harper-poet
  to the hosts of Norsemen;
I was in the White-mount,
  in the court of Cynfelin;
In stocks and chains
  for a year and a day;
I was there to see
  in the land of the Trinity,
And whirled about
  throughout the world;
And till Judgement's day
  I'll be in this place;
And no one knows
  whether I'm flesh or fish;
I was nine months gestating
  in the witch Ceridwen;
Gwion Bach I was then,
  but now I'm Taliesin!

And the story says that this song stunned the king and his people. Then Taliesin sang another song to let the king and his people know why he had come there and what he was going to accomplish, as this poem tells:

> Provincial poets! I am contesting!
> I shall not hold back;
> I speak a prophecy
> to those that will listen;
> I am here to seek
> the loss I have suffered,
> Elphin's release
> from Caer Degannwy.
>
> My Lord will slip
> his fetters and chains;
> for the Chair of Degannwy –
> relentless my drive –
> three-hundred songs and more
> the worth of the song I'll sing;
> the poet who doesn't know it
> deserves neither spear,
> nor stone, nor ring,
> nor even to be in my company.
>
> Elphin son of Gwyddno
> sits under sentence,
> under a dozen locks and more,
> for praising his bardic instructor;
> and my name is Taliesin –
> chief poet of the western world!
> and I shall release Elphin
> from his golden fetters and chain!

Following this, as the text says, he sang a song in aid of Elphin, which is said to have produced such a tempest of wind that the king and his people thought the castle would fall in on them. The king responded by having Elphin brought immediately from his prison and released to Taliesin. Taliesin then sang another song that caused the fetters around

Elphin's feet to spring open. But really, in my opinion it's very difficult for anyone to believe this story. Nevertheless, I will continue with as many of his poems as I have seen in writing. After the poems just mentioned, he sang a series of stanzas that are called "Poets' Posers"; they follow here.

> What man did Alpha
>   make first?
>   What fair language
>   did the Lord make best?
>
> What food, what drink?
>   Who brought clothing?
>   Who introduced denial
>   from the land of lies?
>
> Why is a stone hard?
>   Why is a thorn sharp?
>   Who's as hard as a rock
>   and as salty as salt?
>
> Why is the nose ridged?
>   Why is a wheel round?
>   Why does the tongue declare
>   more than any other organ?

After that he sang the verses called "Bards' Rebuke"; it begins like this:

> If you are a bard in contention,
>   with fierce poetic inspiration,
>   don't test your ferocity
>   in the court of a king
>   unless you know
>   the name of *rimin*
>   the name of *ramin*
>   the name of *rimiad*
>   the name of *ramiad*
>   and the name of your granddad

27

before he was christened;
and the name of the firmament
and the name of the sky
and the name of your tongue
and the name of the realm.

Stand aside, poets all –
both high and low;
my darling is below,
bound by the chains of Arianrhod;
you cannot for sure
know what I declare,
nor distinguish clearly
between the truth and a lie.

Poets of tiny horizons,
why aren't you fleeing?
The poet who can't shut me up
will get no peace at all
till he goes to the grave,
beneath sand and gravel;
but those who hearken to me,
God will take heed of them.

Following that is the satire called "Bile of the Bards."

Bards practice abuse,
their eulogies Godless ditties,
everything they say a lie;
they poke fun at proper men,
corrupt married women,
violate Mary's innocent maidens;
they waste their time and their lives:
drinking by night and sleeping by day;
they hate the church and love the tavern
roam every village, town, and lane,
never give lodging nor alms;
recite no psalter or prayers;

keep not the Sabbath nor holy days;
fast not on eves or ember days.
>Birds fly
>fish swim
>bees make honey
>worms crawl;
>everthing acts to
>earn its keep,
>save lazy bards, thieves
>and wandering Jews.
I don't revile your bardic profession,
for it came from God to counter blasphemy,
only those who use it recklessly,
to revile Jesus and those who serve him.

When Taliesin had freed his master, proved the fidelity of his mistress, and silenced the poets so that none of them dared utter a single word, he instructed Elphin to make a wager with the king that his horses were swifter than the king's. Elphin complied, and a date was set for the race at a place now known as Morfa Rhiannedd. The king arrived there with his people and twenty four of the fastest horses he owned. Eventually, the course was marked out and the horses made ready to run. Taliesin was there with twenty-four sticks of holly, burnt black. He had his master's jockey put them under his belt, and instructed him to let all the king's horses get ahead of him and then, as he overtook each of them, to strike the horse across the rear with the stick and then let it fall to the ground. He instructed him to do that to each of the horses in turn as he caught up to them, and to pay special attention to the place where his horse surged into the lead and mark the spot with his cap.

The jockey accomplished both these things, striking each of the horses in turn across their rumps and throwing his cap to the ground where his horse took the lead. When the horse had won the race, Taliesin brought his master to the marked spot and had Elphin set men to digging a hole there. When they had dug down to a certain depth, they found a huge caldron full of gold. "Elphin," said Taliesin, "you see here payment and reward for rescuing me from the fish weir and for raising me till now." A pool of water stands on that spot, known ever since as Y Pyllbair or 'Caldron-pool.'

Afterwards, the king had Taliesin brought to him, and questioned him about the beginnings of the human race. Taliesin responded with the verses that follow here, now known as one of the four principal divisions of poetry.

> Almighty God made,
> in the Vale of Hebron
> with his blessed hands,
>> Adam.
>
> He made a fair one
> in the garden of Paradise,
> from a rib woven,
>> wonderful woman.
>
> Seven hours they were there,
> tending the orchard
> before Satan's siege,
>> persistent plague.
>
> From there they were driven,
> through the frost and cold,
> bringing their lives
>> to the world we know.
>
> To bear in travail
> daughters and sons
> and gain the sovereignty
>> of Asia.
>
> Twenty eight in all,
> in labor she bore,
> a mixed brood withal,
>> male and female.
>
> Among those many souls,
> she brought forth Abel,
> and Cain – without control,

unredeemable.

To Adam and his mate
was given a spade
to turn the soil
        to earn their bread.

To sow the plain
with clear, bright grain
to feed everyone
        till the day of Doom.

An angelic messenger
from the Heavenly Father,
brought the seed grain
        down to Eva.

But a tenth of the gift
she concealed;
so planted only part
        of the field.

Black rye grew up
instead of wheat crop,
revealing the evil
        of thievery.

Because of that deception,
Saturn says that everyone
must first give to God
        that tenth as tithe;

Of the deep red wine,
planted in full sunlight;
by the light of the waxing moon
        comes white wine.

From the privileged grain

and the virtue of red wine
is made miraculously
    Christ's own body.

His flesh is the wafer,
His blood the wine,
and the words of the Trinity
    make them holy.

Every sort of sacred book
authored by Emmanuel
was brought by the angel Rafael,
    a gift to Adam

When he stood in the Jordan
with the water swirling
around his jaws,
    fasting.

Moses was made strong,
as he stood in the Jordan,
by the power of the three rods
    most potent.

Samson was given,
in the tower of Babylon,
the skills and arts
    of Asia's land.

To me alone belong,
through my bardic song,
the skills and esoterica
    of Europe and Africa.

I know their careers,
their dwellings and wars,
their tributes and destiny
    till Doomsday.

Dear God! how loathsome,
and with great lamentation,
the prophecy will come
        to Troy's descendants.

A serpent, armor plated,
proud and without pity,
her wings gilded,
        coming from Germany.

She will overcome
England and Britain,
from the North Sea's shore
        to the Severn river.

Then will all Britons
be as prisoners,
status of foreigners
        to Saxons.

Their god they'll worship,
adopt their language,
and lose their land –
        save wild Wales,

Till a new world commence,
after long penance,
when the two powers
        are equal.

Then will the Briton
gain country and crown,
and the foreigner
        will be no more.

And the words of the angel,
concerning peace and turmoil,

> will be assured and true
> for all Britannia.

And he went on to speak numerous prophecies concerning the world to come.

ATHIRNE AND AMAIRGEN

Athirne is an important figure in the traditions about poets in early Ireland, and he turns up in several tales. His name is interesting in that it is related to Latin *paternus* and means 'fatherly.' Though he is hardly the 'fatherly' type as we find him here, his name recalls that of one of the Welsh poets named in the *Historia Brittonum*, Talhaearn Tad Awen 'Talhaearn Father of Poetic Inspiration.' Thus Athirne is a kind of archetypal figure in early Irish poetry. In the present story he is called chief poet of all of Ireland, and, as we see, he fosters Amairgen who, upon the death of Athirne himself becomes chief poet of all of Ireland.

While Athirne epitomizes the mean-spirited side of poets, our tale presents an even more sinister side of him. Here he is willing to kill without hesitation to forestall the career of a potential rival. But there is a good deal more to the story than just the homicidal tendencies of a certain Irish bard, and I have discussed it in detail elsewhere (Ford 1990). Suffice it to say here that competition between and among poets was rife in the early period. See, for example, Taliesin's challenges to the poets of Maelgwn Gwynedd's court in the preceding story. But the process of becoming a poet in itself entailed a sort of ritual death: a poet had to be born again, as it were, and this is reflected not only in the sort of mock death that occurs in this story but also in the re-christening that we see in the stories about Finn and Taliesin. There seems to be a reference to poetic ritual death in "The Gododdin" too; see Ford 1987.

Amairgen appears in the medieval Irish pseudo-historical work *Lebor Gabála Érenn* or 'The Book of the Taking of Ireland.' That rather long text purports to account for all of the successive waves of peoples who came to Ireland, from the ante-deluvian Cesair and her three companies of women to the sons of Mil Espáine, the Gaels themselves. In this account, Amairgen, both poet and judge, is the first of the sons of Mil to set foot on Ireland. As he does so, he recites a poem in which he claims to exist in all matter (see Introduction, p. xxi). Thus it can be seen that in Amairgen we are dealing with a figure very much in the mold of the Welsh poet Taliesin, a figure who embodies all knowledge, is protean, having existed in a variety of shapes, perhaps simultaneously. Amairgen is the archetypal poet at the horizon of Irish culture. Nonetheless, our tale takes us one step further back, to the ersatz slaying and subsequent training of Amairgen by Athirne, who would thus seem to be what his name suggests, the father of poetry, fosterer of Amairgen. But whatever of these ruminations on the mythical pedigrees of primeval Irish poets, Athirne remains best known in the Irish literary tradition as a mean-spirited and hard-hearted individual, feared for his powers of satire. This side of him is perhaps best revealed in the tales "Athirne the Insistent" and "The Siege of Howth." The translation is based on the edition of Best 1954, lines 13565-617.

Bibliography: Best 1954; Ford 1987, 1990, 1992a; Morris-Jones 1918; Thurneysen 1918

Athirne and Amairgen

There was a famous smith in Ulster named Ecet Salach or Ecet the Foul. He was also known as Echen. He was a master of every art, and there wasn't before him or after him a better smith. A son was born to him, and they named him Amairgen. He reached the age of fourteen years without speaking. His belly grew till it was as huge as a big house, sinewy and fat. The snot ran from his nose into his mouth. His skin was black, his teeth white, his face pallid. His legs and thighs were the size of the handles of a smith's bellows. His feet were cloven, under huge, gnarly ankles. He had high cheekbones and a very long face. His eyes were dark red and sunken, under long, hairy eyebrows. The hair on his head was rough and spikey, and his back was humped, bony, and scabby. And so he was not handsome. And if he were left sitting for a long time without cleaning up after him, his excrement would pile up as far as his hips. His favorite foods were boiled curds, salt made from burnt seaweed, unripe blackberries, bright rowanberries, burnt ears of corn, stems of wild garlic, hollow nuts, all upon a table for his delectation.

One day Athirne sent his servant, Greth, to Ecet Salach to put an axe into the forge. Greth saw the ugly, misshapen creature there in the middle of the house. The creature scowled at him, and Greth rose to go. Ecet's daughter was there in the house, seated in an exquisite chair and clothed in a beautiful garment. She alone was watching the house, and the boy was beside her. Then they heard something, the boy speaking to Athirne's servant: "*In ith Greth gruth* ('does Greth eat curds')?" he intoned three times. Greth did not answer but hastened to go. The boy spoke again: "blackberries, sloes, stems of garlic, pine nuts, nuts without fruit; *In ith Greth gruth?*"

Greth fled from the house, ran across the bridge leading to the fort and into the marsh. He kept going until he reached Athirne. "You have seen warriors!" exclaimed Athirne, "you have a frightful look about you."

"And with good reason," replied Greth. "a fourteen-year old lad who has never spoken addressed me today, and he will leave you without office if he's not destroyed."

"What did he say to you?" asked Athirne.

"Not hard," answered Greth, "he said, *'In ith Greth gruth,'*" and he told him the rest of it. Then Athirne asked him how things were in that court. Greth told him everything and the manner in which he left the place.

Meanwhile, Ecet returned home, and his daughter said to him, "Amairgen spoke today, to Athirne's servant who had come here to fix his axe."

"What did he say to him?"

"*'In ith Greth gruth,'*" she began, and told him all of it.

"This is what will come of that," said Ecet, "Athirne will come to kill the boy so that the boy won't surpass him, for the lad who spoke those words will possess great poetic learning!"

So the maiden took the boy out of the court to a summer milking-place on the south side of Slieve Mis. Ecet meanwhile made a clay likeness of the boy and clothed it in a fine garment. He laid it down, as if the boy were sleeping, on his left side between himself and the bellows.

Athirne and his servant Greth arrived, and they saw the boy lying there. They put their axe together, and they were good at it; the head was driven onto the handle. Athirne brought the axe down onto the head of the effigy there, thinking it was the boy himself. They ran out of the house, then, and the hue and cry was raised after them. The host pursued them, and Athirne gathered his goods and possessions into the fort.

Afterwards, the wrong was redressed. The Ulstermen came and a settlement was made between them. Twenty-one cows, the honor price of a chief poet, were paid for Amairgen, and a contract was made between them. Athirne took Amairgen in fosterage, and the lad learned the poetic art from him. Later, when Athirne languished in old age, Amairgen became the chief poet of Ulster.

THE SPIRIT OF POETRY

Among the numerous Celtic words for poetry inherited from Indo-European culture is Welsh *awen* and its Irish cognate *aí*. The Welsh word means 'poetic gift, genius, or inspiration, the muse.' The Irish word, the earliest form of which is *auí*, is defined as 'poetic inspiration, learning; metrical composition.' The basic meaning underlying the root of these words is 'blow': poetic inspiration is just that, something that 'blows' into the poet. That, of course, is the meaning of our 'in-spiration': a blowing in. The poet, then, is a kind of medium through which the muse speaks. Thus, in "The Story of Gwion Bach, Who Became Taliesin," we read that Ceridwen realized that the only way her ugly son was going to get recognition in this world was if she could make him full of *yspryd proffwydoliaeth* 'the spirit of prophecy.' In other words, she wanted him to become a poet, one with powers of divination such as Taliesin and Finn have. Her son does not profit from her labors, of course, but Gwion Bach, reborn as Taliesin, he of the radiant brow, does have such powers. Indeed, in the court of Maelgwn Gwynedd he is identified as a *spirit*.

Our story occurs in the early Irish compilation known as *Sanas Cormaic*, 'Cormac's Glossary,' where it is given in explanation of the Irish word *prull*. Cormac mac Cuilennáin was king and bishop of Cashel and ruled the province of Munster until his death in the early tenth century (see "Gormlaith daughter of Flann Sinna"). His glossary, an important text for Celtic scholars, gives explanations of words and names, supported sometimes by brief narratives. Although these explanations are 'fanciful' by modern linguistic standards, they do provide important clues to Irish culture as perceived and understood in Cormac's own time. In the present narrative, the gifted poet figure has no name other than 'Spirit.' He is given a Latin appellation by the scribe, *Spiritus Poematis*, 'the Spirit of Poetry.' As I have argued elsewhere (Ford 1990), this story fits the paradigm of Celtic myths about the archetypal poet in several ways. Like Amairgen and Ceridwen's son Afagddu, the Spirit of Poetry is exceedingly ugly at first. Like Amairgen and Taliesin, he speaks in riddles. In our story, the woman known as daughter of Úa Dulsaine is much sought after and, while her state is pitiable, she controls the situation. She catechises the great poet Senchán Torpéist, but he remains dumb, unable to complete the verses she quotes him. The Spirit of Poetry can cap the verses, however, and thus helps Senchán to save face. When the test is over, she is dressed in fine clothing and brought back to Ireland in the company of Senchán. In her splendor, she is strongly reminiscent of Amairgen's beautiful sister, who, beautifully dressed, sits upon a kind of throne, guarding the house where her brother sits in his own filth. It is she who transports her ugly brother to the cowshed and protects him while Athirne and his servant are butchering his effigy in the symbolic death of the boy.

Senchán Torpéist is chief poet of all of Ireland in a number of tales, including "Guaire's Greedy Guests," in which he plays a central role. The name Senchán means something like 'Mr. Custodian of Tradition'; *Torpeist* is explained fancifully in the course of our story. The translation is based on the edition of Meyer 1912.

Bibliography: Meyer 1912; Ford 1990

The Spirit of Poetry: *Spiritus Poematis*

Prull: it means 'great increasing and enlarging', as the poetess, daughter of Úa Dulsaine ('descendant of satire'), said to Senchán Torpéist on the Isle of Man:

> my ears burn me greatly (*prull*)!

And one of the poets in Senchán's entourage replied:

> the song of a son of Satire,
> from the doctor of the district of Tull.

This is how that came about. Senchán happened to go on a poetic circuit to the Isle of Man. He was accompanied by fifty poets as well as by apprentice poets. Rarely did any other poet ever wear the kind of regalia that Senchán wore, including his cloak of feathers and all the rest. The very finest of the garments of the Gaelic nobility, that's what the poets themselves wore.

When they had embarked on the sea and were headed away from land, a weird, unnatural-looking lad called out to them from land, "let me go with you!" They all looked at him, and they were not at all pleased to have him come along, for they judged that he was not a bird fit for their flock – his appearance was repulsive. Truly, if anyone pushed on his forehead with his finger, a gush of putrid matter would spurt out and run down to the base of his neck. A rough membrane covered his head right

39

down to his shoulder blades; it looked as though the gray matter of his brains had burst through his skull. His eyes protruded like the eggs of a blackbird. As fast as a beast of the wild, black as death, his teeth yellow as gold; his butt green as the trunk of a holly tree. His lower legs were bare and skinny, his heels blotchy-black and pointed. If the rag he wore were removed, it is certain that it would move out by itself because of all the lice in it – unless someone put a rock on it. He called out loudly to Senchán and said to him, "I will be more valuable to you than any one or two or the entire bunch of fools who surround you!"

"Can you jump onto the rudder and from there into the boat?" asked Senchán.

"I'll give it a go," he replied. He leapt from the shore onto the rudder, as swiftly as a mouse along a weaver's beam, and hopped into the boat. The boat almost capsized when the occupants fled from him to the other side of the vessel, and they cried out as one, "a monster has attacked you, Senchán, and if we should ever reach land, he'll be your only company!" And that's why he is called Senchán Tor-péist, because a monster, a *péist*, attacked him.

They land at the Isle of Man and leave their boats at the shore. As they were crossing the strand, they saw a big, gray-haired old hag on the rock. As the poet said,

> Old hag and old geezer,
> may their pubic hair be their shroud
> if they don't serve the son of God
> and don't offer up first-fruits.

There on the strand, the old hag was harvesting seaweed and other produce of the sea. Her feet and her hands were refined and elegant, but she was not wearing fine clothing, and the pinched look of hunger was upon her. And that was sad, for she was the poetess, daughter of Úa Dulsaine from Muscraige Líach Tuill in the territory of the Uí Fhidgenti. She had gone on a circuit of Ireland, Scotland, and Man, and her entire retinue had died. Afterwards, her brother, the son of Úa Dulsaine and a wonderful poet, was seeking her throughout Ireland, but didn't find her, and so on.

The old hag saw them, then, and inquired who they might be. "Those you ask about are good people – Senchán, poet of all of Ireland, is here."

"Senchán," she said, "would you grant me the favor of responding to me?"

"I will indeed," he replied.

> "I was not acquainted with hardship,
> though I reap swollen seaweed;

What's the other half of this quatrain?" she asked.

Senchán was dumb struck; so were the other poets. Then this fellow we spoke of before springs to Senchán's side and says, "Hush, you hag! Don't speak to Senchán – it's not proper for you. Talk to me, for none of this company will converse with you."

"Fine," said the poetess. "What's the corresponding half-stanza?"

"Not hard," said the lad:

> "From the rock of the sea of Man
> was made sea salt here."

"That's correct!" she said. "Now how about this one?

> my ears burn me greatly (*prull*)!

What's the last half of that would you say, Senchán!"

"So, trying to engage Senchán, are you? He won't answer you."

"All right then, what do *you* say it is?" she asked.

"Not hard," he said:

> "the song of a son of Satire,
> from the doctor of the district of Tull."

"It's true, then," said Senchán, "you're the daughter of Úa Dulsaine, the poetess they've been seeking throughout Ireland!"

"It is I indeed," she replied. Senchán then had her bathed and clothed in splendid garments, and she returned with Senchán to Ireland.

As they drew near to Ireland, they looked at the lad we spoke of before. What they saw was a radiant, regal, great, broad-eyed, valorous youth. His curly hair was yellowish-gold, like gold thread, wavy as the spine of a small harp. He wore an elegant, princely cloak, fastened with a gold brooch. Against his body he held a four-sided, purple, embossed shield, full of carbuncles, precious stones, pearls, crystal, and sapphires. A straight-edged sword with red-gold hilt lay in his right hand. And upon his head was a silver tiara with a gilded crown. His was the most magnificent and elegant form that ever adorned man.

He goes righthand-wise around Senchán and his people, *et nusquam apparuit ex illo tempore. Dubium itaque non est quod ille Poematis erat spiritus* ['and he was never seen from that time on. Therefore, there is no doubt that he was the spirit of Poetry'].

SINANN: THE SHANNON RIVER

The present text takes us into a branch of Irish tradition known as *dindshenchas*. The word means 'traditional lore' (*senchas*) about 'well-known places' (*dind*). It is a kind of didactic verse, like the Irish proverbs and genealogical poems. And like the genealogical material the *dindshenchas* collections are extensive. This is not surprising since the *filid* were expected to know the meaning and origin of every place name, just as they were expected to know the pedigrees of princes, the histories of battles and other exploits, etc.

The story of Sinann, 'Shannon,' is meant to explain the origin of the Shannon river. It tells us why it is called Shannon and who the person was for whom it was named. For our purposes it is important because of its references to Connla's Well, the magic of the hazel nuts of Crimall the sage, and the salmon of wisdom. "The Boyhood Deeds of Finn" tells of the poet Finnéces, waiting on the banks of the Boyne (see below) for the salmon which would give him the powers of divination. And we recall that Taliesin, when found by Elphin, was trapped in a dam designed to catch salmon, and that he refers to himself as a catch that will be worth far more than ordinary salmon.

Additional stanzas at the end of our poem identify the pool in which Sinann drowned as *Lind Mná Féile* 'the Well of the Modest Woman.' Another version of the Sinann legend (Gwynn 1913, pp. 286-91) adds the information that the name of the pool into which the nuts of Crimall (called Crinmond in this other version) fall is Segais.

In the *dindshenchas* poem of Boand, eponym of the Boyne River, we are told that that river had fifteen names, one of which was Segais. In the poem, Boand is the wife of Nechtan, owner of a secret well "from which gushed forth every kind of mysterious evil." We are told that none could look into the well for fear his eyes would burst from his head. Boand, through pride it is said, went to look into the well. It rose up against her and pursued her as she fled from it toward the sea. She drowned in what is now the estuary of the Boyne river. I have argued elsewhere (Ford 1974) that what Nechtan's well (Segais) contained was the brilliant and illuminating essence that characterizes poetry (*imbas forosnai*). The translation is based on the edition of Gwynn 1913.

Bibliography: Bowen 1975-6; Ford 1974; Gwynn 1913; Ó Concheanainn 1981-2; O Daly 1965; Stokes 1885; Stokes 1894

Sinann: The Shannon River

The river Shannon: why it is called so
I'll say now in language true;
I'll speak clearly, without complication,
of the name itself and of its origin.

I'll declare to each and every one
the origin of the bright waters of Shannon,
concealing nothing of its lofty fame,
or the means by which it got its name.

The raucous, gushing well of Connla –
beneath the blue-bordered sea it lay;
six streams flowed from it,
Shannon, the seventh, was above the rest.

The nine hazels of wise Crimall
strew their fruit upon the well;
they possess the power of sorcery,
enveloped by the dark mist of druidry.

Strange to say, their leaves and flowers
begin to sprout in the same hour;
and though it seems a great virtue,
the fruit is ripe at the same time too!

When the crop of nuts has ripened so,
they drop from the tree to the well below;
they sink and settle on the bottom
and salmon come and consume them.

From the juice of the nuts – important this –
come the magical bubbles of *imbas*;
and the bubbles drift, hour by hour,
down the green, flowing rivers.

There was a girl, then, her hair golden,

sprung from the Túatha Dé Danann;
bright-eyed and sprightly Shannon,
daughter of Lodan Luchair-glan.

One night this lovely maiden,
this sweet, full-mouthed woman,
thought she had nearly everything,
only the *imbas* was she lacking.

So one day, this shapely beauty
came to the river to see;
she saw, indeed couldn't miss,
the glorious bubbles of *imbas*.

The girl, proud as she was,
leapt in to seize the bubbles;
but the effort came to nought there
for she drowned; and thus the Shannon river.

IMBAS FOROSNAI: ILLUMINATING INSPIRATION

This text, like "The Spirit of Poetry," is drawn from Cormac mac Cuilennáin's famous glossary, *Sanas Cormaic*. *Imbas forosnai* is one of the three things that characterize a poet; the other two being *teinm laida* and *díchetal di chennaib* (see "The Boyhood Deeds of Finn"). *Imbas* is defined as 'great knowledge; poetic talent, inspiration; fore-knowledge; magic lore; referring especially to knowledge or fore-knowledge obtained by magic or occult means.' *Forosnai* means 'lights up, illumines; brings to light, makes manifest.' Thus it is the Irish equivalent of that which Ceridwen wished to aquire for her son Afagddu in "The Story of Gwion Bach, Who Became Taliesin." Of the other two terms there is much uncertainty. O'Rahilly 1946, pp. 318-40, discusses these terms in connection with Finn's acquisition of wisdom. He suggests that *teinm laeda* means 'chewing of pith or marrow,' indicating the way that Finn would put his thumb in his mouth and chew it to the marrow whenever he needed something revealed to him. It also calls to mind the hazel nuts which contain magical knowledge and which, presumably, must be chewed through in order to ingest the pith. *Díchetal* is 'incantation, spell,' and it is accomplished *di chennaib* 'from ends' or 'tips' or 'heads,' etc. In his account of it, Cormac adds that it is 'from the ends of bones,' but it is not clear what he meant by that.

Whatever of the exact meaning of these three terms that are the distinguishing features of poets in early Ireland, it seems clear that they were acquired only in the process of initiation into the poetic orders and that they represented cult practice of some sort. One is reminded of Giraldus Cambrensis's account of the *awenyddion* or 'folk possessed of *awen*' in his twelfth-century *Description of Wales* (see the Introduction). Gerald's description is that of an unsympathetic outsider, but it suffices to show us that Welsh poets practiced a form of divination that was not unlike that practiced in Ireland, and that it most likely derived from inherited Celtic practices. The translation is based on the edition of Meyer 1912.

Bibliography: Chadwick 1935; Ford 1974; Meyer 1912; O'Rahilly 1946; Scott 1930; Thorpe 1978; Thurneysen 1932

Imbas Forosnai: Illuminating Inspiration

Imbas forosnai, i.e., it reveals whatever thing the *fili* pleases and what he needs to have revealed. This is how it is done: the *fili* chews a piece of the raw flesh of a pig or a dog or a cat. Then he puts it upon a stone behind the door, chants over it and he offers it to false gods and he summons them to him. He remains at that the next day, and chants over the palms of his two hands. He summons idol gods to him in order that his sleep may not be disturbed. He puts the palms of his two hands about his cheeks and sleeps, and people are watching over him so that no one might interfere with him or disturb him. And then the thing that he is after is revealed to him, for as long as three days, or twice that, or three times, or whatever time, long or short, that he may be involved in the offering.

And that is why it is called *imbas*: to wit, a palm [*bas*] on this side and a palm on the other around [*imm-*] his face or around his head. Patrick forbade that thing and the *teinm laída*, and he pledged his word that there would not be heaven nor earth for anyone who practiced it, for it is a denial of baptism. *Dichetal di chennaib*, however, was left as an integral part of poetic art, for it is learning that causes that: offering to demons is not necessary to accomplish it, rather narrating from the ends of bones straight off.

POETS ON TOUR

ATHIRNE THE INSISTENT

Athirne, as we have noted, represents the more unpleasant side of poets and poetry in early Ireland. Because of the power of satire and the belief that satire could ruin reputations and even bring injury and death, and the perceived ability of the poets to actually create fame and reputation for the objects of their poems, poets enjoyed very high standing in society. With these tools of satire and praise, the one greatly feared and the other greatly desired, the poets were able to demand substantial favors from their patrons. And just as poets could, by law, claim payment from patrons for their poetry, so was refusal of payment likely to be met by painful satire. Poets, then, were persons to be feared, and this situation was likely to lead to an abuse of power by them.

In Celtic tradition, the crane is associated with stinginess, meanness, and to some extent with war and warriors. Hence, the cranes that Athirne brings to Midir deny him the opportunity to exercise a prince's primary virtue, that of generosity. They also rob warriors of their mettle. One of the Fenian ballads (Mac Neill 1904) gives an account of the origin of the famed crane-bag, which we learn about in "The Boyhood Deeds of Finn." Two women were in love with the same man. One of them, through her magical powers, turned the other into a crane, and she was consigned to the house of Manannán Mac Lir, the Irish sea divinity, for two hundred years. When she died, Manannán made a bag from her skin, and in it kept his greatest treasures. It is this bag that eventually came into the possession of Finn, as we see in "The Boyhood Deeds of Finn."

Athirne's nickname, *ailgesach* is an adjectival form of *ailges* 'demand; request,' of the sort made by a poet. Poets had the right to make requests of patrons in return for the services they provided, but the word came to have a negative connotation associated with inordinate or unfair demands (see "Guaire's Greedy Guests"). So Athirne came to typify such unfair demands and was called 'the demanding,' or 'the importunate,' or, as here, 'the insistent.' The translation is based on the edition of Best 1954, lines 13550-564.

Bibliography: Best 1954; Ross 1967; Thurneysen 1918

Athirne the Insistent

Athirne 'the Insistent' son of Ferchertne was the most grudging and inhospitable person who ever lived in Ireland. He visited Mider of Brí Léith and brought him hostile and inhospitable cranes out of churlishness and meanness. Not one of the men of Ireland used to visit Mider's house for hospitality or entertainment. "Don't come, don't come!" screamed the first crane. "Go away!" said the second. "Walk on by!" ordered the third. Any of the men of Ireland who looked upon them would fail in a fight that day.

Athirne never ate when anyone else was present. Once he went off with a cooked pig and a flask of mead to eat by himself. As he settled down with the pork and mead, he saw this man coming toward him. "You'd eat that by yourself!" he said, taking the pork and mead from him.

"What is your name?" asked Athirne.

"It's not well known," he began, "Sethor, Ethor, Othor, Sele, Dele, Dreng Gerce, Mec Gerce, Ger Gér, Dír Dír – that's my name." Athirne didn't get the pig back, because he wasn't able to compose a satire on such a name. It was probably someone sent by God to take the pig, for Athirne did not lack proper manners from then on.

LOMNA, FINN'S FOOL

The ability of Finn mac Cumaill (here called Finn Ó Baiscne) to call upon his powers of divination are illustrated in this brief episode. The story occurs in *Sanas Cormaic*, 'Cormac's Glossary,' under the entry for the phrase *orc tréith*, where it is given in explanation of the meaning 'salmon' for the Irish word *orc*.

Lomna is called Finn's *drúth*. The term originally seems to have referred to a congenital idiot. But it came to be used for a professional entertainer, perhaps one who imitated an idiot as part of his act (Kelly 1988). At times it seems to have been confused with *drui* 'druid,' and could be used as a term for a poet. We don't have enough information in the present text to decide the precise meaning of the appellation here, but it is clear that he is a member of Finn's household, that he is skilled in *ogam* and in riddling verse, all of which would be true of a professional poet.

That Lomna's head should be capable of speaking, indeed, versifying, after it has been removed from his body comes as no surprise to us. We see another famous example of that in "The Battle of Allen." The head looms large in the traditions of the Celts as far back as the commentaries of the Greek Poseidonius. The Celts revered the head, and there is plenty of evidence for a cult of the head (Ross 1967). In warfare, heads of slain enemies were taken as trophies and proudly displayed. In the medieval Welsh tale of "Bendigeidfran" (second branch of *The Mabinogi*), the mortally wounded Bendigeidfran instructs his followers to remove his head and carry it with them as they make their way back from Ireland to Britain. He promises that his head will be as good company for them as it ever was when on his body. He further instructs them that upon their arrival in Britain they should bury the head in the White Mount in London, where it will be a protective talisman to keep Britain free from all oppressions. Heads, then, were potent and separable parts of the body, and the present story is but one example of how well it might function entirely on its own. The translation is based on the edition of Meyer 1912.

Bibliography: Ford 1977; Kelly 1988; Meyer 1912; Ross 1967

Lomna, Finn's Fool

Orc tréith, that's the name for the son of a king, for a king is called a *tríath*. The assembly of an *orc tréith*, to wit food and valuable clothing, down and feather beds, draughts and chess, horses and chariots, hunting dogs and other household pets.

Now *orc* is also a word for 'salmon,' whence the head of Lomna the fool said after it was struck from his body, "the speckled, white-breasted salmon bursting with spawn in the seas; neither talkative nor silent is the chief of a tribe who does not get his fill. Coirpre apportioned in a way that was not fair." And here is how he came to say that.

Lomna the Fool was Finn Ó Baiscne's fool. One day Finn went hunting. Lomna remained back. Now Finn had a woman from Leinster with him. You see, in every mountain and every forest that Finn used to frequent with his warband, there would be a woman set aside for him in the territory closest to him. These were women hospitallers and they were excellent for sustaining the warband, for their wealth used to extend across lands and no one would dare trespass against them.

It happened once that Finn was in Tethba with his warband, and he went out hunting. Lomna, however, remained back, and as he was going outside, he espied Coirpre the warrior lying furtively with Finn's woman. The woman begged Lomna not to tell, but Lomna was vexed at the thought of betraying Finn. Then Finn came home. Lomna cut an *ogam* [coded] message on a four-sided stick, and this is what it said:

> A slat of wood in a silver fence,
> a hellebore among edible plants;
> as the saying goes, the man whose woman is horny is a cuckold,
> and I point my finger at the woman from Leinster.

Finn got the point and became disgusted with the woman. The woman knew that it was Lomna who told on her. She sent word to Coirpre who came and killed the fool, cut off his head, and carried it away with him. Finn came to the hunting lodge at the end of the day and he noticed the headless body.

"There's a body here without a head," said Finn.

"Find out for us whose body it is," said his men. So Finn put his thumb into his mouth and he chanted through *teinm láida* and said,

54

Nicon ruba doine, nicon arlaig,
nicon topaig nais, nicon derg raigi,
nicon ruba torc, nicon fornae,
nicon torgrae, nicu rarbairt a lighe Lomnae.

"This is Lomna's body," said Finn, "and enemies have taken his head from it." They gathered the dogs then and set them loose on the trail of the warriors, and came upon them in a deserted house cooking a fish on a griddle; Lomna's head was on a spike beside the fire. The first serving from the griddle was divided by Coirpre among his three companies, and not a single morsel was offered to the head. That was taboo for Finn. Thereupon, the head said to them:

"The speckled, white-breasted salmon bursting with spawn in the seas; that is, a salmon from the spawn, that is what it comes from."

The second serving from the fire or from the griddle Coirpre divided *iterum priori modo*, and again they heard something: the head was saying,

"You have divided out portions a second time in the manner of one addicted to drink; it's only right to bring me my portion now; the warriors of the *fian* will be after you Leinstermen."

"Put the head outside, it's taunting us," said Coirpre. They heard the head from outside saying,

"I was killed by a leader of swift running hosts…when there was dissension it was the same to you driving me away, dissatisfaction with food, Finn will make a bonfire of the Leinstermen!"

Thereupon, Finn went up to them and he killed Coirpre.

THE BATTLE OF ALLEN

The Battle of Allen (*Cath Almaine*) is the last historical event about which a saga was composed in Ireland. The battle took place in December of the year 722, and it was fought over the *Bórama* or 'cattle-tribute' which the Uí Néill attempted to collect from the Leinstermen. Another tale (Stokes 1892; O'Grady 1892), a long one, tells of the origin of this tribute. Eochu, king of Leinster, married the daughter of Tuathal Techtmar, ancestor of the Uí Néill and high-king of Tara. Dissatisfied with her, he told the king she had died and then married her sister. When the two sisters met, they died of shame. Tuathal raised an army, invaded Leinster, killed Eochu, and imposed a fine (the *bórama*) on Leinster in perpetuity. This was the fine: 15,000 each of cows, swine, wethers, mantles, silver chains, copper cauldrons; a huge copper cauldron that would hold twelve swine and twelve oxen; thirty white cows with red ears, with their calves of the same color, tethers and bronze pails (summarized from Byrne 1973).

This heavy fine was imposed, usually by force, by a succession of Tara kings until the Leinstermen, aided by Finn Mac Cumaill and his men, successfully resisted. On another occasion, as our story says, the saint Mo-Ling, at the urging of the Leinstermen, went to the northern king Finnachta, who was mustering a force to levy the tribute, and tricked him by asking him to delay the campaign until Monday. Finnachta agreed. What Mo-Ling meant was the Monday of Doomsday, so that the tribute would never have to be paid by Leinster. Finnachta had thus surrendered his right to impose the tribute.

Our interest in the story centers on the figure of Donn Bó and the role that poets and other entertainers played in military expeditions. One of the major functions of poets traditionally was the creation of fame for their patrons through the celebration of their generosity and valor. They accompanied the patrons into battle and thus witnessed at first hand the qualities they would celebrate in their poems. This function is surely what lies behind the unwillingness of Fergal's men to join him in battle unless Donn Bó came along. The poet of "The Gododdin" accompanies the army to Catraeth, and in his poems praises their courage even in defeat. In "The Battle of Gwen Ystrad," the poet Taliesin begins several lines with "I saw," making clear that he personally witnessed the bravery and ferocity of his patron. We note too that another kind of entertainer is present on this expedition, the *drúth* or 'fool, jester' Úa Maiglinne. Though Donn Bó is a versatile entertainer, he insists that he cannot attend to Fergal on that occasion, and he suggests that the jester take his place.

Úa Maiglinne then tells stories of various famous battles. It has been suggested, and reasonably so, that telling tales of battles on the eve of a great battle was intended to urge the audience on to great deeds on the following day (Rees 1961).

Another point of interest is the ability of the poet to continue to function even after his head has been severed from his body! On the significance of the head see the introductory note to "Lomna, Finn's Fool." The translation is based on the edition of Ó Riain 1978.

Bibliography: Byrne 1973; O'Grady 1892; Ó Ríain 1978; Rees 1961; Ross 1967; Stokes 1892

The Battle of Allen

The battle of Allen was fought between the Leinstermen and the Uí Néill on the eleventh of December. The cause of the battle was the tribute, which Fínnachta had resigned to Mo-Ling, being levied by Fergal. The Leinstermen would not give it. They had not given it to Loingsech mac Aengus nor to Congal Cinnmagair, though they endured much grief from Congal, and they weren't going to give it to Fergal. They trusted in the words of Mo-Ling, who had pledged that the tribute would never again be levied against the Leinstermen.

Fergal was angered by the fact that the Leinstermen would not fulfill what had been promised to him, and so to take the tribute by force he proclaimed an immense and huge hosting upon Conn's Half, the northern half of Ireland, mustering the men of Eogan and Conall and the Airgialla and Meath. This occurred in the fourth year of his own sovereignty, or in the thirteenth year, *ut quibusdam placet*. He was a long time assembling the troops, for every man of Conn's Half summoned used to say, "if Donn Bó comes on the hosting, I will go."

Donn Bó, now, he was the son of a widow of Fir Rois, and he never went out of his mother's house day or night. In all of Ireland there wasn't anyone who was handsomer or had better shape or form or appearance than he. There was not in all of Ireland anyone who was more valorous or more accomplished than him, and no one had more amusing verses or better tales of kings than he. He was better at

57

harnessing horses, riveting spears and plaiting hair, and his wisdom more evident in his face than any other; *de quo dicitur*:

> More beautiful than other boys, lovely Donn Bó,
>> People speak of the sweetness of his songs;
> Finer than the youths of Inis Fáil,
>> The cause of a hosting of warriors.

Donn Bó's mother did not let him go with Fergal until Máel mac Faílbe meic Erannáin meic Chrimthainn, successor to Colum Cille, had been pledged for his safe return, and Máel swore on behalf of Colum Cille, then, that Donn Bó would return safely from Leinster to his own house.

So Fergal set out. He had guides to lead him, but they didn't give him good information. They led him into the narrow and rough parts of every trail until they reached Clúain Dobail in Allen. Áedán, the leper of Clúain Dobail, was at that place. The host was unruly, killing his only cow and roasting it on spits in his presence, and taking his house and burning it.

The leper said that the punishment the Lord would bestow upon the Uí Néill for that deed would last forever. He went to the tent of Fergal, where all the kings of Conn's Half were gathered just then. The leper complained of his suffering before them all. But none save Cú Brettan mac Congusa, king of Fir Rois, felt compassion, and that indeed was not a cause of regret for Cú Brettan, for not one of the kings who were in that tent escaped from the forthcoming battle except Cú Brettan mac Congusa alone. And then Cú Brettan said:

> I fear it: battle bloody-red,
>> O Fergal, I see it;
> Sad the followers of Mary's Son
>> After taking the house away from him.

> The leper's cow killed,
>> After his ox was slain;
> Woe to the hand that pierced his cloak,
>> Since he has not subdued mac Brain.

Then Fergal said to Donn Bó: "entertain us, Donn Bó; you are the best entertainer in Ireland: in whistling, flute-playing, harping, in verses, story-telling, tales of the kings of Ireland. Entertain us, for tomorrow morning we give battle to the Leinstermen."

"No," replied Donn Bó, "I cannot entertain you tonight and I do not have a single bit of any of that to parade before you tonight. But wherever you are tomorrow, and wherever I am, I will entertain you. Let the royal fool, Úa Maigleine, entertain you tonight."

So Úa Maigleine was brought to them. He began telling the battles and the contests between Conn's Half and Leinster from the destruction of Túaim Tenbath, i.e., Dinn Ríg, in which Cobthach Cáelbreg was killed, up to that time. They didn't sleep much that night because of how much they feared the Leinstermen and how bad the weather was on the eve of the feast of Finnian that winter.

As for the Leinstermen, they went to Cruachan Cláenta, for they were never defeated if they held their battle-councils there, so it was from there that they would go into battle. After that they went to Dinn Canainn.

The battle-lines of either side joined then on the morning of the following day: nine thousand Leinstermen and twenty thousand of the men of Conn's Half. Cruelly and fiercely was the battle waged on both sides as the men waded in. Exceedingly great was the narration of the triumphs of the heroes of Leinster and the heroes of Conn's Half.

It is told that Brigit was seen above the Leinstermen, and that Colum Cille was seen above the Uí Néill. In the end, Murchad mac Brain and Aedh Menn mac Colcan, king of South Leinster, were victorious. Fergal was killed. It was Aedh Menn and Dúnchad mac Murchada who killed Fergal, and Bile mac Báin, king of Scotland too; it is from Bile that we have the name Corrbile in Allen. And it was this same Aedh Menn who killed Donn Bó; Fergal did not fall in battle until Donn Bó fell.

One hundred and sixty attendants were slain there. The Leinstermen killed a number of Uí Néill warriors equivalent to the size of their own force in that battle, namely, nine thousand, and a hundred of their kings. Nine others were driven mad by the din of battle and went into *geltacht*, fleeing in terror;. Cnoc Fergail 'Fergal's Mound' is there. The Leinstermen let out a cry of triumph.

Unde dixit:

At the end of day at Allen,
 after contending for the cattle of Brega,
the raucous, red-mouthed Badb shrieked
a shout of victory over the head of Fergal.

Murchad rose to the occasion,
 pressed warriors into the ground,
turned his sword against Fergal,
 with a huge host at south Allen.

A hundred generous kings dead,
 proud, protective, powerful;
nine fled in terror, gone mad,
 nine thousand armed men.

Then the fool Úa Maigleine was seized, and he was compelled to do 'the fool's roar,' which he did. Great and melodious was that roar, so that ever since then the fools of Ireland speak of 'Úa Maigleine's roar.' Then Fergal's head was cut off, and the fool's head was cut off. The echo of the fool's roar remained in the air for three days and three nights. That's where 'the roar of Úa Maigleine pursuing the men in the bog' comes from.

Then Aedh Laigen mac Fithchellaig, king of Uí Maine of Connaught, turned to flee, and he called out to his sons, "Don't leave me, lads! Your mother will be all the better to you if you bring me with you!"

"They will not bring you," say the Leinstermen, and they kill Aedh Laigen. His sons came with Aedh Alláin mac Fergal to Lilcach, where the holy men Mo-Díchu mac Amairgin and Gall Cráibdech were. There the Uí Néill and the Connachta, disguised as clerics, dug the ditch of the church, and that's how three miracles were performed by the saints, and as a result there is a covenant of Uí Néill and men of Connaught with that church since that time. *Unde* Aedh Alláin *cecinit*:

We have not found on earth
 anything as peaceful as Allen;
We have not come after battle

60

to any place as splendid as Lilcach.

That day, thus, was victorious for the Leinstermen. But Cú Brettan mac Congus, king of the Fir Rois, was spared on account of the stanzas he had made the night before.

That evening, the Leinstermen were in Connal of the kings, drinking wine and mead after the battle, happy and in high spirits. Each of them, garrulous and effusive, was telling of his encounters. Then Murchad mac Brain said, "I would give a chariot worth four *cumals* and my horse and my battle gear to the hero who would go into the battlefield and bring us a token from it!"

"I will go!" said Báethgalach, a warrior of Munster. He put on his harness of conflict and combat and came to the place where Fergal's body lay. There he heard something, a proclamation in the sky above him, and it said,

A command to you from the King of seven heavens! Make entertainment for your lord tonight, for Fergal mac Maíle-Dúin! Though all of you professional entertainers have fallen here, including flutists and hornists and harpists, let neither terror nor weakness impede you from entertaining Fergal tonight!

Then Báethgalach heard the piping and the plaintive song, and from the tuft of rushes beside him he heard a warrior chant that was sweeter than any music. He warrior went toward it. "Don't come toward me," said this head to him.

"Question: who are you?" asked the warrior.

"Not hard to say; I am the head of Donn Bó,' replied the head, "and a pledge was enjoined upon me last night to entertain the king tonight, so don't harm me."

"Where is the body of Fergal?" asked the warrior.

"Over there."

"Question: shall I take you with me?" asked the warrior.

"You're the one I most prefer to take me," said the head, 'but by the grace of Christ, if you take me away, you must bring me back to my body again."

"I will indeed," promised the warrior.

The warrior returned, the head with him, to Connal, where he found the Leinstermen still drinking. "Did you bring a token with you?" asked Murchad.

"I did," replied the warrior, "I brought the head of Donn Bó."

"Put it on the post over there," says Murchad. The whole host recognized it, that it was the head of Donn Bó, and they all said: "Too bad for you, Donn Bó, you were so handsome. Entertain us tonight, as you did your own lord just now." His face is turned aside then, and his woeful warrior chant rose on high, so that they were all weeping and grieving.

Afterwards, Báethgalach conveyed the head to his body as he had pledged, and he put it in the proper position onto the trunk. Anyway, Donn Bó got back to the house of his mother! For these are the three wonders of this battle, to wit: Donn Bó reaching his house alive because of the pledge of Colum Cille, the roar of the fool Úa Maigleine three days and three nights in the air, and the nine thousand overcoming the twenty thousand. *Unde dicitur*:

> The battle of Allen, enormous slaughter,
> great the deed of December
> when Murchad mac Brain in great endeavor
> won with the men of Leinster.

> Fergal of Fál was beaten,
> the son of great Maél-dúin
> and mills on the battlefield
> turned from the streams of bright blood.

> Eighty-eight kings, it is true,
> and nine thousand men at least;
> from Conn's Half a famous host,
> fell there altogether.

> Nine gone mad from the battle,
> fled to the wood of Fid Gaible,
> where they soon deteriorated;
> and the Battle of Allen is concluded.

Haec sunt nomina regum qui interfecti sunt in hoc bello. Hi sunt quidem do Shíl Chuinn:

[There follows a long list of the names of the contestants, and the so-called "B" text ends with this list; what follows here is from the "Y" text.]

Leinster had gone into the battle in the absence of Cathal mac Findguine, and he was displeased by that. The Leinstermen heard of Cathal's displeasure with them, and so they took counsel. They decided to give the head of Fergal to Cathal, that he might participate in the victory celebration. So the head was brought to Cathal, and it was then that Fergal's poet, Rumann, sang this verse:

> Fair yet furious Fergal dead!
> warrior of glorious deeds;
> like thunder the peal of a groan
> from Mayo to the Isle of Man.

At the time, Cathal was at Glennaman of the Kings and Slieve Crot. Cathal attempted to kill the company that brought the head, for he was angry at the killing of Fergal in violation of his peace.

Afterwards, Cathal allowed the smooth-combing and braiding of Fergal's hair, and a satin scarf was put around it after that. Then seven cooked oxen, seven rams and seven sides of bacon were placed in front of Fergal's head, and it blushed with all the men of Munster looking on. The head opened its eyes toward God, taking pleasure in the great respect and honor that was bestowed on him. After that, that food was distributed to the indigents of the monastic cells nearby, that is, Áth Chros Mo-Laga and Tulach Min Mo-Laga.

Then Cathal went with a choice muster of the men of Munster to escort the head of Fergal and bring it to the Uí Néill. The kingship of the Uí Néill was bestowed upon Flaithbertach mac Áeda, and Cathal left them so, and came to Glennaman of the Kings at the end of a fortnight and a month. Later on, a great war was waged in Leinster against Cathal mac Findguine. Cathal and a large force of Munstermen went against Fáelán, king of Leinster, and all his men, and the battle of Féile was fought between them. Fáelchar, king of Ossory, fell there, and the Leinstermen were defeated.

Thus far the separation of Cathal and Leinster. Finit. Amen. Finit.

LLYWELYN AND THE FOOL

This tale concerns Llywelyn ap Iorwerth (1173-1240), also known as Llywelyn Fawr or 'Llywelyn the Great.' Indeed, he was one of the greatest of the rulers of Wales in the age of the princes (see the poems to him by Prydydd y Moch, below). The key figure in this narrative, however, is a fool, a sort of court jester. Like the Irish *drúth* in the two preceding tales, this particular figure is at times indistinguishable from his more elevated counterpart, the court poet. The tale shows that as late as the 1530s or so, there was belief in the magical powers of poets and their poetry. It tells how Llywelyn went to London for his betrothal to Joan (known in Welsh as Siwan or Sioned), daughter of King John. This occurred in the year 1205. The event is not widely noticed in chronicles of the time, perhaps because just then Joan was still bastard daughter to John, though later on she became legitimate by papal decree. The present narrative is found only in Elis Gruffudd's "Chronicle of the Six Ages of the World" compiled by him while in the service of the English government as part of the garrison at Calais in France (see the introductory note to "The Story of Gwion Bach"). Elis was writing in the first half of the sixteenth century, and he was using extant French, English, and Latin sources, as well as those written in his native Welsh. As a conscientious historian, he makes constance reference to 'my copy,' 'the books,' etc. Much of his Welsh material comes from oral as well as written sources, and he often refers to 'the people' or to 'the opinion of the people' or the sayings of 'old people,' and so on. The present text no doubt comes from oral traditions about the marriage of Llywelyn. There is no question of where Elis's sympathies lie, and the story itself is a kind of political fable. The Welsh magician outdoes his English counterpart, and Llywelyn ap Iorwerth saves face in the end, thanks to the gifted fool. As it turns out, the fool is not Llywelyn's own, but rather a *spirit* who has appeared to save the day for the Welsh. The translation is based on the edition of Parry 1944.

Bibliography: Parry 1944

Llywelyn and the Fool

After the death of Iorwerth Drwyndwn ab Owain, Llywelyn, his son, took the crown of the principality of Wales. In the fifth year of the reign of King John, Llywelyn or Lord Llywelyn was engaged and married to Elsabeth, the second daughter of King John, as the English chronicle says. But the Welsh chronicle says that it was Sioned, the youngest of the three daughters that he married. But indeed, it scarcely matters which of the two it was, since all the books say clearly that he married one of King John's daughters and that the prince made great preparations to go to England for the marriage. At the time, as the story says, the prince's fool begged and pleaded with his master to be allowed to go on that journey with his master the prince, but the fool's request was denied.

Soon, Lord Llywelyn mounted his horse and rode from Maenan to Rhuddlan. The next day he continued his journey from there to Caerleon on Dyfrdwy. It was then, as some of the books of Wales say, that the prince encountered a spirit that looked and acted like the fool he had left behind, and who followed him to Caerleon. There, he handed him over to his innkeeper to keep under close guard until he could find someone to take him back to Trefriw.

Then the prince mounted his horse and rode on, pushing forward determinedly until he had nearly arrived at the king's court. Then suddenly the fool appeared in the presence of the prince and his company. The fool, as the text says at great length, had the prince dress him in flamboyant clothes, as was proper for a person of that sort of learning.

Soon thereafter the prince arrived at the court and married the king's daughter. At the wedding feast, as my copy says, there was no shortage or lack of every sort of species of rare and excellent provisions to place before the rustic and lowly Welsh. These were consumed amid merriment and entertainment by every kind of minstrel and magician, the sort that were at that time very much in vogue in the courts of kings and princes.

Then one of the king's magicians stepped forward to demonstrate the power of his art for the entertainment of the people at the feast. To mock the ignorant Welsh, he conjured up through the magic of his art two or three men in Welsh boots and frocks, driving a herd of goats before them into the hall or the chamber where the wedding was taking place. As soon as they had come into the upper part of the hall or chamber, the goats began leaping on the seats and benches and tables, running from one place to another, with the people laughing and shouting, 'Look! Here's an offering from Wales!' This stunned the prince, causing the blood to rise in his cheeks from embarrassment as he asked the magician why the goats signified the Welsh rather than some other people.

The magician answered and said, "because they're ready to leap and run about from one place to another all over this kingdom and over land and sea to other realms to do the wretched things that goats do." On hearing this the prince lowered his head and fell silent.

Just then the prince's fool came and stood beside his master and asked permission to show the crowd the power of his magic. The prince answered, saying, "Indeed, I have cause enough to be embarrassed here without giving you permission to give me more reason to be red-faced."

But anyway, the story says that by the fool pleading and others pleading for him the prince gave permission to the fool to do what he thought appropriate. As my copy says, the fool, through his magic, conjured some men driving a herd of pigs before them into the hall or chamber in the same way the other magician had made men driving goats earlier. As soon as they came into the upper part of the chamber, they began to root up the ground and overturn tables and do other piggish activities which would be too long to rehearse here. And the Welsh laughed at that, saying, "Look! Here's a fine offering of English pigs for the prince to send to Llanrhychwin to root up bracken!" This stunned the English, who asked the fool what the pigs indicated.

He answered them saying that that they signified the English people, whom he said were pigs, unmindful of their faith, and who were turning up the ground to make fields and ditches to put the land into the hands of a small number of them, all of whom were stranger to each other than dogs and pigs are to each other. All this cheered the prince.

Eventually the prince took his leave from the king and began the journey back to Wales. He pushed on steadily until he came to Y berth Ddu above Llan Eurgain. There the fool said to the prince, "Sire, 'tis here I met you and 'tis here I leave you. Know and be assured that I am not the same as nor akin to your own fool, whom you suppose I am. You'll find him in your court, from which he hasn't moved, when you return home.' And so saying, he vanished abruptly from their midst.

The prince continued on his journey from there to Trefriw, where he found the fool, who had never left home. The prince and his people were amazed at all that.

THE SIEGE OF HOWTH

The title of this tale in the twelfth-century Book of Leinster is *Talland Etair*. *Talland* is a 'holding of land,' but its semantic range is quite broad, apparently including the abstract senses of both 'talent, gift' (as in 'talent for poetry, gift of poetry') and 'reproach, insult, disgrace.' Elsewhere, the tale is called *Forbais Etair*, using the word which means 'siege' or 'encampment (under siege).' While there certainly is a siege at Etar (Howth), it is worth noting that the story is motivated by the poetic practices of Athirne and his insulting behavior that follows from it. In the Book of Leinster, the story is followed immediately by three other narratives about Athirne, including "Athirne and Amairgen" and "Athirne the Insistent." So whatever of the conflict between the men of Ulster and Leinster, the story has as its motivating force a poet and his poetry.

There are other elements in the story that link it to the practice of poetry. When his poetic circuit takes him to South Connaught, the king, Eochu, tells Athirne there will not be *éra* 'refusal' of any request the poet might make. In "The Vision of Mac Con Glinne," we are told that Mac Con Glinne was called Anér "for there was never before him nor will there be after him anyone whose praise or satire was more troublesome. So that's why he was called Anér 'Non-refusal,' because no one could refuse him." Here, then, is a word closely connected with the consequences of a poet's request. The Irish word for a poet's request, especially used of a preposterous or impossible request is *ailges*, and that is precisely what Athirne makes on the men of Brestine in Leinster, living up to his nickname *Ailgesach* 'Insistent.'

Toward the end of the narrative we find some rather bizarre incidents, they too connected with the practice of poetry. Mes Gegra's charioteer, though not identified as a poet in the story, falls asleep and has a vision. While this is going on, Mes Gegra sees a large nut floating on the water. The charioteer, whose body has been levitating during his sleep, apparently has seen this nut in his vision, for when he awakens, he asks whether Mes Gegra has eaten the nut. It's difficult to make sense of this episode except by reference to divinatory practices such as "Illuminating Inspiration," and the nut floating on the water recalls the source of poetic inspiration as recounted in "Sinann."

Bibliography: Dobbs 1949; Stokes 1887.

The Siege of Howth

There was a hard and merciless man in Ireland, namely Athirne the Insistent, an Ulsterman. He was a man who would ask a half-blind person for his one good eye and force his attentions on a woman about to give birth. All that happened when he went on a poetic circuit at the request of Conchobar. He started out left-hand wise, visiting Connaught first. Then he went off to visit the king in the middle of Ireland, between the two Áth Clíaths, Eochu mac Luchtai, king of south Connaught. Eochu afterwards escorted Athirne to Munster, on the southern bank of the Shannon.

"So that you may not be dissatisfied with us, Athirne, if there are any treasures or valuables of ours that you would like, please take them," said Eochu.

"In fact, there is." replied Athirne. "I'd like that one good eye of yours put right here in my hand."

"You will not be denied," said the king, "you shall have it." And with that he put his finger into the socket, tore out his eye, and put it into Athirne's hand.

"Take my hand, lad," said the king, "and lead me to the lake so that I can rinse my face." He splashed water over his face three times, and said to his servant, "is the eye gone from my head?"

"Alas!" exclaimed the lad, "the socket [derc] is red [derg] with your blood!"

"Then let Dergderc be the name of this lake forever!" proclaimed the king.

Because of the king's generosity, giving his only good eye for the sake of his honor, God gave him a miraculous gift in return, restoring both his eyes to him. These verses were sung concerning that:

> The eye of the renowned king –
> For Athirne it was a legal thing;
> The poet's eyes stared ahead
> And pierced the proud king's head.
>
> Between wrathful Athirne
> And the good though reddened Eochu,
> God the Creator made things right

And gave the king perfect sight.

After that, Athirne called upon the king of Munster, Tigernach Tétbuillech. There was nothing he would accept to preserve the king's honor but to have the king's wife sleep with him that night. Otherwise, he said, he would destroy the honor of all of Munster forever. So on the night the woman was about to give birth, she was bedded by Athirne for her husband's sake, that his honor might not be destroyed.

Then Athirne went to Leinster, to Ard Brestine in the southern part of Mag Fé. The men of south Leinster came to meet him, and offered him treasure to stay out of their country; they were afraid of his satires. The treasures of any whom he visited were worth nothing if he did not have a share of them. Besides, any tribe or people by whom he might be killed would forfeit their right to legal redress from then on. So a man would give Athirne his wife, or his one good eye, or whatever he wanted of treasure and wealth.

What Athirne had in mind was to satirize the Leinstermen heavily, so that they would kill him, and then the Ulstermen would forever avenge his death upon Leinster. So he made a demand of the Leinstermen in Brestine: as he saw nothing of their treasure or wealth that he wanted, he would reproach them with words to the extent that they would never be able to raise their faces among the Gaels, unless they gave him the fairest treasure on the mound where they stood. No one knew what that treasure was or where on the mound it was.

That was an insult and an embarrassment to the people. Together they beseeched Tigernach to come there and help deliver them from the straits they were in. It so happened that there was a rider exercising his horse on the mound just then. He would ride toward them where they were assembled and then turn and charge off in the opposite direction. On one occasion, as the horse turned its legs sharply, it threw up a large clod of dirt with its hooves. No one in the assembly noticed it until it landed in the chest of the king, Fergus Fairge. The king saw a brooch, embedded in one side of the clod of dirt, worth eighty ounces of red gold. "What's this!" exclaimed the king. And Athirne said,

A brooch there is in Ard Brestine,
Brought out by the hoofs of a horse;
It engendered a just decision

In the mantle of Maine mac Durthacht.

"That's the treasure I wanted – the brooch!" exclaimed Athirne. My father's brother left it, and buried it after the battle of Brestine, where the Ulstermen were defeated!" So the brooch was given to him.

After that he went to visit Mes Gegra, king of Leinster. Mes Gegra was brother to Mes Roídia, and they were the two sons of the the two dumb ones; that is, their mother and father were deaf and dumb. Mes Gegra welcomed Athirne warmly.

"That's fine," said Athirne, "provided your wife stays with me tonight."

"Why should I give her to you?" asked the king.

"For the sake of your honor," said Athirne. "Otherwise, just kill me, so that the men of Leinster will be shamed forever and so that the Ulstermen will never cease avenging me on them forever!"

"You won't have your way with me because I fear the Ulstermen," said the king, "but to save my honor you may have the woman. There isn't a single Ulstermen who could take her from me if I didn't give her to you for my honor's sake."

"Right," said Athirne. "And I shall not depart from you until a single one of the Ulstermen has taken both your wife and your head."

"That will not be argued," said the king, "you shall have her." The woman, Buan, Mes Gegra's wife, spent the night with Athirne. Athirne stayed on circuit in Leinster for a year, and then he took the wives of a hundred and fifty princes and nobles of Leinster away with him to his own land.

"Well, my boy," said Athirne to his servant, "go to the Ulstermen and have them come meet me. The Leinstermen are likely to be thinking about me with all this booty, unless I restore their honor to them."

Indeed, the Leinstermen had come to bid Athirne farewell, and were at Tolka, north of Áth Clíath. Athirne said good-bye to them, but he left no blessing or anything else. The Leinstermen didn't very much like their wives being taken off as swag for the Ulstermen. So when Athirne got to Oenach Laigen, the Leinstermen went in pursuit of him and the booty. The Ulstermen arrived to provide protection for Athirne. The two forces clashed at once, and the Ulstermen were beaten. They fled by sea until they got to Howth. They were there nine days without food or drink, unless they drank the briny sea-water or ate dirt. Athirne had seven hundred cows there in the enclosure, but not a boy or man of the Ulstermen tasted a drop of their milk, for Athirne threw it all over the cliff. He didn't want any of them to discover his food or be able to savor it. They'd bring their wounded to him, but he wouldn't give them a drop, and they died from their wounds, abandoned. The Ulster nobles would go to him to plead for a drink for Conchobar, but they got nothing from him. So what nurtured Conchobar was what the girl brought from Emain Macha every afternoon. The girl's name was Leborcham.

There was a slave and his wife living with Conchobar, and they had a child whom they called Leborcham. She was quite ugly: her feet and knees faced to the rear, the backs of her thighs and her heels faced front. But she could race around all of Ireland in a single day, and at the end of the day she would tell Conchobar all the good and all the evil that was done in Ireland that day. Sixty loaves were set before her, next to the fire, besides what she ate with the rest of the company. She's the one who traveled from Emain Macha to Howth everyday with Conchobar's food.

The battle raged day and night around the fort. The Leinstermen say it is they who built the fort at Howth. Cú Chulainn's Gap is there, and it is not closed off. They all used to urge him to stop up the gap, but he refused, saying that it would be his many spears that would close it off. Conchobar counselled Cú Chulainn to hold his battle rage in check until reinforcements should come from Ulster. Leborcham had gone there to muster the troops and bring them by land and by sea to relieve the siege.

Mes Dead, son of Amairgen and Cú Chulainn's foster-son, was stationed to guard the gate of the fort. Every hour of the day he slew nine of the enemy. And three times a day the Leinstermen brought out Ulster hostages, and they too fell by Mes Dead. And it was then that unequal combat was first practiced in Ireland, for as the Ulster reinforcements were landing to the east of Howth, three hundred warriors attacked the lad at the gate. As they were cutting off his head, he let out a horrendous roar, and Cú Chulainn heard it.

"Either the heavens have collapsed, or the sea is draining, or the earth has split open, or my foster-son has roared as they overwhelm him with numbers." And so saying, Cú Chulainn leapt forth, splitting the host as he went. A fierce battle ensued. The warriors raised the contest to a bloody crescendo, fighting from morning till late afternoon. The Leinstermen were defeated, and they raised a wall of red against the Ulstermen, because it was taboo for the Ulstermen to go past a wall of red. There were heavy casualties on both sides in the conflict. A great many Ulstermen fell in the battle, first of all Mes Dead son of Amairgen, Bríannán Brethach, Connla, Beothach, Conaed son of Mornae, and many others.

Then Leborcham went north from the host to prophesy to the women of Ulster, for they had been in fear and dismay, and greatly grieving from the time the men had been holed up in Howth. Among the women were Mugain, she of the furze-like pubic hair, wife of Conchobor mac Nessa; Feidelm of the nine shapes, daughter of Conchobor, so called because she had nine shapes and each of them was lovelier than the others; fair-haired Feidelm, wife of Loegaire Buadach; Findbec, daughter of Eochu and wife of Cethern mac Fintain; Brig Brethach, wife of Celtchar mac Uithechair; Findnige, daughter of Eochu and wife of Eogan mac Durthacht; Findchaem, daughter of Cathbad and wife of Amairgen (who was tonsured at the rear); Derforgaill, wife of Lugaid Riabderg; fair-haired Emer, daughter of Forgall Manach and wife of Cú Chulainn mac Sualdaim; Lendabair, daughter of Eogan mac Durthacht and wife of Conall mac Amairgen; Niab, daughter of Celtchar mac Uithechair and wife of Cormac Connlonges mac Conchobair; and a good many more of the noble ladies of Ulster as well.

Mugain began to question Leborcham, then, and she asked, "Swift Leborcham, girl, which of the glorious Ulstermen did you see there?"

"Gentle, fair lady," Leborcham began, "I saw the warrior Conchobar, your beloved spouse, alive still, toiling in a stream of blood. I saw the perfect Cú Chulainn, everywhere fending off destruction. I saw Celtchar, himself heavily wounded, passing through cascades of red. I saw fierce Loegaire Buadach, wrapped in a hooded cloak full of holes; the glory of his triumph sprang forth. I saw Bríannán, and men he encountered were speckled with blood, consigned to a fine built cairn. I saw Gabliol there, a hacking, high-jumping warrior. I saw Conla, lying in a muddy puddle. I saw Furbaide Fer Benn, a fit man, ready for blood, in narrow straits. I saw Eogan the champion to the right of him; from his two hands a torrent of blood gushes forth. I saw there Dubthach; his two heroic arms were hacking away, severing arms. I saw Lugaid, with his many sons; he went the limit, with bloody resolve. I saw Amairgen, a formidable and proud warrior; his fury fuels combat. I saw Fergna there, a mighty man, foremost of champions; like a hawk he hounded them. I saw Auchride, who drove forward against the choicest foe, testing their mettle, leading good men. I saw Beothach, who got his second wind; he was spattered with blood as they slashed away. I saw the destroyer who ruins royal forts, Rochad, mighty striker, whom hosts gaze upon. I saw the eloquent and witty sage, who has achieved the highest level of noble speech, excelling all men, Ferchertne the king's poet. I saw Fiachra there; no ear ever heard reproach of him. Conaed, slayer of hundreds, foremost in slaughter, fiercely aggressive; the son of Mornae slain; men fled from all around him; he deserves to be laid in a fine tomb. I saw Corpre there, chief of men, eager for the bosoms of women. I saw there the mighty flames that glow like a single spark, weapons relentless in deeds of valor: Glaine, Gormainech, Mane Milscothach, Ailill, Scel, Toscel, Dures, Ret, and Bricriu; bold action from the sons of great Carbad. I saw Conall Cernach with troops and young warriors, with victories, spoils, herds; handsome Conall Cernach, victorious, triumphant warrior, aggressive and undaunted. I saw noble Cethern there, red-bladed, expending great energy. I saw there what has come to pass for the Ulstermen, that they did not lay out the enemy as a bear licks honey and sweet things or as the great sea overwhelms the land. I saw that sods were raised up, around which men were strewed, heads hurled, spears blunted. Swordplay, shields clashing, Ulstermen victorious; then slaughter upon slaughter, massacre upon massacre, the army in bloody rout. I have taken off a hostage from each of the provinces of Ireland except that of the Gailioin. They are at hand; they will come, will be exhibited, and will spend the night in Emain Macha. The great fighting men of Ulster await the troops who are coming to relieve them, if only they do not fall.

And that is the prophecy that Leborcham delivered to the women of Ulster.

Conall Cernach ventured out alone in pursuit of the Leinstermen to avenge his brothers, Mes Dead and Loegaire, who had fallen in the fight. He went through Áth Clíath, past Drummainech, through Uí Gabla, to Forcarthain; past Uachtur Aird and Naas to Cloínud. When the Leinstermen reached their own land, each of them went to his own house. Mes Gegra and his charioteer stayed behind, however, at Cassán Cloínta.

"I'll sleep for a while," said his charioteer to Mes Gegra, "and afterwards you can sleep."

"Fine," said the king. As Mes Gegra sat there looking at the water, he saw this nut come floating along the surface toward him. It was as big as a man's head. He went down and pulled it from the water, cut it in half with his knife, and left the one half for his servant. He noticed that the lad was lifted above the ground during his sleep; afterwards, he awakened.

"What is it with you, lad?" asked the king.

"I have seen an evil vision," he replied.

"Round up the horses, lad," ordered the king. He did so, and then said,

"Did you eat the nut?"

"Yes, I did."

"Did you save half of it for me?" the lad asked.

"I ate some of it first," said the king.

"The man who would eat a little without my knowing would eat the whole thing," said the lad. The king held out his hand with half of the nut clenched in it. The lad struck out with his sword and cut off the king's hand.

"That's a pity, lad," said the king, "open the hand and you'll find half of the nut in it." As he did so and found half of the nut there, he turned the sword on himself and plunged it right through his body.

"What a shame, my boy," said the king.

So Mes Gegra hitched up his own chariot, and he put the hand in it in front of him. As he was heading west out of the ford, Conall was entering it from the east.

"Well now, Mes Gegra!" exclaimed Conall.

"Yes, it's me!" replied Mes Gegra.

"A question," said Conall.

"What else could it be," said Mes Gegra, "but the one from whom you're entitled to satisfaction, go for it with all your might!"

"You have my brothers," said Conall.

"Not in my belt," replied Mes Gegra.

"That's even worse," said Conall.

"It's not fair to fight me, and I having but one hand!" warned Mes Gegra.

"In that case," said Conall, "I shall bind one of my hands to my side." And his hand was bound around three times to his side. They hammered away at each other until the river ran red with their blood. In the end, Conall's skill was the greater.

"Well now, Conall," said Mes Gegra, "I know that you will not leave until you have taken my head off. So take my head onto your own head and add my pre-eminence to your own." Conall struck off Mes Gegra's head then, there at Cassán Cloínta, and went to set it upon a standing stone beside the ford. A drop of blood flowed from the head into the pillar and straight through it into the ground. Conall placed the head upon the stone, then, and it bore the stone right down into the ground, and ended up facing the river.

Now at that time, Conall was known as Conall 'wall-eye.' There were three men known for their blemishes then: wall-eyed Conall, one-eyed Cú Chulainn, and Cuscraid the stammerer. The women of Ulster fell into three groups, each group loving one of these three. The group that loved Cú Chulainn used to shut one eye when conversing with him; the group that loved Conall used to let one eye wander as they conversed with him; the group that loved Cuscraid used to stutter when they spoke with him.

Anyway, Conall put Mes Gegra's head over his own head so that it came right down to his shoulders, and from that moment on Conall's eyes looked straight to the front.

Conall went into his chariot by himself, and his charioteer went into Mes Gegra's chariot. They proceeded to Uachtar Fine, where they encountered a band of fifty women, Mes Gegra's wife Buan and her entourage heading south from the border.

"Whose are you, woman!" demanded Conall.

"I am the wife of Mes Gegra," she replied.

"You are commanded to come with me," said Conall.

"Who gave the command?" she asked.

"Mes Gegra," answered Conall.

"Do you have some token or sign?" she inquired.

"You see his chariot and his horse," said Conall.

"He gives gifts to many," she countered.

"And I have his head," added Conall.

"I'm lost to him now!" she cried. Just then the head began turning alternately red and white.

"What's wrong with the head?" asked Conall.

"I know," the woman said. "It was a bet between him and Athirne. Mes said that no one person of the Ulstermen would ever take me off. It's losing the bet that's bothering his head now."

"Get into the chariot," commanded Conall.

"A moment, please, that I may mourn my mate," she pleaded. She let out a wail and cry that was heard as far as Tara and Allen, and then fell back, dead. Her grave is on that road, known now as Coll Buana, 'Buan's hazel,' after the hazel tree that grew up through her grave.

"Get the head, boy," ordered Conall.

"I can't take the head with me!" the lad pleaded.

"Then take its brains," said Conall, "split the skull with your sword and take out the brains. Mix them with lime and make a ball of it." The lad complied, and the skull was left with the woman. The two of them then proceeded to Emain Macha, where the Ulstermen were filled with the sense of victory at having slain the king of Leinster.

And that is the story of Athirne's poetic circuit, the death of Mes Gegra at the hands of Conall Cernach, and the Siege of Howth.

GUAIRE'S GREEDY GUESTS

This text is known in Irish as *Tromdámh Guaire*. *Trom* means 'heavy, burdensome,' while *dámh* means 'a company, a legitimate number of guests, party; a bardic company, poets.' The sense of the compound, then, is a heavy, inordinate or overbearing company of persons, in this case poets. That is what visited itself upon Guaire, a seventh-century king of Connaught. Guaire's renown in the literary tradition extends beyond the present tale. There is a tenth-century poem in the form of a dialogue between Guaire and his brother, Marbán. Marbán had become disaffected with the courtly life of noble and warrior, renounced his possessions, and took up residence in the wild. There, a great oak or yew tree provides his shelter; fruits, berries and herbs his food, natural wells and streams his drink, and the local fauna his neighbors and guests. In the dialogue poem, Marbán extols the glories of nature, celebrating it in ways not unlike Finn does in his poem on Summer. The relationship between Guaire and his brother is representative of the tension between the civilized, courtly life, the life of kings and their retinues, and the raw world that exists outside of that. We see this tension in the person of the poet himself (see Introduction), and we see it too in the discrete worlds inhabited by, on the one hand, the hero Cú Chulainn in the court of Conchobor (the Ulster Cycle of tales) and, on the other hand, Finn Mac Cumaill and his *fiana* who belong to the land.

In opting for nature over culture, Marbán is on the side of the saints. The early Irish saints sought out remote places to erect their tiny oratories, and they led lives governed by a strict asceticism designed to bring them closer to God through a closeness to nature. Not surprising, then, that it is through the intercession of the saints of Ireland that Marbán succeeds in combating the greediness of the company of poets. He also rescues the poets from potential oblivion by recovering for them the great tale, "The Cattle-raid of Cooley."

Needless to say, this story presents poets in a very bad light, while it presents the saints, the monastic clerics, Marbán's ilk, in a very positive light. That these two groups, the poets of the old order and the Christian clerics and literati, feuded is a matter of record. The present tale was surely composed by the clerics to mock the professional poets. In the tale that follows this one in the present collection, we shall see that the poets had their day in court too.

We meet two famous poets in the story. Dallán Forgaill is called Eochaid Rígéces, that is Eochaid (apparently an honorific appellation) Royal-poet or King-poet. He is depicted as perhaps the chief poet of all of Ireland, but one who enjoys esteem throughout Britain and Europe. Dallán is the author of the earliest datable Irish poem, the extremely difficult *Amra Choluim Chille*, composed shortly after that saint's death in 597. It is a poem in praise of Colum Cille to thank him for saving the poets of Ireland from being banished due to their extravagant demands – just as in the present story. Dallán dies as a result of making an unjust satire against the king of Oriel, who has refused the poet's unjust request.

Next we meet Senchán Torpéist, who has been elected chief poet in place of Dallán. It is interesting to see the process by which this took place. The poets gather together to select a new chief poet. They call upon Dallán's widow, who is called the foster-mother of the poetic orders, and her trio of hags. She recalls Dallán's high regard for Senchán, and upon that recommendation Senchán is made *ollam*-elect. There follows an inaugural ode by the new chief-poet, and then a bardic circuit of Ireland. The process calls to mind the central role of women in the stories about "The Spirit of Poetry" and "Athirne and Amairgen." It also calls to mind the words of Caesar (*Gallic War*, vi.13), that upon the death of the chief druid, the druid deemed by the others as most eminent succeeds to the post.

The Celtic poets cultivated difficult language; indeed, one might say that they had a dialect of their own. The Greek commentators noted that the Celts were fond of speaking in riddles, and it is surely part of the parody here that the king of Oriel is able to understand neither the poems in his praise or the subsequent satire directed against him. It is up to Dallán to explain the poems to him. A similar reference to the obscurity practiced by poets in Wales is found in the Welsh tale, *Breuddwyd Rhonabwy* 'The Dream of Rhonabwy.' It says that bards came to declaim their poems to Arthur, and no one there, except for Cadriaith, could understand the poems except that they were in praise of Arthur (Richards 1948, 20.13-16). And Cadriaith (meaning 'fine-speech') appears to have been a poet himself (Bromwich 1978). The translation is based on the edition of Joynt 1941.

Bibliography: Bromwich 1978; Connellan 1860; Joynt 1941; Meyer 1901; Ó Coileáin 1977; O'Connor 1989; Richards 1948

Guaire's Greedy Guests

There was once a noble and famous king of Oriel by the name of Hugh son of Duach the Black. Hugh Finn son of Fergnae son of Fergus son of Muireadach Mael was king of Bréifne during the same time. The two of them were very competitive. Anything that the one of them would do, the other one would want to do something better. They weren't much alike, for Hugh Finn was triumphant and prosperous many times over while Hugh son of Duach the Black, king of Oriel, was fierce and aggressive. It was natural for him to be the fiercer of the two for he had this shield, Dubhgilla or 'Black Oppressor.' Among its virtues was that any of his enemies who faced it in battle would have no more strength than a woman in labor, and it was victorious wherever it went, even when accompanied only by its bearer.

Now at that time, Eochaid Royal Poet (whose real name was Dallán Forgall) was with the king of Bréifne. He had a very large retinue, and he liked Bréifne best because of its extensive herds and wealth. One night in the drinking lounge the king said to Dallán, "Dallán, you enjoy great honor and esteem with me."

"No wonder," said Dallán, "I am honored among the Scots, the Saxons, the Britons, and the Franks, and I hold the office of ollam in all those lands."

"Even so," said Hugh, "I give you more than all of them put together. When you go on your professional poetic rounds into distant lands, if you're short a cow I make it up to you, and if you're short a horse or property or money, I make it up to you so that your goods and wealth remain undiminished."

"Why are you telling me this, my king?"

"So that you will know it's proper that whatever you may ask of the king of Oriel you will get from him, for his practice is no less than mine."

"There is nothing apart from his sovereignty that he wouldn't give me."

"Ah! but there is!" replied Hugh Finn.

"What?" asked Dallán.

"He has a shield, Dubhgilla the Black Oppressor. That's how he has always seized power and how he continues to hold it and to defend the borders of Oriel. He will not give that to you!"

79

"That's not a proper request for a true poet;" countered Dallán; "if it were, I would ask for it."

"I'll reward you mightily if you go ask for it," said Hugh Finn, "I'll give you a hundred head of every herd!"

"I'll do it!" said Dallán, "and if I don't get it I'll satirize Oriel's king!"

They passed that night, and the next morning Dallán rose early. His horse was brought and he and his twenty-seven attendant ollams went to the fort of Oriel's king. When the king heard that Dallán had arrived he went out, kissed him three times, welcomed the company of poets, and made to escort Dallán to the fort.

"I won't come," he said, "until I know whether my request will be granted."

"What is your request?" asked the king.

"Your shield, Dubhgilla," replied Dallán.

"That's not the proper request of a true poet," said the king, "if it were, I would give it to you."

"I have brought you a poem in exchange for it," said Dallán.

"I'd love to hear the poem," said the king. So Dallán sang this song:

> Hugh! hero of hubris
> O venom valor-hard!
> Gifts from great seas
> Given to appease.
>
> Star vacant sun
> That stuns me;
> You board of brilliance,
> We well up, O warrior!

"A fine poem," said the king, "for whoever could understand it."

"You're right," said Dallán, "and whoever composes a cryptic poem, 'tis he who must explain it. As I made the poem, I shall explain it.

'Hugh! hero of hubris!' – that means you are the honorable and valorous hero of Ireland.

'Venom valor-hard!' 'Venom' means poison, and your valor is like a poison to opponents in battle.

'Gifts from great seas'; that is, if you possessed all the wealth of the world's seas, you would give it all away to poets and minstrels.

'Star vacant sun'; that refers to the sun after the stars have gone out, for that's when it appears best, though not better than your own form.

'You board of brilliance!'; that is, though a man have seven sets of chessmen they would do him no good if he didn't have a board. You are the board on which the men of Ireland stand.

"That's good!" exclaimed the king of Oriel. "I'll give you money and cattle for that!"

"You can only give it if I agree to take it," cautioned Dallán. "But I have composed another praise poem in exchange for the shield:

> O Hugh! Lofty, noble hawk!
> Your shield a hewer,
> Its point a cresting wave,
> Head of our people, our prince.
> We bear its powerful frame
> Over every fair and seemly stream
> Unenvied by the prince –
> His shield and mine,
> Multi-hued, raven's delight,
> Screaming Badb's perch,
> Powerful, splendid shield
> Of Hugh son of Duach.
> Before I wend my way,
> From Duach's son we'll carry
> That Powerful, splendid gillie
> As proper pay for poetry!

"That's a fine poem, Dallán," said Hugh, "and you'll have a proper reward for it – gold, silver, treasures, all that."

"I won't accept it," replied Dallán, "because I composed the poem to get the shield. And I have yet another poem for it:

> O Dubhgilla! O black beauty!"

And he sings the rest of it.

81

"That's a fine poem, Dallán," said Hugh, "and I will pay well for it with gold and silver, and a hundred head of every flock to boot."

"Right," replied Dallán, "but you could name all the gold, silver, and wealth in the world, and still I would only accept the shield."

"I won't give it to you," said Hugh.

"Then I'll satirize you," said Dallán.

"May the miracles and wonders of the King of heaven and earth protect me and shield me from you! And remember, Dallán," Hugh warned, "that the saints of Ireland made a contract between you poets and us: if any of you made an unjust satire on any of us, three disfiguring blisters would appear on the maker, but on the other hand if we deserved it and you made it justly, then the same would happen to us. These are the saints who confirmed that: Columcille mac Feidlimid, Ciarán of Clonmacnoise, Senchiarán of Saigir, Finnian of Clonard, Finnian of Mag Bile, Senach son of Caitin, Ruadhan Lothra, Brendan of Birr, Brendan of Clonfert, Mo Cholmóc, Comgall of Bangor, Dolua of Derry, Caillín of Fenagh."

"All of those together won't save you from being satirized by me, and my satire works best if it is sung in your presence!" And he intoned these words:

O Hugh son of Black Duach!
O piddling puddle!
O arrogant cuckoo!
O non-lasting blackbird's nest!
Flowers and plants sucked dry!
Hungry stream of guests!
O brazen candle – unlit!
O cold, wooden barge!
O leaky boat!
O haunt of cockroaches!
For shame, O Hugh!

"In all conscience," said Hugh, "we cannot say whether that poem was worse or better than the first one you recited."

"I'm not surprised to hear a person of your wits say that," said Dallán, "and since it is I who composed the satires, I will explain them.

'O Hugh son of Black Duach! O piddling puddle!' That's like a little puddle in the summer when someone steps in it after a long drought; the water splashes out and the hole doesn't fill up again until the rain returns. That's you, for you will not be able to get enough praise to restore your honor in the wake of this satire.

'O arrogant cuckoo!' meaning a pet cuckoo, for there is no worse house pet than a cuckoo. He hardly ever sings, and then only in winter. And some people say that another bird raises it, a falcon, that the cuckoo puts the other bird's chick out and this bird feeds the baby cuckoo until is fully fledged. Then the cuckoo flies away, and has no more love for the falcon than for any other bird. That's the same as between you and the poets of Ireland: they won't remember anything good you have ever done as a result of my satire.

'O non-lasting blackbird's nest!' That's like a blackbird flushed by a man in the middle of the night. He lets out a cry and a whistle and then, seized by fear, is silent for the rest of the night. That's you: your hospitality is widely known, but after this satire no one will hear of it again.

'Flowers and plants sucked dry!' That's a reference to bees, for if seven horse-loads of plants sucked by bees were placed in a pot and put on the fire, there'd only be charred remains."

"Enough, Dallán!" exclaimed the king, "don't satirize me to my face any longer! I leave you to your company of poets now."

"Fine," said Dallán. "Bring my horses so I can leave." Their horses were brought around, and Dallán and his poets departed.

"May God Almighty and the saints get you if you have satirized me unjustly!" Hugh called after him.

They had not gone far when Dallán said to the poets, "I'm amazed at what the storytellers say, that it will go badly for whoever makes unjust satires. Now I believe that never have more unjust or more undeserved satires been made than the ones I myself have just made and yet I'm better for having made them — for when I came to the fort I was blind and now I have two perfectly good eyes!"

"Royal bard," they said, "that is good news — but hard to believe!"

"But it's true," replied Dallán.

"If it is," said the poets, "then tell us how many are now in front of you and how many behind."

"There are two groups of nine in front of me and one group of nine behind me."

"That's right!" they all said.

"Perhaps these are not good signs," Dallán reflected. "I got Colum Cille son of Feidlimid to promise that I would see a miracle just before my death, and what greater miracle could I experience than going to the fort blind and coming back with two good eyes? Take me home." So they brought him home then, and he lived for three days and three nights and then he died. Afterwards, all the poets convened. These are their names: Maol Gedic son of Fir Goboc, the bard of Scotland; Arrachtan son of Onsclann, bard of Brittany; Srubchaille son of Sreabchaille, bard of the Saxons; Niamchaemh the bard of Ulster; Dael Duileadh the bard of Leinster; Ollmhor high-poet, bard of South Munster; Oircne Aitemain bard of North Munster; Senchán the poet, seer and chief-ollam of Connaught. When they had gathered together they were asked who should be made ollam in place of Dallán.

"Have the foster mother of the poetic orders brought to us," they said, "Muirean daughter of Cuan Chuillede, Dallán's wife, and the trio of crones, Grucc, Gracc and Grangait."

The women were brought and the company asked them which one ought to be made ollam. Muirean spoke: "You went on a poetic circuit into Scotland once, and I asked Dallán then who should be made ollam after him if he should die. His reply was that if there was anyone in the world who could give him stanza for stanza and word for word it was the old poet Senchán."

"If that's the case," said the poets, "let's make Senchán ollam-elect." So Senchán was inaugurated as ollam and he was instructed to go to Dallán's corpse and compose an elegy for him. Senchán did so and made this elegy, which he sang over Dallán:

> A beloved body has fallen here;
> Though he was mighty, he was mere:
> Slight in figure, mighty in work;
> Lord of a multitude of men.
>
> A hundred and fifty poets at a time,

Orphaned now from knowledge of rhyme;
Had the number of us been even more,
Every day would bring new lore.

Depths of a Deluge, deep below,
Force of ever-falling Assaroe,
Flood of the fabled Red Sea:
Thus the mind of Dallán raged.

Until we go beyond the bright sun
Created from God's own mouth,
No seer, whether from north or south,
Will surpass the wisdom of Eochaid-Dallán.

O God in heaven! he was wise,
Our chief poet, noblest alive,
Till lapped by the waves of death;
Ah, he was beautiful and beloved!

The company agreed that they had a fully competent ollam in the man who sang that elegy, and they asked where they should go first on a bardic circuit of Ireland. Each of them was promoting his own province, but Senchán said that it was proper for them to go first to the one person who had never been satirized or shamed with respect to gold or proliferation of wealth.

"Who's that?" they asked.

"Guaire son of Colman son of Cobthach son of Goibniu son of Conall son of Eogan son of Eochu Brecc son of Dathi son of Fiachra," Senchán replied. The company agreed that it was right for them to go there since that's what Senchán wanted.

They had messengers sent ahead to Guaire, to tell him that Senchán and his troop of poets were coming to visit. "I welcome them," said Guaire. "I welcome the good and the bad among them, the lofty and the lowly; I welcome their women and their men." Guaire built an eight-sided lodge for them, with a door between each two sides, eight couches between each two doors, and a smaller couch just below each main couch. The reason he arranged it that way is so that if anyone in the compartment caused trouble or contention and jumped up out of his main couch, he'd have the smaller couch right there in front of him.

Then he made eight wells for the men and eight for the women, because he didn't want the women to wash their hands in the water used by the poets or the poets to have to wash their hands in water used by the women. He prepared feasts and provisions for them, and when all that was done he sent messengers to invite them. Senchán's response was, "Though Guaire's reputation is great, I will not take this entire company there and ruin Connaught; two-thirds of us is enough, and we'll leave the rest behind." And so it was done; he brought only a hundred and fifty poets and a like number of apprentices, a hundred and fifty dogs, a hundred and fifty lads, a hundred and fifty female attendants, and twenty-seven of every sort of craftsman to Guaire. And that's how they came to Durlus.

Guaire went out to meet them. He kissed the noblest of them and gave warm welcome to the sages. "I welcome you all," he said. "Welcome to your nobles and to the lowliest of you. I bid a great welcome to you all, to ollam and anruth, poet and apprentice, lads and ladies, dogs and servants. Were it not for the size of your company – I don't say there are too many of you, mind – I would welcome each of you individually. But welcome to all anyway."

They were conducted into the great lodge and food was served to them. Guaire told them to ask for whatever they wanted and they would receive it. But it proved very difficult to satisfy all their requests, for each of them required their meals apart and a bed to themselves, and they never retired a single night without grumbling nor rose a single day without wanting some unusual and rare desire satisfied. And those impulses had to be satisfied or Guaire would be satirized and shamed.

One night one of the company, Muireann, foster-mother of the poetic orders and wife of Dallán, had an unusual craving, and she let out a great groan. "What's the matter?" they asked.

"I've got this craving," she said, "and I'll die if it's not satisfied!"

"What is it you want?" Senchán asked.

"A bowl of milk, still warm, with the marrow of the anklebone of a wild pig, and a pet cuckoo on an ivy branch before me during the twelve days of Christmas." She also wanted a heavy load of the ruddy fat of a gleaming white boar around her back and belly, and to be mounted

86

on a long-haired bay with a crimson mane, wearing a garment made from a spider's web, crooning as she rode forth to Durlus.

"That's a tough one," said Senchán. "Not just a single craving but a bunch of strange desires that'll be hard to satisfy." They passed the night. Now Guaire used to come to visit the lodge each day to ask how they were getting on, and he came that day. "How is everything with this fine and good company today?" he asked.

"We have never spent a worse time," they said.

"Why is that?"

"One of us has developed a craving," said Senchán.

"Who?" asked Guaire.

"Muireann daughter of Cuan Chuillede, Dallán's wife, foster mother of the poetic orders," replied Senchán.

"What does she crave?" asked Guaire. Senchán told him. "That's not just a craving," said Guaire, "that's a bunch of cravings, the easiest of which would be difficult to get." Guaire left sad and gloomy. The only one of his own people with him at that time was a servant, and Guaire asked him, "Can you keep a secret well, boy?"

"Why do you ask?" said the boy.

"I want to go to Seiscenn Úarbeóil," replied Guaire, "where Fulachtach son of Eogan is. I'm the one who killed his father, his four sons, and his three brothers, and I'd rather he kill me and my reputation for hospitality live on than that I live on with my reputation ruined. Those cravings will never be satisfied!"

"I can keep a secret well," said the servant, "but if you are seen leaving, there's not a soul in this place who won't be at your side." Guaire didn't like that, so he went off to a little oratory called Finnairecal na Féle, the Blessed Oratory of the Nobly Generous Ones. Whenever he had trouble with the poets and the men of learning he would go to Finnairecal na Féle, prostrate himself, pray, and beseech Jesus Christ. And he would get from God everything he asked for by virtue of his noble generosity – and that is why it's called the Oratory of the Nobly Generous Ones. Guaire was there prostrating, praying, and beseeching God that he might die before he would see himself satirized and shamed by the company of poets. He probably had never had a request that he found more difficult than the one the old crone made, and was praying God fervently that He would deliver him from that need and that He

87

would help him satisfy the desires of the bardic company. Trusting in God, he made a little lay at Finnairecal na Féle:

> O Son of God! sad for me,
> The bunch who showed up yesterday;
> Thrice fifty poets who came as one,
> A troublesome lot, with Senchán.

> Though the crowd was harsh
> That came to Durlus,
> Fun and laughter was the lot of all
> Till the old crone came to call.

> Great the task I meant to try,
> Waiting on folks who live so high;
> If anyone leaves lacking aught,
> My work till now comes to nought.

> Why would the King of the heavens above
> Bestow his own image on me with love,
> If He would not give me grace
> To save that image and protect my face?

> I pledged to Mary's Son
> That I would deny nothing to anyone;
> If he should take from me my fame,
> Wouldn't that sadden Him the same?

Guaire spent the entire night there, and early the next morning he heard the sound of footsteps coming toward him. Such was his dejection and state of mind that he did not look up. Afterwards he did recognize him: it was Marbán the swineherd, chief-prophet of heaven and earth. He and Guaire had the same mother, and he was Guaire's swineherd. The reason he was a swineherd was that it afforded him a better opportunity, there in the woods and open spaces, to practice his faith and piety. He greeted Guaire.

"And the same to you, O chief-prophet of heaven and earth," said Guaire.

"Why so sad?" asked Marbán.

"Someone in the poets' lodge has had a craving," Guaire replied.

"What is it? And who wants it?" asked Marbán.

"Muirean daughter of Cuan Chuillede, Dallán's wife and foster-mother of the poets," said Guaire.

"She's the one of them we hope dies first!" said Marbán. "What does she crave?"

"A bowl of milk, still warm, with the marrow of the anklebone of a wild pig," said Guaire.

"That'll be hard to find," said Marbán, "but hard or not, I'll find it in Glen in Scáil, the Phantom's Glen."

"She wants something else, too, a pet cuckoo warbling on an ivy branch before her," added Guaire.

"This is a strange time of year to be asking for that," mused Marbán, but strange though it be, we know where to get it."

"There's more," Guaire continued, "she wants to be mounted on a bay horse with a red mane and pure white legs."

"Those things, the cuckoo and the horse, are in the same house," said Marbán.

"Who has them?" asked Guaire.

"The daughter of Damhán daughter of Iubhdan, your own powerful paramour, she has them," Marbán said.

"Well then, I'll get them. And there's another thing: she wants to be wearing a multi-colored garment made from a spider's web," said Guaire.

"I'll get that as well in Glen in Scáil," said Marbán.

"There's one more thing she demanded," said Guaire, "a heavy load of the ruddy fat of a gleaming white boar around her back and belly."

"She asked for that?" asked Marbán.

"Yes," replied Guaire.

"My curse on the one who demanded that!" exclaimed Marbán. "That boar is mine and I'd hate to kill him. He's my herdsman, my medic, my messenger, my musician."

"How does he do all that?" asked Guaire.

"Well," said Marbán, "when I come from the herd at night and the thorns of Glen in Scáil have torn the hide from my feet, he comes and licks them. And if I had all the doctors and healing ointments in the world, his tongue would heal me sooner. That's how he doctors me. He's my herdsman in that when the pigs are in Glen in Scáil and I'm weary, I give him a kick and he takes off after the pigs. There are nine ways into Glen in Scáil, and there's never a fear that thieves or rustlers or predators will get them before he drives the last of them in. And he is my musician, for when I want to sleep, I give him a kick and he lies on his back with his belly up and he croons to me. And the song he sings is as melodious to me as the sounds of a fine harp in the hands of a skilled performer. They say it is the thrush that is most tuneful but even more so is that boar's crooning. I find it hard to kill the creature," said Marbán, "so you send someone for him, because I will not do it. And I swear," he added, "that one of these days I'll pay a call on the poets' lodge and avenge the white boar on them, and they'll live to regret it!"

Thanks to Marbán all those cravings were satisfied. The white boar was killed, its lard was put on the crone's back, and she was astride the horse, crooning, as she rode toward Durlus. As she was going, she passed over a rough road; her horse stumbled and she fell beneath it. She broke her thigh, her forearm, and her neck, and so she died. And that's where the expression "the crone's load of lard" comes from.

Another craving seized one from the poets' lodge, meddlesome Medb, Senchán's daughter. She gave out a great sigh. "What's the matter?" asked her father.

"A craving," she replied, "and if it's not satisfied I'll die!"

"What is it you want?" asked Senchán.

"My cloak full of ripe blackberries," she said (and it was in February she demanded that), "so that I can go like that to Durlus and when I get there, I want to find Guaire's people in sorrow and sickness."

"Why do you say such a thing," asked Senchán, "when Guaire is maintaining us and taking such good care of us?"

"Don't you know, father?" said Medb. "I am like the stinger – you know, the nettle, which would as soon sting the one that builds a house around it as anyone. That's how I am: I'd just as soon the one who gives me goods and gold die like anyone else!"

They passed that night, and on the following morning Guaire went to the poets' lodge. "How's this great and good company today?" he asked.

"We never had a worse day!" replied Senchán, "My daughter, meddlesome Medb, has had a craving."

"What is it?" asked Guaire. Senchán told him, and Guaire's heart sank. "There's no way such cravings can be satisfied!" And so saying, he turned on his heel and left the lodge. A short time later he encountered Marbán.

"Greetings, Guaire!" said Marbán.

"And the same to you, O chief-prophet of heaven and earth!" replied Guaire.

"Why so sad?" Marbán asked.

"Another of the poets' company has had a craving," Guaire said.

"After the white boar?" asked Marbán incredulously.

"That's right," said Guaire.

"What is it?" asked Marbán.

"A cloakfull of blackberries."

"I can get those in Glen in Scáil," said Marbán.

"How so?" asked Guaire.

"Well, one day you were hunting in Glen in Scáil, and you had a dog on a leash. The dog saw some creature and pulled you forward. There was a bramble bush beside you that pulled your cloak from you. You let it go willingly, for you have never refused anything to anyone. You had scarcely gone from it when I came up. I found a lot of berries on the bush, and I spread the cloak over them it in such a way that neither rain nor foul weather has touched them till now, thanks to Almighty God and my own powers. And those that were red then are black now, and those that were ripe then taste like honey now."

"She wants something else, too," said Guaire. "She wants to see my people in sorrow and sickness."

"That's a hard request," said Marbán. "Go tonight to Finnairecal na Féle, the Blessed Oratory of the Nobly Generous Ones, and I'll go to Glen in Scáil, and together we'll pray that your people be in sorrow and sickness, but that they'll be healthy again the same day." They went their way and beseeched God ardently that night. Medb got the berries, came to Durlus, and found all of Guaire's people near death, thanks to the prayers of Guaire and Marbán, but she had scarcely left the place when both men and women were fully restored to health. And that's how those cravings were satisfied by God and by Marbán.

Another craving seized a member of the poets' lodge, Brigit daughter of Onithchern the Oppressive, wife of Senchán, and she gave out a great sigh. "What's the matter, princess?" Senchán asked.

"I have a craving," she replied, "and if it's not satisfied I'll die!"

"Tell me what it is," said Senchán.

"All I can eat of the fatty flesh of the water blackbird, and all I can eat of a white, red-eared cow without a liver, but with lard where the liver should be. Also, I want my fill of ripe wild strawberries and purple berries, and, to wash it all down, a honeyed drink made from honeysuckle."

"Those cravings will be hard to satisfy," said Senchán.

That night wore on, and early the next morning Guaire came to the poets' lodge. "How's everything with the great and good company today?" he asked.

"We were never worse," answered Senchán, "for one of us, Brigit daughter of Onithchern, my wife, has had a craving."

"What does she want?" asked Guaire. Senchán told him. "Those cravings can never be satisfied," said Guaire, and wearily he left the lodge. Not long after, he encountered Marbán, and the two of them greeted each other.

"Why so sad?" asked Marbán.

"One of the poets' company has had a craving," said Guaire.

"Even though they got the white boar?" asked Marbán.

"Yes," Guaire replied, and he described the cravings.

"I know where I can get those things," said Marbán, "from the old crones of Túaim Dá Ghúalann. There are a hundred and eighty crones living there in a single house, and they have their fill from a single milking of that cow. And they also have that blackbird. When the last of the crones goes off to bed, it sings them song that would lull wounded men and women in labor. And I tell you, that cow is better than a hundred and eighty cows and a calf with every cow; and the blackbird is worth more than a hundred and eighty regular blackbirds."

"She wants something else, too," said Guaire, "strawberries, purple berries, and honey from honeysuckle."

"I can get those in Glen in Scáil," said Marbán. And all those things were procured, just as Marbán had promised. A hundred and eighty cows and blackbirds were given to the crones in exchange for their one cow and one blackbird, and the nobles of Ireland said that the entire poets' company was not worth the lives of those two creatures.

Another craving came over one of the poets' company, Senchán himself, and he gave out a great sigh. The entire company responded as one, and they asked him what was the matter. "I have a craving," he answered, "and if it is not satisfied I'll die! I must have my fill for myself and my people and for the nobles of Connaught of the fat of a pig that has not yet farrowed and of ale made from a single grain. If I don't get those things by this time tomorrow I'll be dead!"

That was made known to Guaire during the night, and he didn't even wait till morning to go to the lodge. "What's going on over here tonight?" he asked.

"We have never had a worse night," they replied.

"What's the matter?" Guaire asked.

"One of us has had a craving."

"Who?" Guaire asked.

"Senchán the ancient seer, the royal ollam himself!"

"What does he want?" Guaire asked. They told him, and Guaire's heart fell, for he figured those cravings could not be satisfied. He left the lodge, and before long he met Marbán.

"Why the long face, Guaire? he asked.

"One of the poets' company has had a craving," said Guaire.

"Even after the white boar?" asked Marbán.

"Yes," Guaire replied.

"What is it?" asked Marbán, "and who wants it?"

"Senchán, the ancient seer, and this is what he wants: all he and the poets and the nobles of Connaught can drink of an ale made from a single grain."

"I can get that in Glen in Scáil," said Marbán.

"How so?" asked Guaire.

"Well, one day, your own steward, Guaire Beiceinig the tightfisted, came from sowing seed. He felt a lump in his shoe, a grain of wheat no smaller than an acorn. He brought it to me, and I planted it. And in the second year, it sprouted twenty-seven ears. That was eleven years ago, and since that time I have not allowed a single grain to mingle with it, so that I now have four major stacks of grain from that single seed. I have given directions for a fabulous feast to be prepared in Glen in Scáil, and I am sure," added Marbán, "that if all the nobles of Connaught converged on the spot they would find their fill of food and drink from that single grain."

"He wants something else, too," said Guaire. "He wants himself and his people and the nobles of Connaught to have all they can eat of the fat of a pig that has not yet been born, and if it hasn't been found by this time tomorrow then there's no need of it ever being found."

"I can get that in Glen in Scáil," said Marbán.

"How so?" asked Guaire.

"Well, one day your lead sow was wandering about in Glen in Scáil, about to bring forth her litter when she met up with a wolf. The wolf ripped her open so that her guts spilled out. She in turn ripped off the wolf's head, and the two had just fallen when I came upon them. I found the sow's uterus on the ground, with all the piglets struggling to break out. I helped them out – nine male piglets and one female. Then I killed some inferior piglets so they'd have a sow to nourish them. That was nine years ago, and those nine males are now mature boars with curved tusks. And if the nobles of Connaught gathered together, I'm sure they'd have their fill from the fat of those pigs. Give them their choice: they can either have the feast brought to them or they can come and dine in Glen in Scáil."

Their decision was relayed to the poetic company, who said that the nobles of Connaught should be assailed with satire for suggesting that they, the poets, leave their own lodge. So the feast was brought there, and all were seated as Senchán deemed proper. They began to drink and enjoy themselves, and each of the nobles had whatever he wanted of music and performance from the company. Three days and three nights it went on.

When Senchán saw the huge amounts of food and drink being consumed by the servants and rabble, he became sullen and he pouted, saying that he would eat or drink nothing until the nobles of Connaught had been told to go. They were told to go, but even so, Senchán remained without food and drink for three days and nights.

"This is bad for us," Guaire lamented, "the entire company eating and Senchán there in the middle of them fasting." So he sent a favorite foster-son of his to Senchán. He told him to get a long, white hazel spit, put a goose on it, hold two-thirds of the spit in front of him and one-third behind him, and cook it in front of Senchán. The lad did that.

"What are you doing with that goose?" asked Senchán.

"Fixing it for you, royal bard," said the youth.

"Why are you the one that was sent with it?" asked Senchán.

"Guaire wanted someone of fine manners and cleanliness to attend to you," he replied.

"I don't think he could have found anyone more ill-suited than you!" Senchán hissed.

"Why do you say that, royal bard?" the lad asked.

"Because I knew your grandfather! He had pustulous tumors on his fingers, and that's why I refuse to take food from your hands!" The lad departed sadly, and related all that to Guaire, who took it badly. Three days and nights passed. Guaire summoned another fosterling, a daughter of Beg Bainnech, and told her to take some wheat flour and salmon roe and prepare a dish for him in his presence.

"What are you doing with that?" asked Senchán.

"Making something for you, royal bard," she replied.

"Why are you the one that was sent to do it?" asked Senchán.

"Well, Guaire wanted to send someone of cleanliness and purity with your food," she answered.

"I'm absolutely certain," Senchán boomed, "that there is not a servant in this place more unsuitable than you!"

"Why do you say that, royal bard?" the girl asked.

"Because I knew your grandmother, and once she was up on a rock giving directions to lepers. She stretched our her arm and pointed the way for them, and because she did that, there's no way I could accept food from your hand!"

The girl returned dejected and told Guaire what had happened. "Damn the mouth that said that!" said Guaire. "I pray the King of heaven and earth that, before he departs this world, Senchán kisses a leper full on the mouth!" Senchán remained without food for a day and a night.

Brigit daughter of Onithchern told her serving girl to take her leftovers to Senchán.

"What's left?" asked Senchán.

"A chicken's egg," said Brigit.

"That'll almost fill me up," said Senchán, "it's a lot right now!"

The serving girl, who was called Bé Aidgell because she ruined things, went for the egg. She searched for a long time but couldn't find it.

"You probably ate it yourself," said Senchán.

"No, it wasn't me, royal bard," said Be, "it was those clever little creatures, the mice!"

"That was wrong of them!" exclaimed Senchán. "There's no king or lord, however exalted, that they would not love to leave their tooth marks in his food. And that's disrespectful, for food they've sunk their teeth into should not be consumed by anybody. I'm going to satirize them!" he proclaimed, "and that won't be hard at all." And he began the satire:

> Mice, however sharp their teeth,
> Are no match for warriors' wrath;
> I'll bring death to the biters,
> In avenging Brigit's leftovers.

A mouse answered:

> Small indeed the amount you left,
> And of very little are you bereft;
> We'll pay you back, take the reward,
> Don't satirize us, O learned bard!

Senchán continued:

> O mouse beyond the wall,
> Who speaks from behind a hole:
> You with the claws not short,
> 'Tis you, from spite, who ate my ort!

The mouse again:

> No! my own son, white-bellied Bianán,
> Innocent of regulation,
> 'Tis he, O great and glorious poet,
> Who is bound to pay his debt.

Senchán answered:

> Abandon your far-fetched wiles,
> For we are about to begin your trials;
> Out from the wall, slow and nice,
> And on the floor, you mice!

They say that ten mice fell dead in front of Senchán. Then Senchán said, "It's not you I should be satirizing but the corps that's supposed to keep you in check – the cats! I'll satirize them good – and I'll satirize their chief, their leader, their judge, Irusán son of Arusán. I know where he is, too, in the cave of Knowth, east of blessed Cíarán's Clonmacnoise. I'll satirize Riachall Rinnfhíaclach 'Pointy-tooth' daughter of Claibaithinne, his wife; Reng Gérfhíaclach 'Sharp-toothed', his daughter; Cronanach 'the Crooner of Cruachan' and Gruaman Gairbhfhíaclach 'Surly saw-toothed', his two brothers. And of course I'll satirize Irusán himself, for he's the best and noblest of them and he's their chief. And he sang:

> Irusán, pawer of claws,
> Otter ort,
> Backside of a cow in heat,
> Cheek by jowl.

"'Irusán, pawer of claws,'" he explained, "that's when the mouse is in the wall, and all he can do is paw at the wall with his claws.

"'Otter ort,' because long ago the ancestor of the cats was sleeping on the shore of a lake, and an otter came up and gnawed the tops of his ears. So from that time to this cats have had ugly, chopped ears.

"'Backside of a cow in heat,' for a cow in heat doesn't tuck her tail any faster than Irusán does when a mouse gets away from him.

'Cheek by jowl,' that's the way the cat and the mouse are, like a team of horses; with a thin wall between them, she's forever listening for him and he's always listening for her. And that's the satire," said Senchán.

News of that poisonous satire reached Irusán, who was in the cave at Knowth. "Senchán has satirized me," he said, "and he will be punished for it."

His daughter Reng Gérfhíaclach 'Sharp-toothed' said to him, "we would prefer that Senchán be brought to us alive so that we too can avenge the satires on him."

"Okay," said Irusán, and he set out, telling his daughter to have her brothers follow him. Senchán was told that Irusán was coming for him to kill him, and so he told Guaire to gather the nobles of Connaught about him to protect him from Irusán. They all did that. Before long they could hear a shaking, powerful, pounding thunder, and a sound like the roar of a wild fire burning out of control, and they thought there was no plow-ox in Connaught mightier than that. Irusán was blunt-nosed, boisterous, bellowing, and proud; chop-eared and broad-chested; noble, known, and sharp-nailed; sleek, slit-nosed, sharp-toothed, rough, growling, restless, and rash; wide-flanked, wrathful and raging; an odious, dagger-eyed, demented droner. He approached them like that and moved among them freely. Weapons didn't stop him until he reached Senchán. He seized him by one arm and threw him on his back and went out the way he came in, for he had no purpose other than coming for Senchán.

Senchán now began praising Irusán, his leaping and movement, his running, strength, bravery, and quickness. He sang,

> Irusán son of Arusán,
> Of the race of otter's ort,
> We adore the same God –
> Gad, he's going to eat me!

But Irusán didn't put Senchán down until he reached the blessed Cíarán's Clonmacnoise. As he was going past the smithy, Cíarán looked up and saw Senchán on Irusán's back. "Good Lord!" exclaimed Cíarán, "Guaire's reputation destroyed and the high-poet of Ireland on a cat's back!" There happened to be a hunk of smelted iron in the smith's tongs, and Cíarán made a lucky but well-aimed shot at the cat, which struck him in the side and went straight through, leaving him dead. Senchán jumped off and swore an oath. "Damn the hand that made that throw!" he exclaimed.

"Why?" asked Cíarán.

"I'm angry at not having been left for Irusán to eat, so that the company of poets could satirize Guaire. I'd rather have Guaire satirized than me alive and him safe from satire." And so saying he went back to Durlus. The nobles of Connaught wanted to welcome him, but he would accept neither kiss nor welcoming words from any of them. He went to the poets' lodge where they continued to feast amid plenty.

One day in Glen in Scáil, Marbán the swineherd mused, "It's been a long time since I vowed revenge on the company of poets for what they did to the white boar." This is the kind of person Marbán was: he was a saint, a prophet, a seer, and a host to all in Glen in Scáil. He was Guaire's brother, and the one who helped Guaire in every difficulty. He was even the one who had helped him to obtain the kingship of Connaught, and every misstep Guaire made, it was Marbán who set things straight again. He was also a faithful servant of God.

So he set out for the poets' lodge then and, as he was looking for the place, he encountered the poets' women-folk washing their hands in the well. The first one he met was meddlesome Medb, Senchán's daughter, and he asked where the lodge was. "Well, young man," said Medb, "you must have been out of the country for a while if you don't know the poets' lodge and haven't heard their stories and songs!"

"That's not why," replied Marbán; "you see, I'm a swineherd by profession, and I've heard that a man could have whatever music he wanted in that lodge."

"Not true," said Medb, "unless he has a blood-relationship with poetry and learning."

"I have that," replied Marbán, "you see, the grandmother of my servant's wife was the granddaughter of a poet!"

So Marbán proceeded to the lodge. He didn't go for the door of the lodge that was open but for the one that was closed. It was opened for him, and he came in with his cloak billowing in the wind, which blew against every single person in the place. The company rose as one and Senchán asked him how he managed against such a wind.

"Silly question," said Marbán, "I came *with* the wind, and if proof were needed, I have brought a good deal of it with me."

"Do you come to contest?" Senchán asked.

"I do," replied Marbán, "provided I can find someone to contest with."

"All right," said Senchán, "from what was poetry first made?"

"From the nuts of the well of Segais," Marbán answered.

"That's right," said Senchán. "Are you Marbán, chief prophet of heaven and earth?"

"I am indeed," said Marbán.

"What is your pleasure?" asked Senchán.

"I've heard that a man could find whatever music or performance he wanted among you, and so I've come to ask for whatever performance I want from you."

"You'll have it," replied Senchán, "provided you have a blood-relationship to learning."

"I do," said Marbán, "the grandmother of the wife of my servant was the granddaughter of a poet."

"Then you shall have whatever art you like, even though your kinship with poetry is a rather distant one!" said Senchán. "Now tell us what you'd like."

"There's nothing I'd like better right now than my fill of crooning," said Marbán.

"Nothing could be easier," said Senchán. The crooners were brought out, twenty-seven of them, and they chose to perform the standard croon. But Marbán would have none of that; he wanted the low, guttural crooning. The reason he chose that sort was so that they would burst their heads, their necks, even their feet, and would run out of breath sooner than with the standard crooning. So there were twenty-seven crooning like that, and when they would be on the point of finishing, Marbán would say, "Give us our fill, like you promised!" The choir was soon exhausted, and Marbán asked again for his crooning. Only one forlorn group of nine was found to respond to his request, and they were at it a much shorter time than the first group. "Let's have our crooning!" demanded Marbán.

"I'll perform for you, Marbán," said one of the company.

"Who are you?" asked Marbán.

"I'm Dael Duiled, the ollam of Leinster."

"What can you perform for me?" asked Marbán.

"I'm an expert riddler," said Dael.

"Are you good at that?" asked Marbán.

"You cannot put to me a question I cannot answer," said Dael, "and I can ask questions the whole bardic company cannot solve. So tell me, what good thing did man find in the earth that God did not find? What two trees' branches remain green until they wither away? What animal lives in the sea, drowns when he is removed from the sea, and lives when put back into it? And what creature dwells in fire and is burned when taken out of it, but lives when put back into it?"

"Good questions, Dael Duiled," said Marbán, "and I have good answers. What man found on earth that God did not find is the fullness of lordship. For there never was a man, however good or bad, if he was not satisfied with temporal lordship, who did not turn to the King of heaven and earth as his Lord. That's not the case with God; he could never find an adequate lord for He Himself is the Lord of lords. The two trees that do not lose their green, those are the Eo Rosa and the Fidh Sideng, that is, the holly and the yew. The creature who drowns when taken out of the sea is called Gnim Abraein, and the one that burns when taken out of the fire used to be called Tegillus but is now called Salamander. Those are the answers to the questions you have put to me, Dael Duiled," said Marbán.

"I beg your pardon, chief prophet of heaven and earth," said Dael; "leave me in peace and I'll bother you no more."

"Let's have my crooning, men!" demanded Marbán. One of them answered him and said, "I'll perform for you."

"Who are you?" asked Marbán.

"I'm Oircne Aithemuin, the ollam of North Munster."

"What learning are you going to show me?" asked Marbán.

"I can show you splendid learning, for I am knowledgeable and well-informed."

"It seems to me," said Marbán, "that though there are plenty of ignorant men in this lodge there is none as ignorant as you."

"How so?" asked Oircne.

"Well, there are two men paying court to your wife right now and you know nothing of either of them. One of them is the son of the king Findfholtach the White-haired, and the other is the son of Fraiged Dairine, Guaire's fosterling. Your wife gave the gold ring that Guaire gave you to one of these men and gave your sword to the other one." Oircne leapt up and looked for his ring and his sword. When he found neither, he said, "I beg your pardon, chief prophet of heaven and earth. Leave me in peace and I'll bother you no more."

"Fine," said Marbán, "now let me have my fill of crooning!"

One of the company spoke up. "I'll perform for you," she said.

"And who are you?" asked Marbán.

"Crinlaid Caillech the Crone," she replied.

"What art can you perform for me?" inquired Marbán.

"The noblest art in the world," answered the crone, "something neither king nor abbot nor bishop nor pope can do without: I'll be a perfect lover for you."

"I suppose," said Marbán, "that you were fond of that way of life when you were in the vigor of youth, since you're fond of it now in your

101

old age. As for me, that which I didn't do when I was young I won't do at this age with a skinny, hunched over, wrinkled, gruesome old crone like you!"

"I beg your pardon, chief prophet of heaven and earth. Leave me in peace and I'll bother you no more."

"Fine," said Marbán, "now let me have my fill of crooning!"

"I'll perform for you," one of them said.

"What can you do and who are you?" Marbán asked.

"I'm a fine master in my art to Senchán, and my name is Casmhael the Harper."

"Well tell me, Casmhael," said Marbán, "how did harp playing originate? Who made the first song? Which came first, the harp or the timpan?"

"I don't know, chief prophet," said Casmhael.

"Well I know," said Marbán, "and I'll tell you. Once upon a time there was this couple, Macuel son of Miduel and Cana Clothmor 'Great-praise,' his wife. His wife grew to hate Macuel and she ran away from him into the woods and desolate places. He pursued her. One day she came to the sea of Camas and was walking along the shore when she encountered the remains of a whale. She heard the sound of the wind playing upon the sinews of the whale, and the sound lulled her to sleep. Her husband came upon her, and he figured that it was that sound that caused her to sleep. He went into a grove of trees that was nearby, made a harp frame, and put strings made from the whale's sinews into it. And that was the first harp ever made.

Now Lamech Bigamus had two sons, Jubal and Tubalcain. One of them, Tubalcain, was a smith, and he perceived that the sound of his two hammers in the forge was of the same duration as a verse, and so he composed a verse, and that was the first verse ever composed."

"I beg your pardon, chief prophet of heaven and earth. Leave me in peace and I'll bother you no more."

"Fine," said Marbán, "now let me have my fill of crooning!"

"I'll perform for you, Marbán," said one of the house.

"Who are you?" asked Marbán, "and what skill do you have?"

"My name is Corche Ceóilbhinn 'Sweet-music,'" he replied, "this company's timpan master."

"Tell me, Coirche Ceóilbhinn," said Marbán, "why is the timpan called the 'timpan of the saint' when no saint ever played a timpan?"

"I don't know that," said the timpanist.

"Well," said Marbán, "I know, and I'll tell you. When Noah son of Lamech went into the Ark he took a great deal of music with him, in particular the timpan, for Noah had a son who could play it. They were in the Ark all while the flood was over the earth. Afterwards, Noah and his family left the Ark, and the son wanted to bring the timpan with him. "You may not," said Noah, "unless I get something in return." The son asked what that was. Noah said he wouldn't mind having the instrument named after him. The boy granted him that favor, and Noah's timpan is what it has been called ever since. You ignorant timpanists don't call it that, you call it timpan of the saint, and that's because you can't tell the difference between the name *Nai* 'Noah' and the noun *naem* 'saint'!"

"I beg your pardon, chief prophet of heaven and earth. Leave me in peace and I'll bother you no more."

"Fine," said Marbán, "now let me have my fill of crooning!" Marbán had asked for that three times and still had not got it.

Senchán was embarrassed by that, and since no one else could be found to satisfy Marbán he said that he himself would provide the crooning. "I'd rather hear it from you than from anyone else in the world!" said Marbán. Senchán lifted his beard on high, but Marbán would only have the low, guttural crooning. When Senchán would be on the point of finishing, Marbán would say, "I haven't had enough yet!" Senchán was abashed, and he strained so hard at the low crooning that one of his eyes burst from his head and landed on his cheek. When Marbán saw that, he was concerned lest that reflect badly on Guaire, so praying on his beads with his right hand, he restored the eye to its proper place. Then he said, "more crooning!"

Then one of the party said, "I will perform for you, Marbán."

"Who are you?" inquired Marbán, "and what is your specialty?"

"I'm the best storyteller in this company and in all of Ireland," he replied, "and my name is Fis son of Fochmhairc or 'Knowledge son of Inquiry.'"

"Well," said Marbán, "if you're the best storyteller in Ireland, then you know the principal tales of our land."

"I do indeed!" the storyteller said.

"All right," said Marbán, "relate 'The Cattle-raid of Cooley' to me." The storyteller fell silent and his face reddened.

"What's the matter with you?" Senchán demanded, "why don't you tell the story to Marbán?"

"Royal bard," the storyteller began, "I didn't even know that such a raid took place in Ireland, and I certainly don't know who carried it out!"

"In that case," said Marbán, "I put you under taboos until you can narrate the tale of this 'Cattle-raid' for me. And I put the entire company under taboos that they shall not spend two nights in the same house until they have knowledge of 'The Cattle-raid.' Furthermore, in the sight of God I deprive of you of your poetic faculties, so that from this moment on you'll have the ability to make but a single poem, until you get "The Cattle-raid of Cooley" for me. I'm going now," said Marbán, "but I swear, if it were not for Guaire I'd avenge my white boar well on you, you stupid, feckless bards!"

Marbán departed, leaving the company weary, gloomy, and distressed, not knowing what to do. "Marbán put us under taboos not to stay in the same place for two nights," said Senchán, and since we were here yesterday we can't be here tonight, under the terms of the taboo. We have to go off and look for 'The Cattle-raid.'" At those words, the company bounded to their feet and went out from the lodge, both ollam and anruth, seer and poet, men and women, dogs and servants, young and old. There's this: though they were called 'greedy guests' and were much despised, their appetites were small. Brigit daughter of Onithchern, Senchán's wife, had the biggest appetite, and for that they used to call her 'Hungry Brigit'; Senchán himself would be satisfied with a hen's egg.

The company went outside and came to where Guaire was. Guaire was surprised to see them there on the lawn. He went out to greet them, and gave Senchán three kisses. "Tell me, royal bard," he said, "why have you moved out of your lodgings?"

"Bad news," replied Senchán. "That swineherd Marbán, chief prophet of heaven and earth, came to see us to take revenge for the white boar. He asked for his choice of art and music, and that was granted him. He chose crooning, and twenty-seven of our people fell trying to please him. Finally I myself tried to provide the crooning, and every time I tried to bring it to a close he'd ask for more. I strained so hard that one of my eyes popped out onto my cheek, but with God's help he healed me. Then one of our people said that he would tell him a story, and

Marbán asked for 'The Cattle-raid of Cooley.' The storyteller said he didn't know that one, so Marbán put us all under taboos that we couldn't put two poems together or spend two nights in the same house until we got 'The Cattle-raid' for him. Since we were in our lodge here last night, we can't stay there tonight."

"Where do you plan to look for 'The Cattle-raid'," asked Guaire.

"In Scotland," Senchán said.

"Don't go there," said Guaire, "it's not likely you'll get word of it there, because that 'Cattle-raid' was brought into Ireland. I know what you should do."

"What?" asked Senchán.

"Stay here with me," Guaire said, "and you'll be honored by me and by the men of Ireland just as you have been up till now, even without being able to practice your art."

"That would just be charity." said Senchán.

"Okay, then," said Guaire, have your women, boys, and servants stay here with me and you and your ollams, seers, and minstrels go off to find 'The Cattle-raid.'" That seemed right to all, and they decided to do that.

"It is only right that the one poem that we have been allowed should be composed in honor of Guaire," Senchán announced, "for we have been with him here in Durlus a year, a quarter, and a month. During that time we have never lacked for food or drink, for gold or silver, treasures or wealth, nor were any of our cravings left unsatisfied. The hospitality we received here will never again be found in the halls of high kings or the kings of provinces." And Senchán began,

> We leave you now, dear Guaire
> Bless you as we retire;
> Four months and a year,
> Noble king, we were here.
>
> Three fifties of poets proven,
> And three fifties yet to learn;
> Each with two women, servant and dog,
> All maintained in a single lodge.
>
> To every man his meal apart

To each his separate cot
Yet never rose a single day
Without dispute or jealousy.

In good conscience I say to you,
This prophecy will come true:
If we succeed in what we learn,
Though we leave, we will return.

"Where will you be tonight?" asked Guaire.

"In Naas of the kings, if we make it," replied Senchán, "in the fort of Connra Caech 'the Blind,' king of Leinster." They go off in the direction of Naas, and as they were traveling they met a leper on the road.

"Where have you come from, you motley crew?" asked the leper.

"This is no motley crew," one of them said, "this is the senior poet Senchán, with his poets and his entourage."

"I know your names," the leper said, "but it would take too long to say them. I pity the country you're coming to; lucky the land you've left! Where do you plan to go tonight?"

"To the fort of Connra Caech king of Leinster," they replied.

"You have no business going there because you don't have any poems," said the leper.

"Who told you that, scurvy?"

"Now's the time for you to see if that's true," said the leper, "for that's what will earn you passage to Scotland."

"He's right," said the ollams, "we ought to see if we'll be able to compose a poem for the king of Leinster." They tried to do it, each of them trying to contribute a stanza, but even when they could come up with a single word they couldn't find another one to go with it properly.

"If you were willing to pay me, I could compose a poem for the Leinster king for you," said the leper. They said he could have whatever reward he chose.

"Swear it," said the leper, and they all gave their word. "All right," he said, "the reward I want is for Senchán to give me a kiss." Senchán said that even though it meant going back on their word, he would not give the leper a kiss. The ollams replied that they would return to Guaire and no longer accompany him if he didn't do it. So even though he hated it, Senchán did kiss the leper.

Afterwards, they proceeded to the fort and banged on the gate. The porter asked who was there. The leper replied that it was Senchán and his ollams. The porter asked if they had a poem for the king. "We do," said the leper, "and I'm the reciter of it."

"You're ugly for a reciter," said Senchán, "and we're worse off having you with us." They were admitted, and the king gave them a warm welcome and asked them where they were headed.

"To Scotland," they said, "and we'd like to have a ship and provisions from you." The king asked if they had a poem for him. "We have," said the leper, "and I'm the one who will recite it." He sang out:

> Connra Caech, Dairbre's son,
> Irish women's fair-haired lover;
> Give us a ship to plow the waves
> O'er the sea, into safe harbor;
> O shining name, we sought your fame
> In renowned Bregmag's border;
> We bring in exchange your good praise
> O king, O lord of loyal supporter;
> Send us away, O generous lord,
> Across the sea, to the wind, with vigor.

As a result of that poem, they were given sleeping quarters and they spent that night happy and in high spirits, lacking nothing of service or attention, till the next morning. A ship was prepared for them and was provisioned. The leper asked if he could go with them in the ship. Senchán said that if he did, he himself would not go. So Senchán and his ollams boarded and left the leper ashore. They sailed on till they came to the rocks of the Isle of Man. They saw a single person on one of the rocks, and at the same time they saw the leper on the prow of the ship performing low, guttural crooning. The person on the rock called out to them, ""Who's there in the boat?" The leper replied, saying "Senchán and his poets."

"All right," said the person on shore. "I put you under taboos that none of you shall come ashore until you can answer this half quatrain with its other half."

"Proceed," said the leper.

"We're worse off having the leper with us," said Senchán, "because he doesn't care what happens to us."

"You can't come to land here, royal bard," the leper told him, "until you have a half-quatrain to answer his. Sing it, man," said the leper to the fellow, "for there is nothing I want from Senchán." The man sang this half-quatrain:

> Mountains high, oceans deep,
> Every mariner has a crew

The leper countered:
> Snow will fall, lightning flashes,
> From forests will call the cuckoo.

"That's right!" said the man from above, "and there's no one in the boat but you who could supply the right lines. I have another half-quatrain for you."

"Sing it," said the leper.

> The wise one is keen against the guilty,
> The branch tied tightly to the root;

And the leper replied:
> O'er the rock of the sea of Man
> Here you have made a great salt.

"That's it!" exclaimed the man above, "and I have yet another half-quatrain."

"Sing it," said the leper.

> Because of my burning and my mixing
> And my cutting on the sea,

And the leper finished it,
> Woman doctor who does fine work,
> Great your toil above the briny.

"That's a woman doctor who has been conversing with you," he explained to Senchán. One year she's a doctor, the next year she makes salt. She lives in a stone house, and she's got a chest there that contains sixty pounds. She will share that with you tonight, giving you half, and that will support you during your stay in Scotland. And you have me to thank for that, not her." And so saying, the leper disappeared, and no one knew where he went.

They came to land then and they spent that night with the woman doctor with the best welcome and attendance. The following morning, the woman gave Senchán thirty pounds and told him, "This is your last compensation until you regain your ability to compose poetry. Your trip to Scotland would bring mockery to you without you having the power to compose a single poem." They boarded the ship then, and sailed on to Scotland, where the royal ollam, Maol Gedhic son of Fer Goboch, prepared a feast for them. They spent the night with him enjoying the choicest hospitality and welcome; and that was the night in which they got the most respect in Scotland.

They traveled Scotland from south to north and from east to west and spent a year there, but still they had no news of 'The Cattle-raid.' Senchán was depressed at having heard nothing of the tale, and he said he wanted to return to Ireland. Their ship was made ready and they set out across the sea and made harbor in Dublin. As they went ashore, they saw Saint Caillín coming toward them. He was Senchán's brother by the same mother. He kissed Senchán three times and asked him what he was up to. Senchán told him that he had been looking for "The Cattle-raid" and had failed to find it.

"Just as it should be," said Caillín, "because you did a great deal of wrong and injustice to Guaire. He prayed God that you would have to kiss a leper – do you know who that leper was you kissed?"

"No," said Senchán.

"It was me," said Caillín, "and you had to do it."

"Okay, then, dear brother," said Senchán, "then help me find 'The Cattle-raid of Cooley.'"

"I will," said Caillín, "and I'll go with you to Durlus where Guaire is and we'll fetch Marbán from Glen in Scáil, for he's the one who knows how to find that story."

They set out together, Caillín and Senchán with his company, and came to Durlus where Guaire was. Guaire kissed Caillín and

Senchán and welcomed the entire company of poets. He asked Senchán to give an account of himself, and Senchán told him that he had got no word of 'The Cattle-raid' since he left him. They sent word to Marbán in Glen in Scáil, and he joined them in Durlus. They asked him who could narrate 'The Cattle-raid' to them. Marbán said there was only one man among the living or the dead in Ireland who could narrate that story.

"Who's that?" asked Senchán.

"Fergus son of Roech," Marbán replied, "for he's the one who knew of the deeds of the men of Ireland and the Ulstermen on 'The Cattle-raid of Cooley," and it is on account of him the raid was carried out."

"How do we go about it?" they asked. Marbán told them to send for the saints of Ireland and to bring them along to Fergus's gravestone. There they should fast for three days and nights and beseech the Almighty to send Fergus to them to narrate 'The Cattle-raid.'

Caillín went off and brought the saints of Ireland to Durlus, where they spent a night feasting. The following day they went to the gravestone of Fergus, and they beseeched Jesus Christ to send Fergus to them. Fergus appeared and wanted to narrate 'The Cattle-raid' to them standing up, but they couldn't hear any of it until they had him sit down, and that's how he recited the tale to them. Cíarán of Clonmacnoise wrote it down from him, and where he wrote it was on the hide of the dun-colored cow. Fergus narrated the tale right through to the end, then went back into his grave. The saints gave thanks to God for having answered their prayers in the matter of Senchán's request to them, through the intercession of the saints of Ireland and the guidance of Marbán the swineherd. The saints who had come there were Colum Cille son of Feidlimid, Caillín, Cíarán of Clonmacnoise, Cíarán the Elder of Saighre, Finnian of Clonard, Finnian of Mag Bile, Senach son of Gaitre, Brendan of Birr, and Brendan son of Finnlug. They all went off to Durlus and spent that night feasting. The next day the company of poets went off to Glen in Scáil to invite Marbán to come and hear them recite 'The Cattle-raid.' Marbán said he wouldn't come unless the company promised to abide by the judgment he would give. The company said they would abide by it. Marbán came to them then, and 'The Cattle-raid' was recited to him. Afterwards, the ability to compose poetry and their arts were restored to Senchán and the poets. Marbán then took them along to his own place in Glen in Scáil and prepared a fabulous feast for them. He hosted them for a week, during which time they lacked nothing of food, drink or entertainment. Then Marbán asked to give his judgment on them, as they had promised.

"Proceed," they said.

"Swear by the saints of Ireland that you will comply," said Marbán. They so swore. "The judgment I give is this, that each ollam return to his native district and that the company of poets exist no more." And so each of the ollams went off to his own territory at the instigation of Marbán and the saints of Ireland and the company of poets have roamed no more in Ireland from that day to this.

THE VISION OF MAC CON GLINNE

Robin Flower called this tale, "an amazing composition...Mac Con Glinne, it will be seen, is an example of the type of truant scholar, the *scholaris vagans* of European literature, the happy-go-lucky vagabond who goes singing and swaggering through the Middle Ages until he finds his highest expression and final justification in François Villon" (1947, pp. 75-6). Indeed, this eleventh-century composition is an amazing tale. Its hero is Mac Con Glinne, who, at the beginning of the tale, is a clerical scholar or student at Armagh. Dissatisfied with the life of a poor student, he decides to take up poetry. His success in that profession is explained by his nickname, Anér or Aniér, meaning that, because of his powers of praise and satire, he could not be refused whatever he desired.

As Jackson points out in his edition of the work (1990), there are two major themes governing the story. The first is the widely-known practice of curing a tape worm by starving the victim and then drawing out the worm by holding food in front of the victim's open mouth. The second is the voyage to the otherworldly land of plenty. The otherworld is often depicted in early Irish and Welsh literature as a land reached by sea voyage, and the literature abounds in descriptions of the particular beauty and sumptuous provisions of such a place. In our story both of these themes are parodied: the tape worm turns out to be the devil (demon of gluttony) and the otherworld is depicted as a place made entirely of foods, mostly milk products and fatty meats.

Jackson also discusses in some detail the elements that are specifically mocked by the author. He makes fun of monks, especially of the monastery at Cork, the chief monastery of Munster. He is blasphemous in claiming that the angels are all waiting for him, and that his position in Heaven is assured. He parodies the sacraments, the use of relics and religious amulets, even the Passion of Christ. The literary methods of the monastic scribes are mocked, e.g., opening the story with reference to the four things required of compositions, a device originally reserved for ecclesiastical literature of a very serious kind. Then there is the gross exaggeration that one expects to find in the heroic sagas, such as the Ulster Cycle tales. Genealogical lore is parodied brilliantly in the recitation of Manchín's pedigree. And so on.

Whatever of the identity of Mac Con Glinne, Cathal mac Finguine is an historical figure, king of Munster from 721-742; see "The Battle of Allen."

Bibliography: Flower 1947; Jackson 1990; Meyer 1892

The Vision of Mac Con Glinne

The four things that are asked of every literary composition are asked of this one as well, to wit: the place, the person, the time, and the reason for it. The place was Cork City in Munster, and the person was Anér Mac Con Glinne of the Eoganachta of Glennamain. It was composed in the time of Cathal mac Finguine son of Cú cen Gairm or Cú cen Máthair. The reason it was composed was to expel the demon of gluttony that was in Cathal's gullet.

How the demon came to be

Cathal mac Finguine was a great warrior-prince who ruled Munster. He was hungry as a dog and could eat like a horse. Satan, the demon of gluttony in his throat, used to consume all of Cathal's food. A pig, an ox, a good-sized bullock, sixty loaves of the best wheat, a vat of new ale, and thirty eggs from grown hens – that was for starters, along with side dishes, until his main meal was ready for him. As for the main meal, there isn't room enough to enumerate it all.

The reason the demon of gluttony dwelt in Cathal's gullet was because Cathal fell in love, sight unseen, with Lígach daughter of Mael Dúin, the king of Ailech, and sister of Fergal son of Mael Dúin, another king of Ailech who was Ireland's defender against Cathal at that time. This is clear from the contention of the two hags who exchanged these verses in Achad Úr:

> There in the North
> Across the rocks, is Mael Dúin's son
> Beyond the Barrow,
> Though he rustles, he won't remain.

> He will! He will! (said the hag from the south)
> And be grateful to get out!
> I swear by my father,
> If Cathal comes, Fergal won't get cows!

Lígach daughter of Mael Dúin would send nuts and apples and other goodies to Cathal out of love and affection for him. Fergal heard about that and summoned his sister to him. He promised he would bless her for telling the truth but curse her if she lied to him. His sister said that, whatever of her love for Cathal, she feared her brother's curse, so she told him the whole story.

Her brother told her to bring him some apples. Then he summoned scholars and promised them great rewards if they would put spells on those treats in order to destroy Cathal mac Finguine. So the scholars infused those tasty things with magic and spells and gave them to Fergal, who sent servants to bring them to Cathal. The servants urged him, in the name of the eight elements of the world, to wit, the sun and moon, fresh water and salt, heaven and earth, day and night, to eat the apples, since it was out of love and affection that they were sent from Lígach daughter of Mael Duin.

So Cathal ate the apples, and they turned into magical creatures in his guts, and those creatures in turn gathered together and grew into a single beast which became the demon of gluttony. And the reason that demon of gluttony was created to dwell in the gullet of Cathal mac Finguine was to destroy the men of Munster in a year and a half, and it's likely it would destroy all of Ireland in another half year.

Mac Con Glinne introduced

I have heard of an eight-some tonight,
In Armagh, after midnight;
I swear with all my might,
Their other names are not so nice.

Comgán was called 'Son of Two Arts,'
Famous on the trail of quarry;
Noble Crítán was called Mac Rustaing,
Women passed his grave a-farting.

'Black of Two Tribes,' a famous handle,
The name of Stéléne's son;
'Dark Raven'; the fair 'Hag of Beare';
'Rough one of Oak,' Mac Samáin's burden.

'Non-refusal' Mac Con Glinne's name,
From the banks of sweet-surfaced Bann;
'Little man,' 'Little woman,' bellows for slaughter,
Father and mother of Marbán 'dead man.'

My King, King of heavenly glory,
Brings victory in battle to hosts,
That one may not die, Son of modest Mary,
These eight, gathered together, I have heard.

One of these eight, Anér Mac Con Glinne, was a famous scholar with a great deal of knowledge. The reason he was called Anér is because he used to either satirize or praise folks. A good name, too, for there was never before him nor will there be after him anyone whose praise or satire was more troublesome. So that's why he was called Anér or 'Non-refusal,' because no one could refuse him.

A great desire seized this scholar: to take to poetry and abandon learning, for learning made for a wretched life. He thought about where he should go to practice poetry first, and he decided to visit Cathal mac Finguine, who was on royal circuit at Iveagh in Cork. The scholar had heard of the quality and quantity of dairy products to be found there, and he had a passion for such foods.

Now all this occurred to the scholar one Friday evening in Roscommon, where he was engaged in learning. He sold what little wealth he had for two loaves of wheat bread and a piece of streaky bacon, which he put into his book bag. That evening, he made a pair of pointed, leather shoes for himself from brown hide folded seven times.

He rose early the next morning. He put on his tunic, hitched it up over his buttocks, then his white cloak, tucked up in folds and secured by an iron brooch. He threw his book bag over his shoulder, grabbed his well-balanced staff (five hands long in each direction) by the middle in his right hand, and went clockwise around the graveyard. He bade his teacher – that is, his tutor, farewell, and a copy of the gospels is hung around his neck for good luck. He set out on his journey and travelled across Connaught, to Slieve Aughty, then to Limerick, Carn Fheradaig, Berna Trí Carpat, Slieve Caín, Fir Fhéne (called Fermoy these days), past

115

Móin Mór, and came to rest a little before vespers in a Cork guest house.
All the way from Roscommon to Cork on Saturday.

    This is how the guest house, standing open before him, looked.
It was a day of three things: wind, snow, and water standing in the
doorway. There wasn't a piece of thatch or trace of ash that hadn't been
swept past the other door, under the benches and beds and along the
walls of the royal house. The blanket there was rolled up on the bed, full
of lice and fleas. And no wonder, for it was never aired in the sun by day
nor taken up at night, because it was never out of use long enough for
that to happen. The bathtub had water from the night before in it, and the
heating-stones were lying beside the door.

    The scholar found no one who would attend to him and wash his
feet. He kicked off his sandals and put his feet into the fetid water. Then
he rinsed his sandals in it. He hung up his book bag on his staff, against
the wall, hung up his sandals, took hold of the blanket and wrapped it
around his legs. But the lice and fleas nibbling at his legs were as
numerous as the sands of the sea or the sparks from a fire or the dew on a
May morning or the stars in the sky, and he grew weary. No one came to
enquire about him or to see to his needs.

    So he took down his book bag and got out his psalter and began
chanting the psalms. The scholars and books of Cork say that the sound
of his voice was heard for a thousand paces beyond the city, singing the
psalms in their spiritual mysteries, in hymns of praise, commemorations,
in categories, with pauses and choral singing, groups of ten, with
paternosters and canticles and hymns at the end of each group of fifty
psalms. Every man in Cork no doubt thought that those sounds were
coming from his next-door neighbor's house. What caused that was the
primal guilt, his original sin, his own obviously working ill-luck, so that
Mac Con Glinne was kept from food and drink and a bath until everyone
in Cork had gone to bed.

    After he had gone to bed, Manchín, the abbot of Cork, said,
"Lad, have we any guests tonight?"

    "No," replied the servant.

    "I saw someone," said another servant, "boldly and impatiently
crossing the green a little before vespers a while back."

    "We should find out who he is," said Manchín, "and bring him
his food." Mac Con Glinne was reluctant to retrace his steps for his
food, and besides it was a terrible night.

They brought his provisions out to him, and this is what it was: a small bowlful of oatmeal porridge made with whey water from the church, two embers of fire in the middle of a wisp of seed husks of oat, and two pieces of undried peat. The servant came to the door of the guest house. Fear and terror seized him at the prospect of the darkened structure standing wide open. He didn't know whether anyone was inside or not. As he put his foot across the threshhold he called out, "is anyone here?"

"Someone is," answered Mac Con Glinne.

"It is breaking taboo to arrange this house for just one person."

"If its taboos have ever been broken, they've been broken tonight; they were destined to be broken, and it is I who have done it."

"Come forward and have your meal," said the servant.

"I swear," he replied, "since I have been kept waiting until now, I will not come forward until I know what you've brought me."

The lad put the two embers in the middle of the wisp of oat husks into the hearth and added another wisp taken from the bed. He arranged the two pieces of fresh peat around them, blew on the ember until the wisp caught, and presented him with his meal.

Ut dixit Mac Con Glinne:

> Lad! (Mac Con Glinne said,)
> Let's trade verses;
> You sing some lines about bread,
> And I'll do the same for the spread.

> Cork with its sweet bells,
> Its sand is hungry
> And its soil is sandy;
> It grows no food at all.

> Unless a famine should happen,
> Never would I indulge
> In a bowl of the porridge of Cork,
> A bowl full of Cork porridge,

> Take back this piece of bread
> Over which you just now prayed;
> For him who would eat it, woe!

117

And that's my story, my boy.

The scholars memorized the stanzas, for their minds were sharp.

They returned with the food to where Manchín was, and they recited the stanzas to him. "Hmm," said Manchín, "smart-alecky words are the work of a boy. And little boys will be singing those verses unless the one who composed them is punished."

"What are you going to do?" said the servant.

"I'm going to go to the culprit, strip his clothes from him, take whips and sticks to him until his skin and his flesh are split and torn off his bones – but his bones won't be broken. After that, soak him in the muddy waters of the river Lee, then put him over there in the guest house without any covers." (And, of course, there was nothing there anyway except the blanket, with fleas and lice as thick as the dew of a May morning!)

"Lock him in the house until morning so he can't escape, so that my judgment regarding him and the judgment of the monks of Cork can be implemented before the Lord and before St. Barre, whom I serve. There is no sentence for him but hanging, for the sake of my honor, St. Barre's, and the church."

That's how it was done then, and it's there that his primal guilt, his original sin, his own obvious sin came against him. As you shall see, his clothes were stripped from him and he was beaten and whipped and put into the River Lee until he had more than enough of its muddy waters. Then he spent the night in the guest house.

Manchín rose early the next morning and summoned the monks of Cork to the guest house. It is opened for them and they go in and rest on the benches and beds. "Well, you wretch," said Manchín, "you were wrong to mock the church last night."

"The church folk were no better," replied Mac Con Glinne, "not giving me food, and I but a party of one!"

"You were not without food, as long as you got even a small loaf or a drink of whey water in the church. There are three things that one ought not to complain about in the church: fresh fruit, new ale, and the Saturday evening meal. For even though there's little on Saturday evening, the next day we have psalm singing, then the bell, preaching, celebrating mass, and satisfying the needy. Saturday evening's lack is made up on Sunday and Sunday evening. You complained too soon."

"We confess," said Mac Con Glinne, "that we have been humbled and have done more than enough of atoning for it."

"But I swear before the Lord and St Barre," said Manchín, "that you'll not satirize again! Take him away," he said to the monks, "and let him be hanged on the green for the honor of St. Barre and the church, and my own honor as well."

"O Cleric!" exclaimed Mac Con Glinne, "don't hang me! Let a fair and just judgment be pronounced on me rather than hang me." So they set about bringing judgment on Mac Con Glinne. Manchín began to prosecute him, and each of the monks of Cork in turn did the same. But though they had a great amount of learning and knowledge and teaching, they did not find any passage in legal argument by which they might hang him.

But regardless of the law, they brought him to Ráthín Mac nAeda, a green on the south side of Cork. "Grant me a favor, Manchín and you monks!" cried Mac Con Glinne.

"What, to spare you?" asked Manchín.

"No, not that," said Mac Con Glinne, "though I'd be happy if that came of it."

"Speak!" said Manchín.

"Not until I have sureties for it," said Mac Con Glinne. Sureties, strong guarantors, and bonds were placed upon the monks of Cork for the fulfilment of the favor, and he bound those guarantors.

"Now speak," said Manchín, "what do you ask?"

"All right," said Anér, "I wish to consume a portion of the Host which is in my book bag before I die, for one should not go on a trip without receiving communion. Bring my book bag to me." It is brought, and he opens it and takes out two wheaten loaves and a piece of cured bacon. Duly and lawfully, he breaks off a tenth of each of the loaves and cuts a tenth of bacon. "Here's a tithe, you monks," he said. "If we knew someone more deserving or poorer than another, we'd give the tithe to him."

The poor who were present rose up when they saw the tithe and held out their hands. Mac Con Glinne looked them over, then said, "By God, I'm not sure whether any of you need this tithe more than I do! None of you travelled more than I did today, all the way from Roscommon to Cork. I didn't eat a bite or drink a drop after I arrived, and I consumed nothing on the way. When I arrived I didn't find the

119

welcome due a rightful guest, rather I found misery and insult, you curs, robbers, dogshit, you monks of Cork! My clothes were torn from me, I was beaten and whipped, dunked in the Lee, I was dealt with most unjustly and given no true justice. As God is my witness," he continued, "there's one thing the Devil won't charge me with when I go down there, and that's giving this tithe to you, for you don't deserve it." So that was the first bit he ate, the tithe, and then he ate the rest – the two loaves and piece of bacon. Then he raised his hands and gave thanks to God.

"Take me to the Lee now," said Mac Con Glinne. With men to secure and guard him, he is brought toward the Lee. When he reached the well called Bithlán or 'Ever-full', he removed his white cloak and laid it down. He lay on his back on it, the book bag under him for support. He stuck his finger through the ring of his brooch and, passing it over his head, dipped the point of the brooch into the well. As the drops of water trickled down the point he would hold it over his mouth.

"The trick's on you, you curs, thieves, you monks of Cork! When I was in my cell at the monastery, I used to hoard whatever scraps of food would come my way over a five or six day period, then eat them in a single night and drink my fill of water afterwards. That would last me for several days without anything else, and it didn't bother me. I'll last several days on what I ate just now, several days doing penance, and a few more days drinking water. I swear to God and St. Barre, whom I serve, that none of the monks of Cork, high or low, will leave the place where they are now, but will all die in a single night, Manchín above all, die and go to Hell. I am sure to go to Heaven, and I will be in the presence of God, on whom there is neither end nor decay."

That harangue was conveyed to the monks of Cork, and they convened a hasty council. This is what was decided: to bless Mac Con Glinne if he should go humbly to his hanging, or to guard him with a company of nine men until he died where he was so they could then hang him. That was told to Mac Con Glinne. "It's a dog-decision" (i.e., it is the decision of a cur, or the one by whom the decision was given is a cur), "but anyway, whatever may come of it, I will go humbly, just as our Master Jesus Christ went to his passion." He turned himself in to the monks, and that was during the time of vespers.

"Manchín, a favor!" said the monks.

"In God's name, what favor?" asked Manchín.

"To delay hanging this wretch till morning. We haven't rung the bells, haven't preached or said Mass, haven't fed the poor. And let us not go the entire Sunday without feeding ourselves! Grant us respite till morning?"

"I assure you," said Manchín, "that I'll grant no delay; the day of the crime, that shall be the day of the punishment."

Alas! Then and there Mac Con Glinne is taken to Wood of the Foxes. With people guarding him, he is given an axe. He cuts down his own passion tree and carries it on his back to the Cork green, where he himself set it up in the ground. Vespers being over, their only thought was to hang him right then. "A favor, Manchín and you monks!" cried Mac Con Glinne.

"I swear you'll get no favors from us!" replied Manchín.

"I'm not asking for a reprieve, for if I were it wouldn't be given of your own free will, you curs, thieves, dogshit, ignorant brutes, you know – you shifty, blundering, hang-dog monks of Cork! No, what I want is to fill up on fat, juicy foods and delicious, intoxicating, sweet drinks, with beautiful, lightweight, thin, dry clothes on me to keep out both cold and heat, and feast for a fortnight before I die."

"I swear you won't get that," said Manchín. "But the day is done; it's Sunday and people are asking for a respite for you. Still, what clothing you have will be stripped from you and you will be bound to that pillar over there, and tomorrow there will be preliminary torture before the main event." So that was done; his few clothes were removed from him, he was tied to the pillar with ropes and cords.

The monks returned to their house, Manchín to the abbot's residence. The poor and guests were fed by them, and they themselves ate too. The scholar, who had been sent by the Lord God to rescue Cathal Mac Finguine and the Munstermen and Mog's Half, the southern half of Ireland, as well, was left fasting at the pillar. He was given no justice. At midnight, an angel of the Lord came to him at the pillar and began to reveal a vision to him. When the angel was on the pillar-stone, it was too hot for Mac Con Glinne. When he was away on the ridge, it was quite tolerable. That's where 'Angel's Ridge' at the green of Cork comes from, that was never a morning without dew. When the night was done, the angel left him. Mac Con Glinne then composed a little introduction that would be appropriate for relating the vision that had

121

been revealed to him. He worked solidly on that introduction to his vision until morning.

The monks' assembly bell sounded early that morning, and they went straight off to the pillar. "Well, you wretch," said Manchín "how are you today?"

"Fine," said Mac Con Glinne, "if I am allowed to relate a brief word to you, a vision I had last night. If I am given a respite I'll relate the vision."

"I swear," said Manchín, "if Adam's progeny were under my sway, they wouldn't give you a single night or day of respite. Nor will I."

"We swear," said the community, "that though it may anger you, he will be given a respite so that he might tell his vision. Afterwards, do whatever you want with him."

Manchín's pedigree in food

So then Mac Con Glinne traced Manchín's pedigree, on the food side, back to Adam:

> A blessing on us, O cleric,
> O famed fount of intellect,
> son of Honey-bag,
> son of Grease, son of Lard,
>
> son of Oatmeal, son of Broth,
> son of Fruit, bright, dappled and juicy,
> son of Cream, thick and smooth,
> son of Buttermilk, son of Butter,
>
> son of Beer, best of drinks,
> son of Bragget, sweet beer,
> son of Leek, leafy and green,
> son of Bacon, son of Butter,
>
> son of Sausage, plump and stuffed,
> son of Fresh-milk, very pure,
> son of Mast, son of Produce,
> son of Grease, son of Juice,

son of Lard, son of Kidney,
son of Shortribs, son of Shoulder,
son of Sausage, all sizzly,
son of Thigh, son of Gruel,

son of Butt, son of Cheek,
son of Cartilage, sleek,
son of Gulp, son of Sip,
son of Back, son of Belly,

son of Drink, curdled and thin,
son of Cheese, not yet pressed,
son of Fish from Inber Indsén,
son of Sweet-curds, son of Cheese,

son of Wine, son of Mead,
son of Ale, son of Meat,
son of Wheat, hard and harsh,
son of Tripe, son of Paunch.

son of Gruel, bright and clear,
made from sheep's milk pure,
son of Stew, thick and tender,
piping hot with steaming vapor.

son of Oatmeal, thick and lumpy,
son of Oat-bran, so lovely
son of Thin-soup, sprouted,
with some blackberries added.

son of Kale, smooth tips only,
son of Belly, white and soft,
son of Nutmeat, thick and chewy,
son of Abel, Adam's son.

Good your fine food pedigree,
sweet to the tongue like honey,

O firm and steady of step –
thanks to your pointed staff.

"You can't hurt me with that, Mac Con Glinne," said Manchín. "You think nothing of insulting me and the Church in composing a pedigree of food for me such as has never been composed for anyone before me or ever will be till the end of time!"

"It's not an insult at all, O cleric," said Mac Con Glinne, "it's a vision that was revealed to me last night – that was the preface to it. It's not an unbecoming vision, and if I am given a delay and respite I will tell the rest of it." Again, Manchín said that he would grant no delay. But Mac Con Glinne proceeded to tell the vision anyway, and they say that what follows here is what the angel revealed to him. *Ut dixit*:

The vision that I saw,
a wondrous revelation, I tell
in the presence of all.
A little boat of fatty suet
in the port of Lake New-milk,
Above the sea of the smooth world.

We went into the galley
and bravely took the path
across the billowing sea;
we pulled in strong strokes
o'er the great, heaving sea
so that fish and dulse went flying,
and gravel the color of honey.

Handsome the encampment we found,
with its ramparts all of custard,
there, at lake's edge beyond;
fresh butter the causeway's construction,
inside a rampart of pure wheat
fenced with a palisade of bacon.

Cheerful and pleasant the arrangement
of the strong and well-built house,

to which afterwards we went;
the door itself was of dried meat,
the threshold dried bread,
and its walls were soft cheese.

Smooth columns of aged cheese,
and joists of juicy bacon
arrayed alternately each;
lovely beams of old curds,
holding up the house,
and white posts of fresh curds.

A well of wine just behind,
and rivers of beer and bragget,
every full pool tasty and fine;
a sea of malt to make fine ale,
at the brink of a well of whey,
flows across its middle.

A lake of kale so juicy,
with greasy lard afloat on top
was between it and the sea;
it was ridged around by a butter dyke
cloaked in the lard of a boar
around the wall outside.

A fragrant apple orchard,
boughs topped in pink blossoms,
between it and the hill, upward;
a lush patch of fresh veggies,
just of leeks and of carrots,
behind, at the back of the house.

A worthy and intelligent host
were around a fire inside –
red-haired, strong and vigorous youths;
seven chains, inscribed with a hex,
from cheeses and intestines,

hung about their necks.

I saw this fellow, their leader,
wrapped in a mantle of corned beef,
and his wife noble and dear;
I saw the steward, the server,
at the cooking spit of the cauldron
with his flesh-fork over his shoulder.

Noble Cathal mac Finguine:
happy is he who has minstrelsy,
telling tales of exotic delicacies;
good the work of a single hour,
and pleasant indeed to tell
of sailing around in a galley
over the sea of Lake New-milk.

Then he told the entire vision in the presence of the monks of Cork to the very end, though this is not it here. The virtues of the vision were revealed to Manchín. "Well, you wretch," he said, "go find Cathal mac Finguine and tell him the vision, for it has been revealed to me that the evil that is in Cathal will be healed through that vision."

"What will you pay me to do that?" asked .

"Not much," replied Manchín, "how about leaving you alive – body and soul?"

"I don't care about that. The windows of heaven are open to me, and all the righteous, from Adam and his son Abel to the righteous of the present day who have gone to the kingdom of Heaven just now, are singing as one on behalf of my soul until I get to Heaven. The nine grades of Heaven, including Cherubim and Seraphim, are awaiting my soul. And I don't care if Cathal mac Finguine and the men of Munster and Mog's Half of Ireland, the monks of Cork, and, above all, Manchín, die and go to Hell in a single evening. I myself shall be in the union of the Father, the Son, and the Holy Spirit."

"What payment do you ask?" queried the monks of Cork.

"I don't ask for much," said Mac Con Glinne, "just the little cloak which the clergy of Mog's Half of Ireland were denied and which they fasted a single night to obtain: Manchín's hooded cloak."

"That's not much to you," answered Manchín, "but it's a big thing to me. I tell you this," he continued, "I swear before God and St. Barre that if I possessed all of Cork and its monastic lands, it would be easier for me to do without it all than without that cloak alone."

"It's a pity you won't give it," said the monks, "because saving Cathal and Mog's Half is worth more than that hood."

"All right," said Manchín, "I'll give it on the following condition; and I never have and never will grant a request I find more difficult. I'll give it into the custody of the bishop of Cork to give in turn to the scholar – if he helps Cathal mac Finguine." So it was given into the custody of the bishop of Cork. The monks of Cork delivered the hood, and it was left in the bishop's hands.

"Go now and find Cathal!" ordered Manchín.

"Where is he?" asked Mac Con Glinne.

"Not difficult," replied Manchín, "he's in the house of Pichán son of Mael Finn, king of Iveagh, at Dun Coba on the boundary of Iveagh and Corco Laígde. Go there tonight." Mac Con Glinne started out in all haste, boldly and without delay. He hiked up his five-pleated cloak and tied it around his shoulders. Then he tied his shirt up over his rear end and darted across the green like that, headed for the house of Pichán son of Mael Finn, at Dun Coba on the boundary of Iveagh and Corco Laígde. He sped on his way. When he reached the special assembly hall where the company was gathering, he paused to put on an ill-fitting hooded cloak and garment. The upper parts were too short and the lower parts were too long. In that get-up, he began to perform like a buffoon for the company in the hall, things unbefitting a person of his station: lampooning, farting, versifying. It was said that never before or afterwards was there anyone more accomplished in the arts of lampooning.

As he was engaged in these activities in Pichán's house, Pichán said to him, "though your act is very funny, O son of learning, it doesn't cheer me up."

"What's got you down?" asked Mac Con Glinne.

"Don't you know, scholar?" replied Pichán. "Cathal mac Finguine and the nobles of Munster are coming here tonight, and though the great host of Munster is concern enough for me, Cathal himself is an even greater problem. He's hard enough when it comes to appetizers, harder yet for the starter course, and even harder for the main course.

That main course requires a bushel of oats, a bushel of crab apples, and a bushel of bread made from the finest flour."

"What would you give me if I keep him away from you from now till the same time tomorrow so that those problems won't be visited on you or on your people?" asked Mac Con Glinne.

"I'd give you a gold bracelet and a Welsh pony!" rejoined Pichán.

"By God," exclaimed Mac Con Glinne, "you'll have to do better than that!"

"All right," said Pichán, "I'll also give you a white sheep from every house and every sheepfold from Carn to Cork."

"I'll take it," said Mac Con Glinne, "provided I have kings, hospitallers, poets, and satirists as guarantors for the deliverance of the payment and so that it all might arrive in its entirety. The kings are for enforcing the fee, and the hospitallers for maintaining me in food and drink and caring for me while I'm enforcing the payment. If I am cheated out of my fees, then poets to satirize and lampoon them, and satirists to spread the word publicly and to sing against you, your children, and your people, unless my fee is paid." And he laid that legal obligation upon his guarantors.

The arrival of Cathal mac Finguine

Cathal mac Finguine arrived with the troops and mounted men of Munster, and they sat down on the benches, beds, and couches. Gentle, nubile maidens bathed the feet of the companies and hosts and attended to them. Cathal mac Finguine did not allow a single lace of his shoes to be untied while he was busy with both hands stuffing his mouth full of the apples that were lying in profusion on the tablecloth. Mac Con Glinne was there on the other side of the room, and he began smacking his lips, but Cathal took no notice. Mac Con Glinne bounded up, like one possessed, and leapt as if goosed by the war goddess, with a warrior's leap, across the room. There was a huge block, used to test the strength of warriors, who used to drive spears and rivets into it and sharpen the points and edges of their weapons on it. That stone had been the grave marker of a warrior. Mac Con Glinne hoisted it onto his back and took it to where he had been sitting on the couch. He put one end of it on his knee and the upper part of it into his mouth, and began chewing away at it. The learned and the elders, as well as the books of Cork, say that there was no one, either near the fort, in the middle of it, or outside, who did not hear the noise of his teeth grinding against the stone, smooth though it was.

That got Cathal's attention. "What makes you behave so strangely, O son of learning?" he asked.

"Two things," replied Mac Con Glinne. "Cathal, truly handsome son of Finguine, high king of great Mog's Half, arch-defender of Ireland against the descendants of Conn the Hundred-fighter, a man ordained by the Lord God, noble warrior of the fine race of fierce Eoganachta of Glennamain by paternal inheritance: it grieves me to see him eating anything alone. And if there should be folk from distant lands here in the house seeking boons or favors, they will complain that my jaw is not bobbing up and down in harmony with your own."

"Good point," said Cathal, and he handed an apple to Mac Con Glinne as he stuffed two or three more into his own mouth. You must know that in the year and a half that this demon had been in his throat, giving that one crab apple to Mac Con Glinne was the only kind deed Cathal mac Finguine had done, and that only because he had argued so strongly for it.

"Two things are better than one in learning!" exclaimed Mac Con Glinne. So Cathal tossed him another apple.

"Number of the Trinity!" called out Mac Con Glinne, and Cathal added one more.

"The four books of the Gospel according to the teachings of Christ!" he went on. Cathal threw him a fourth.

"The five books of Moses, according to the ten commandments of scripture!" He got another one.

"The first digit for reckoning which consists of its parts and of its own components, to wit, the number six – for three is its half and two is its third; give me the sixth!" Cathal flung another apple in his direction.

"The seven things that were prophesied of your God on earth: His conception, birth, baptism, and so on!" He is given another.

"The eight beatitudes of the Gospel, O high king of royal judgments!" Cathal gives him another apple.

"Nine orders of Heaven, O royal warrior of the world!" He gets a ninth.

"The tenth order here on earth, O defender of the province!" Another apple from Cathal.

"The incomplete number of the apostles after the betrayal!" He hands over the apple.

"The complete number of the apostles after the betrayal even though there was betrayal!" He supplies another.

"Perfection of perfections and the complete number – the apostles *and* Christ!"   "Enough!" shouted Cathal. "By St. Barre, you'll be eating me if you keep this up!" and he flung the tablecloth with all its apples at Mac Con Glinne. There wasn't a nook or cranny or anywhere on the floor or the couches where there weren't apples. They weren't any closer to Mac Con Glinne than they were to anyone else, but they were farther from Cathal. He was seeing red. One of his eyes leapt backward into his head so that a pet heron couldn't pluck it out. The other eye popped out onto his face and was as big as the egg of a full-grown hen. He leaned back against the wall of the house so hard that not a stud or lath or thatching rod or thatch or post was left in its proper place. Then he sat down.

"Show a little humility, king!" said Mac Con Glinne. "Don't damn me and don't deprive me of Heaven!"

"What made you do that, son of learning?" asked Cathal.

"I had to do it," said Mac Con Glinne, "I had a nasty encounter with the monks of Cork last night, and they made a charge against me. And that's what caused me to do what I did to you."

"Go to, Mac Con Glinne," said Cathal. "By the holy monastery of Emly," he continued, "if it were my custom to kill sons of learning, either you would have had the good sense not to have come or you would never leave here alive!"

The author's digression

We digress here to explain that the reason Cathal would swear by the monastery of Emly is because that's where he used to get his fill of bread made from the finest flour. He'd be there, wrapped in his otter-colored, smooth cloak, with his hard, straight sword in his left hand, consuming portions of food in one monastic cell after another. One day, he went to the cell of a certain student and he got his ration of food from him. He looked at the food. The student kept his eye on the page he was reading. When he reached the end of the page, he stuck out his tongue and turned the page with it. "Why did you do that?" asked Cathal.

"I have very good reason," said the student. "I was sent on a military hosting to distant parts, and for food they gave us a portion of the heel of a loaf of bread that was burned and had ashes in it, was dried out and smoky, so that there was no nutritional value in it at all. We had no bit of bacon or butter or meat, no drink of any kind except muddy water from puddles, so that I was deprived of my strength and vigor, all because of the hosting."

"Alas!" sighed Cathal, 'by St. Barre, as long as I'm alive the clergy will not henceforth go on hostings with me." You see, up till then the clergy of Ireland used to go on hostings with the kings of Ireland, so that Cathal was the first ever to excuse the clergy from hostings. He left his blessing, along with provisions for the pilgrims of Emly and for an abundance of bread of the finest flour. He left even more in the south-western part, because it is there that he always got his fill. End of digression.

"By your kingship, your sovereignty, and the service due you, grant me a small favor before I die!" Mac Con Glinne pleaded.

Cathal summoned Pichán aside, and said to him, "This student is asking a favor of me."

"Grant it," said Pichán.

"All right," agreed Cathal. "Tell me what you want," he said to Mac Con Glinne.

"Not unless there are guarantors to guarantee it," said Mac Con Glinne.

"You'll have them," said Cathal.

"On your sovereign word?" asked Mac Con Glinne.

"You have my word for it; now name your boon."

"It's just this; I had a quarrel with the monks of Cork last night, and they put a curse on me. That's what is causing the misunderstanding between me and you. Because we are kinsmen, I ask that you fast with me against God tonight, in order to free me from the curse of the monks of Cork."

"Don't say it, student!" cried Cathal. "Listen, I'll give you a cow from every courtyard in Munster, an ounce of silver from every tenant, a cloak from every church, a steward to collect it all, and you yourself dining with me while he's out collecting it. Damn! I'd rather you have everything there is in Munster, North, South, East and West, than me spend an evening without food!"

"And damn me!" Mac Con Glinne responded, "you gave your sovereign word, and a king of Cashel can't go back on it! If everything in Mog's Half were given me I would not accept it. And I have good cause not to, O high warrior and royal champion of all Europe, for my only wealth is in Heaven or the earth, in learning or in poetry. And last but not least, I will go to Hell for ever and ever if you do not free me from the curse of the monks of Cork."

"It will be done for you," sighed Cathal, "and nothing more repugnant than that has ever befallen me and never will till Doomsday." Cathal fasted with him that night, as did all the rest there. And the student closed up the house and settled into a bed beside the door.

After nightfall, Pichán son of Mael Finn arose. "And why does Pichán get up now?" Mac Con Glinne said to him.

"To prepare food for all these people," he replied, "and it were better had it been ready since yesterday."

"Indeed, no," said Mac Con Glinne, "we fasted last evening, and the first thing we do in the morning is preach." So they remained there till morning. However many of them there were, not one of them stirred until it was time to rise on the morrow. Mac Con Glinne got up then and opened the house. He washed his hands, went to his book-bag, took out his psalter, and began to preach to the multitude. The historians, elders, and books of Cork say that there was neither high nor low there who did not shed copious tears listening to the scholar's preaching. When it was over, prayers were offered up for the king, that he might live long and that Munster would enjoy prosperity during his reign. Prayers were also offered up for the land, the people, and the province, as is the custom at the end of a sermon.

"Well, now," said Mac Con Glinne to Cathal, "how goes it today?"

"I swear!" said Cathal, "never worse – and never will be till the end of time!"

"It's no wonder you're in a bad way," said Mac Con Glinne, "because a demon has been devastating and destroying you for a year and a half now, and you haven't fasted a single day or night on your own. But now you have fasted with a shameless, low-life wretch like me."

"What good is that, student?" asked Cathal.

"Not difficult;" replied Mac Con Glinne, "since you fasted by yourself with me last night, we can all fast tonight and you yourself can fast until some help comes from God."

"Don't say that!" exclaimed Cathal. "If the first night was hard, the second night will be seven times harder!"

"And don't *you* say that,' rejoined Mac Con Glinne, "just be brave." So Cathal and his company fasted that night till after nightfall.

Mac Con Glinne got up then and said to Pichán, "Is Pichán asleep?"

"To tell you the truth," Pichán answered, "if Cathal remains in his present condition till the brink of doom, I will not sleep, nor eat, nor laugh, nor smile."

"Get up, then," commanded Mac Con Glinne, and he asked for bacon fat, tender corned beef, lots of mutton, comb honey, and English salt, on a beautiful, polished platter of white silver, with four perfectly straight spits of white hazel to hold the food. All that he asked for was brought. He put the great big steaks on the spits, and then put on a linen apron and a flat, linen chef's hat. He made a fine fire that had four ridges, four openings, four sections to it – of ash wood, without smoke, fumes, or sparks, and fixed a spit over each of the four sections. He was as swift about the spits and fires as a hind around its first-born fawn, or a doe, or a swallow, or the bare spring wind in the middle of March. He rubbed the honey and the salt into each steak. However big the steaks were, none of them lost enough of their juices to quench a candle, rather all of it sizzled inside.

Pichán divined that the reason the scholar had come was to save Cathal. When the steaks were done, Mac Con Glinne commanded, "Get me some ropes and cords!"

"What do you need them for?" asked Pichán. But it was a question in conscience, a rhetorical question, for it had already been revealed to him. That's where the proverb 'a question in conscience' comes from.

Ropes and cords were brought to him, the strongest the warriors had. They took hold of Cathal, and he was bound like that against the wall of the house. Mac Con Glinne spent a good deal of time securing the ropes with staples and fasteners. When that was done, he came in holding the four spits on high, his white cloak sitting lightly on his shoulders, and went up to Cathal. He set the spits down on the couch in front of him, sat down, and crossed his legs. He took a knife out of his shirt and cut a hunk of the steak closest to him and dipped it in the honey that was on the white-silver dish. "The lively beast's first!" said Mac Con Glinne as he put the meat into his mouth. That saying has survived. He cut off another piece, dipped it in the honey, and passed it under Cathal's nose before putting it into his own mouth.

"Give us some, student!" Cathal begged.

"I will," said Mac Con Glinne, and he cut a piece of the steak in front of him, dipped it in the honey as before, waved it past Cathal's lips and on into his own mouth.

"How long are you going to keep this up, student?" asked Cathal.

"I'll stop now," said Mac Con Glinne. "But there's this – you've consumed a great amount of excellent and incomparable foods up to now; what little remains I'll eat, and this will just be your 'food from afar.'" Another saying that has survived. Cathal hollered and carried on, and demanded the scholar be killed. But that did not happen.

"Well, now, Cathal," said Mac Con Glinne, "I have been shown a vision, and I hear that you are good at interpreting visions."

"Damn!" shouted Cathal, "If I would interpret anyone's vision, it wouldn't be yours!"

"I swear," said Mac Con Glinne, "that even though you won't, I will tell it to you anyway." So he began to tell his vision, and he did it wafting two or three morsels of food past the mouth of Cathal before he consumed them himself.

The vision proper

> A vision I had last night,
> that I set out with two or three,
> and saw a house brimming and bright
> where food was in abundance.
>
> I saw a Fresh-milk lake
> in the midst of a bright plain,
> and a house bustling and busy apace,
> thatched with pats of butter.

134

As I walked all around it
inspecting its arrangement,
I saw sausages, newly boiled,
used to form its wattle.

The doorposts were of custard,
its terraces butter and curds;
couches of splendid lard,
shields of pliant pressed-cheese.

Men were holding those shields,
of soft, delicious, cheese,
men who'd never wound Gaels,
armed with soft curd spears.

A huge cauldron of gruel –
I thought I could take it on –
leafy, boiled, brownish-white kale,
a copious vessel brimful of milk.

Forty rafters made from rashers,
roof-grid made of gut;
every food a man might ask for,
seemed to me they all were there.
                              A vision I had.

And he said further:

I had a vision last night,
it was most captivating,
a potent force was shown to me:
the kingship of all of Erin.

I saw this arboreal court
with palisades of bacon;
coarse gravel formed its rampart,
pregnant and rife with cheese.

135

> From pigs' little intestines
> were made its handsome beds;
> pleasant the pillars and beams,
> wonderfully constructed of tripe.
>
> I was shown the vision of wonder
> there before my hearth;
> chessboard and men of butter,
> smooth, dappled, and capped.
>
> May God bless what I utter,
> festivity flawless and gay;
> after I went to Mount Butter
> servants saw to my needs.
>
> A vision.

Though the pain of being two days and a night without food was great for Cathal, an even greater torment was this enumeration of so many wonderful and unusual foods – and none of them for him. Afterwards, Mac Con Glinne began this fable:

The fable

"As I was lying there last night in my comfy, well-made bed with its gilt posts and bronze rails, I heard this voice saying to me, 'Get up, Mac Con Glinne, you wretch!' I didn't answer the voice. And why should I; my bed was so comfortable, my body so relaxed, and I deeply asleep. Then I heard it again: 'Take heed, beware, Mac Con Glinne, that the gravy doesn't drown you!' That is, take caution that the meat-juices don't inundate you. I rose early the next morning and went to the well to wash my hands. I saw this huge apparition coming toward me. 'Well, then,' it said to me. 'Yes, indeed,' I replied. 'Well, now,' continued the apparition, 'It is I who delivered the warning to you last night, about the gravy. But then, warning you was like

> a warning to a doomed man,
> mocking a beggar,
> a stone falling against a tree,
> a whisper to a deaf person,

death to one who's depressed,
putting a charm in a wall,
putting a rope around sand or charcoal,
hitting an oak tree with your fists,
trying to suck honey from the roots of a yew,
looking for butter in a doghouse,
a diet of peppercorns,
seeking wool from a goat,
shooting an arrow into a stone pillar,
keeping a mare from farting,
keeping a licentious woman from being horny,
holding water in the bottom of a sieve,
trusting a tied-up dog,
putting salt on rushes,
paying a bride-price after intercourse,
telling a secret to a foolish woman,
expecting wisdom in a fool,
exalting a slave,
giving liquor to the reckless,
telling a king how to act,
a body without a head,
a head without a body,
a nun at the bell,
a sinner in a bishop's chair,
a kingdom without a king,
sailing a ship without a rudder,
hauling grain in a basket full of holes,
spilled milk,
housekeeping without a woman,
berries on a hide,
a vision of judgment day to sinners,
defamation as compensation for insult,
giving back without restitution,
putting seed in bad soil,
providing for a loose woman,
serving an evil prince,
cheating in trade,
rigging the scales,

137

going against a judgment,
flouting the gospels,
advising you about food is like advising the Antichrist, Mac Con Glinne!'"
[The narrator takes up the fable here:]
"Damn!" said Mac Con Glinne, "That was a very harsh admonition!"
"Why?" asked the apparition.
"Not difficult," replied Mac Con Glinne, "because I don't know where you came from or where you're going or anything about you so that I could interrogate you back or reply."
"Not difficult there, either," said the apparition, "I am Buarannach mac Elcaib Essamain, 'Loose-bowels son of Fearless Badmouth', out of the fairy mound of food, Sídh Longthe."
"That being the case," said Mac Con Glinne, "I suppose you have many stories and therefore know tales of food and eating. Do you?"
"I do indeed," said the apparition, "but it wouldn't do any good for someone whose capacity for eating didn't measure up to it."
"In what way?" asked Mac Con Glinne.
"Not difficult to say," replied the apparition. "If he didn't have a very broad stomach five hands wide, angular, very long, fourfold full, and four-sided, which would hold twenty-seven eatings and seven drinkings, with a quantity for nine men in each of those drinkings, seven meals and nine snacks, and food for a hundred in each of those eatings and drinkings, and meals and snacks."
"Since I don't have that kind of belly, give me some advice, because you've stimulated my appetite," said Mac Con Glinne.
"I will," said the apparition. "Go to the retreat from which I myself have come, the retreat of Fáithliaig, 'the Divining-Doctor,' and there your appetite for every food your stomach and your heart craves will be satisfied. A place where your teeth will be exercised on the great quantity of unusual foods we have spoken of, where your hunger will vanish and your taste buds will be tickled, a place where your lips will smack from fine drink and fine delicacies, from eating and downing every delicate, tasty, smooth and sweet food your body desires – and you won't feel guilty! But you must go to Fáithliaig and Becnat Bélaide or 'Fattie,' daughter of Mac Baetáin Brass-Longthig, 'Ravenous-eater', his wife.

"The day you arrive at the fort, that's the day their tent of lard will be set up around them on their seemly, compact fields of wheat: the two Fatties, Sausage, and the good lad Little Food-pot, with his cowl of suet around him. You'll be pleased further on the day you arrive at the fort, Mac Con Glinne," continued the apparition, "because that's the day the leaders of the Tribe of Food will be summoned there."

"And what are their names?" asked Mac Con Glinne.

"Not difficult," replied the apparition, "Sloe-ette son of Juicy-smooth-bacon, Loaf-ette son of Fruit-of-dried-meat, Empty-sides son of Sausage, Milkie son of Little-milking, Strong-arm son of Leather-head, and Lard-lover son of Side-of-bacon."

"And what is your own name, may I ask?"

"Wheatie son of Fresh-milkie
son of Juicy-bacon
is my handle;
Honey-coated Butter
the name of him
who totes my bundle.

Sheep-flank
my dog's name,
handsome in action;
my wife is called Suet,
she smiles
at tops of kale.

Sweet-curds is my daughter,
her cooking feats
enliven the hearth;
my son is Corned-beef,
his cloak covers
his big arse.

Vat-o-grease
my wife's maid's name;
in early morning
she sailed over Lake Fresh-milk.

139

My packhorse is Beef-suet:
outstanding, tender jerky
that urges horses onward;
a saddle of soft cheese
upon his back
protects him from his burden.

When a horse of soft-cheese
is let after him,
his running is speedy:
fat for reins,
food for ribs,
shapely beyond all or any.

A great collar of yummy hard cheese
hangs around his neck,
a halter whose parts
are all of fresh butter.

His bridle with reins of fat
throughout,
saddle-bags of tripe overfilled
with bloody tripe.

Saddle-horn is my horseboy,
a pillar of battle;
who calls him out – no boast –
goes to certain death.

My tunic of stew
around me through and through,
suet slice and tripe
that does not bleed.

"Off to the delightful and wonderful foods, then, Mac Con Glinne!" said the apparition. "You know,

> Foods, many and mellow,
> juicy cuts of every meat,
> dark dishes, reddish-yellow,
> faultless, overflowing;
> corned beef to fill a fork,
> juicy, smooth suets,
> and thick joints of pork.

So off with you to the suets and cheeses now!" said the apparition.

"I'm off!" replied Mac Con Glinne, "and put gospels around me."

"I will, gospels of dry cheese, evenly square," said the apparition, "and I'll put my own *paternoster* around you; no one who wears it suffers from either starvation or hunger." And he intoned:

"Your protection by juicy, smooth bacon, Mac Con Glinne;
your protection by oozing, yellow thick cream;
your protection by a full pot of gruel;
your protection by a caldron of gruel."

"I swear before the Lord," said Mac Con Glinne, "I would love to go to that fort so that I could drink my fill of those sweet, filtered old liquors and eat my fill of those vast, wondrous foods."

"If that would please you, you shall have it," said the apparition. "Go as I instruct you, and if you go, don't go astray."

"How shall I manage that?" asked Mac Con Glinne.

"Not difficult," said the apparition, "put yourself under the protection and safeguard of the bold and unrivalled warriors, the chieftains of the Tribe of Food, so that the gravy will not destroy you."

"Well then," said Mac Con Glinne, "which of the chieftains of the Tribe of Food are most valorous in defence against the heavy waves of gravy?"

"Not difficult," said the apparition, "lards and cheeses!"

"I'm off, then," said Mac Con Glinne, "full speed, bounding, and with a high heart! The wind that blows across that land, may it blow past me, provided I keep my face into it. And that's as it should be, given the heaviness of the malady, the rarity of the remedy, and the longing of the healer. I'm off – swiftly, in haste, impatiently, impetuously, gliding smoothly like a fox slinking past a shepherd, or a commoner jumping a queen in her bed, or a hooded crow heading for dung, or a deer grazing a field of winter rye in the middle of June. So, I tuck up my shirt over my butt, and my swiftness and agility are such that neither gnat, biting fly, or midge will fly up my arse until I have crossed fields, forests, and wilderness on my way to the lake of that fort.

[Mac Con Glinne takes up the narration again:]

"When I arrived at the lake, I saw before me a small, gravy-soaked boat of corned beef, varnished with lard, with benches of curds, a prow of lard, stern made of butter, sculling-oars of bone marrow, and oars made from sides of old boar-meat. The vessel into which we went was steady, and we rowed across the broad plain of Lake Fresh-milk, over a stormy sea of curdled, thin whey drink, past estuaries of mead, through terrifying, billowing storm-tossed waves of buttermilk, under constant showers of fat, past a forest of dewy meat-juice, past a little spring of greasy liquid, among islands of soft cheese, past tough rocks of suety lard, past headlands of sour curds, past beaches of dry, pressed and dry cheese, until we arrived at an attractive, solid landing spot between Mount Butter, Lake Milk, and Curd's Peak, at the mouth of the pass to the territory of the Eager-eater folk, in front of the retreat of Fáithliaig, the Divining Doctor. With every oar we dipped into Lake Fresh-milk, we brought up sea-sand of sweet curds."

(It was there that Mac Con Glinne shouted out these words, "Ho ho! These are not walls to keep me out!")

On hearing that, Fáithliaig said to his people, "There is a company here coming to you tonight, people, none other than Anér Mac Con Glinne of the Munstermen, a noble satirist lad, with splendid poetry and minstrelsy. We need to attend well to him, for he's melancholy, wild, swift, frantic, and impatient; he's eager, a swift eater, greedy, immodest, and ravenous; he's gentle and true, very easy, a good jester, quick to express gratitude as well as reproach. And that's proper, too, for he is capable of both satire and praise in the banqueting hall of a mighty, noble, elegant and convivial house."

"The retreat I was at was magnificent – surrounded by fourteen thousand posts of smooth, cured bacon. The woven blackthorn atop the posts was the greasy, boiled lard of a choice, fine boar, put there to defend against the Butter-pat and Soft-cheese tribes, who were on Lake Fresh-milk and at war with Fáithliaig. The door was made of suet, secured by a sausage bolt. I climbed up out of my boat and went up to the door leading into the porch of the outer entrance to the fort. I took a loaf of bread made from the leavings of coarse meal which was on my right side, just outside the outer entrance, and delivered a blow to the suet door with the sausage bolt on it. I knocked it in as far as the outer entrance of the fort, and went in to the big, bright, principal enclosure of the formidable fort. I planted my ten bright, pink, pointy fingernails into the door of smooth, cured bacon with the cheese-log bolt, pushed it in, and walked through.

"Then I saw the porter. The young soldier was handsome, and his name was Bacon-man son of Butter-man son of Lard. On his feet he wore shoes of smooth, cured bacon, and above that leggings of stew meat. He had on a tunic of corned beef, a belt of salmon skin around that, topped by a hooded cloak of beef brisket. He had seven chaplets on his head, each of them a circular row of fresh leeks. Seven charms inscribed on entrails hung around his neck, each of those stamped with a seal of cooked lard. He sat astride a horse of bacon, with hoofs of coarse oat bread on legs of butter. The horse had ears of curd, eyes of honey, and his breath blew steams of sour cream from his nostrils; a torrent of bragget blew out of his arse. His tail was of dulse, from which were cut seven handfuls every twenty-four hours. He was equipped with a saddle of lard or corned beef, a halter of heifer hide on his head, a collar made from the spleen of an old neutered ram. A little bell made of soft cheese hung from the collar, its clapper a solid piece of narrow gut. The horseman held a whip with many thongs – thirty superb sausages made from fat, white cows, and every grease-laden drop that dripped from those sausages would be enough for the half-loaf of a priest. He had a soft staff of boiled briar-root; each gravy-laden drop that gushed forth every time he set it on the round would be enough to fill seven vats."

"Open up for us," said Mac Con Glinne.

"Come in, you wretch," said the porter.

"When I entered," said Mac Con Glinne, "I saw on the left Fáithliaig's slaves, dressed in hair-shirts of gruel and hairy rags of soft custard, clearing away the manure which was on the causeway of custard, from the outer entry of the greathouse to the outer entry of the fort, using shovels of dry bread. To my right, I saw Fáithliaig himself, wearing gloves of well-marbled rump steak, doing the chores of the house, which was fully covered all around with intestines from floor to ceiling. I went into the kitchen, and there I saw Fáithliaig's son with a fish hook of lard in his hand, tied to a line made from the marrow of a deer's shankbone, on a rod of gut thirty hands in length, fishing in a lake of grease. He would pull out a side of bacon or a corned-beef sausage from the greasy lake mixed with honey onto the curd embankment that was beside him in the kitchen. It is in that lake that the son of Fáithliaig was drowned and for whom this famous elegy was composed:

Mac Eogan, famous his fate..., etc.

Anyway, I went into the big house then, and as I crossed the threshold, I saw this pure white mattress of butter. I sat upon it and immediately sank up to the top of my ears in it. It took the work of eight of the strongest men in the house to pull me from it by the crown of my head.

Afterwards, I was taken to the place where Fáithliaig himself was. 'Pray for me! Pray for me!' I begged him.

'In the name of cheese-log!' he exclaimed. 'The ravaged look of your face is horrible! Alas! it is a look of disease. Your hands are yellow, your lips blotchy, your eyes gray. Your sinews have grown weak and have caused your eyes, your flesh, your joints, and your fingernails to swell. The three hags, Want, Death and Hunger, have attacked you with jaws of fierce hunger. An eye that does not bless has turned upon you; a plague of terrible disease has come to you. Indeed, you don't have the look of a well-cared-for, milk-fed calf in the hands of a good cook, nor the look of a well-cared-for piglet, but the look of a lad ill-cared-for and nurtured in gloom.'"

"Not surprising," said Mac Con Glinne, "given the severity of my disease, the lack of a cure, and the need of healing."

"Tell me your problem, lad," said Fáithliaig.

"I will then," said Mac Con Glinne. "I am being eaten away by something that makes me despondent and desultory, loving luxury, hating hardship, desire for swift-eating, mincemeats, gnawing meat, downing whitemeats. I so hunger, starve, thirst, and crave my food that I neither taste nor savor what I eat. I experience sullenness, niggardliness, refusing to share, unkindness concerning what I possess, so that I grow weary with myself and am not dear to anyone. I am afflicted by hunger, with its twenty-four divisions, in addition to depression, hunger and thirst, being bold in going for food before anyone else, every food disagreeing with me. What I want is abundant, appetizing, varied foods of the world for my gullet to fulfil my desires, to satisfy my greed. But alas, great is the grief of one who can not have all of these."

"I swear," said Fáithliaig, "'tis a horrible disease, and wretched the one to whom it has come. But it will not be suffered for long, for by your journey to my retreat on this occasion, you will take with you to your house a medicine for healing your malady, and you will be healed always from it."

"What is it?" Mac Con Glinne asked.

"Not hard," said Fáithliaig. "When you go home tonight, go to the well and wash your hands, brush your teeth, and comb your hair neatly. After that, warm yourself by a blazing fire of straight, red oak or of eight pieces of firewood from an ash tree that grows in the foothills where little sparrows shit, in a dry hearth that reaches from high to low so that its heat will warm you, but its flame won't burn you nor its smoke choke you. Spread the hide of a yearling calf, hairy side up, on the north-east side of the fire, and lie with your side against a bright, white bed of special alderwood. Have a woman in attendance who is swift, white-armed, intelligent and cheerful, eloquent, of good people, wearing a necklace, a cloak with a brooch, with a black fringe between the two ends of her cloak, that it may not inflict sorrow upon her. Three fostermothers with her of the same rank as she. Three sparks of love and gaiety in her face, and no worry lines in her forehead. A pleasant and very appropriate aspect; a purple, five-pleated cloak around her, closed by a reddish-gold brooch; a fair, broad face, and bright blue eyes, topped by bluish-black eyebrows. High, pink cheeks. Red thin mouth, white teeth shining like pearls. Smooth, soft, white forearms, smooth snowy sides, pleasant, firm thighs, straight and shapely calves, white, narrow feet; long and graceful fingers with beautiful pink nails – a lovely lady, with a sprightly walk and gait; her speech and conversation sweet as harp-strings, tender and warm. A woman with no fault or disfigurement or blemish on her that the keen of sight and the wary could see, from the top of her head to the tips of her toes.

"Have that woman bring you your three nine portions, Mac Con Glinne, with each portion the size of a full-grown chicken. Cram those portions into your mouth violently so that your eyes roll and your head spins while eating them. And don't forget the eight grains, Mac Con Glinne, wherever you find them: rye, wild oats, beardless wheat, red-wheat, wheat, rough-barley, barley, and oats. Eight loaves from each of those grains, eight spreads on each loaf, and eight condiments on each spread. Every mouthful as big as a young heron.

"Off with you to the little pots of fine, sweet curds, now, Mac Con Glinne!

> To the fresh pork, to feasts of fat!
> to ram feasts – or, boiled mutton;
> to the choice, talked-about bits that men contend for – corned beef sausage;
> to the delicacies of noble-folk – to mead;
> to consumption's cure – aged, cured bacon;
> to stew-pot's need – sour curds;
> to the wish of unwed women – new milk;
> to a queen's tansy – carrots;
> to a guest's constraint – ale;
> to what gets you through Lent – chicken;
> to a broken brow – butter;
> to a hand against hand – plain bread;
> to a lumpy hearth – pressed cheese;
> to the bubbly belch – new beer;
> to a priest's darling – greasy cabbage soup;
> to the finest and sweetest treasure of all food – porridge with milk;
> to the fill of a family's guts – gruel;
> to the double-looped twins – a sheep's intestines;
> to what's fit for a wall – a rack of ribs;
> to the banned bird – salt;
> to the gateway of a gathering – sweet apples;
> to the pearls of a household – chickens' eggs;
> to a tiny breast – a nut."

"When he had enumerated those many foods for me, he proceeded to prescribe for me my drink."

"To chase those foods I listed, Mac Con Glinne, drink a small container, not too big – enough for eighty men, of very thick milk, another of milk not so thick, one of viscous but flowing milk, one of medium thick milk, one of yellow, bubbly milk that you can chew and swallow, one of the stuff that makes the gurgling, bleating sound of a ram as it goes down the gullet, in such a way that the first swallow says to the next one, 'I swear to God, you scumbag, though you come down you'll go right back up, for there's no room in this pantry for both of us bitches.'

146

"Whatever disease you may get, Mac Con Glinne, 'tis I myself who will cure you – apart from one, and that's the malady of the wise and the well-born, the malady above all maladies, the disease worth everlasting health: diarrhea!"

That's the vision.

The demon of gluttony appears

Because of that tantalizing narration and the enumeration of so many unusual and delightful foods in front of the king, the barbarous creature that dwelt in the innermost innards of Cathal appeared and was licking around the corners of Cathal's mouth. At the time, the student was inside at the big fire. He put each of the steaks on the grill, and then brought them one by one up to the king's mouth. Finally, as one of the steaks was passed before the king's mouth, the accursed creature leapt forward and laid hold of the steak Mac Con Glinne was holding. Mac Con Glinne took the steak, with the creature holding tight, carried it to the hearth, threw it under the cauldron that hung over the fire, and turned the cauldron upside down on it. So that's why a food cauldron is called a 'creature cauldron,' that is, because the gullet creature that was in Cathal's throat ended up under it.

The historians don't agree; they say that the creature went into the throat of the priest's servant, and that the lad was drowned in the water-mill of Dún Caín in front of the residence of Pichán son of Mael Find in Fir Fhéne. But that's not what is in the books of Cork, which say that he was put into the cauldron and was burned up under it. "To God and St. Brigit we give thanks," said Mac Con Glinne as he cupped his right hand over his own mouth and his left over Cathal's mouth. Then he wrapped a linen towel around Cathal's head and led him outside.

"What now?" asked Pichán.

"Easy," said Mac Con Glinne, "bring everybody and everything outside: kings, queens, retinues, herds, flocks, cattle, and all the gold and silver treasures in the fort; bring it all outside." And the learned say that nothing of greater value than a fly's foot was left of the wealth inside the great, central royal dwelling, except the cauldron that was over the demon. The house was closed from the outside, then, and four huge fires were lit throughout the house. When the house was a blazing inferno and fierce conflagration, the demon leapt up to the roof-tree of the royal dwelling, and the fire could do him no harm. He rested atop the adjacent house.

"Well, now, you Munstermen," said Mac Con Glinne, "there's your friend over there. Close your mouths, so that I may address the miserable, wicked monk.

"So, you wretch, submit to us!"

"All right, I will," replied the Devil, "for I can't not submit; you are a man in God's favor, with a lot of learning, a sharp mind, devoted to service, desirous of goodness, with seven-fold grace from the Holy Spirit. I am a demon by nature, unchangeable, and I will tell you my story. I have been in Cathal's throat destroying Munster and Mog's Half for the past year and a half. Given another year and a half I would destroy all of Ireland. Were it not for the nobility, wisdom, perfection, and innocence of the monks of great Cork of Munster from which you have come to seek me, and the number of their bishops and confessors, and were it not for the integrity of speech and word, honor, and soul of the revered and noble king you rescued, and finally, were it not for your own nobility, integrity, innocence, learning, abundance of knowledge, and poetry, it is in your own throat I'd go, and they'd beat you with dog whips, horse whips, and sticks throughout all of Ireland, and the disease I'd bring you is hunger!"

"And here's the Lord's cross in your face!" replied Mac Con Glinne, and he taunted him three times with the gospels.

"Were it not for St. Brigit, the little fair one from the Curragh of the Liffey, I swear to God, Cathal, that I would have buried you and taken your soul to hell long before this!" And with that he and his hellish host shot off into the air.

"What now, Mac Con Glinne?" asked Pichán.

"Not hard," replied Mac Con Glinne, "fresh milk and fresh butter boiled together with honey as a new concoction for the king." And so it was done. A mixing cauldron big enough to serve a hundred and filled with fully-boiled milk was brought to the king for him alone. And that quaff was the first long drink Cathal had taken since the demon had left him. A feather bed was spread for the king, and musicians and minstrels performed from noon till dusk. Then the king fell into a deep sleep. The other kings slept around Pichán in as dignified and pleasant way as they ever had before. They paid great honor and respect to the scholar that night. The learned (i.e., the historians) say that they slept for three days and three nights, but the books of Cork say that it was but for a single day.

The king rose in the morning and rubbed his face.   The brownish-pink drops of dew on his face were no smaller than sweet-smelling, bright apples. "Where's Mac Con Glinne?" he asked.

"Here," replied Mac Con Glinne.

"Tell us the vision again," said Cathal.

"All right," said Mac Con Glinne.

"However long you may take to tell it today," said Cathal, "it will not seem long to me. Today is not the same as yesterday." And Cathal left favor and blessing on every one who would read and preserve the vision.

"Well," said the kings, "do well now by Mac Con Glinne."

"It shall be done," he replied. "He shall have a cow from every courtyard in Munster, an ounce of silver from every tenant, a cloak from every monastic cell, and a sheep from every house from Carn to Cork besides.   And then he shall have the treasure that surpasses that lot, Manchín's hooded cloak."

Just then Roennu Ressamnach the Satirist, his son Cruit-Fhiach or 'Harp-raven' and his daughter Mael Chiar, 'Cropped Black-hair', came into the house and made these verses:

> Manchín set out, plainly,
> to accuse Mac Con Glinne;
> But it was Manchín who was tricked
> out of the little cloak he wore.

> It was not too much for bright Comgan (said the jester's son),
> although he's not of our people,
> the glorious cloak I see;
> though it be the colors of the raven,
> and worth three sevens bondsmaids,
> from Cathal, king of Munster.

> Nor did I think it too much myself,
> though it was gold all around,
> that he would bring it under his control,
> and through pure reason it might be said,

it is to Cathal – and prudently,
the garment went from Manchín.

Then they send a cow from every courtyard, an ounce of silver from every tenant, a cloak from every monastic church, a gold bracelet and a Welsh pony, a white sheep from every house from Carn to Cork, and two thirds of the fee due a mediator in disputes (and another third from the men of Ireland in addition), and a seat beside Cathal forever. All that he got, as we have said.

The virtues of this tale

A tradition of telling and hearing, from one to another, as sages, elders, and historians told it, as it is read and is written in the books of Cork, as the angel of God ordained it for Mac Con Glinne, as Mac Con Glinne related it to Cathal, and to the men of Munster as well. For any one who hears it there will be nothing of sorrow and there will be protection for a year.

There are thirty chief virtues in this story; a few of them will suffice as examples. The married couple to whom this story is told on their wedding night will not separate without offspring; they will want for neither food nor clothing. A new house in which this is the first tale told, no dead will be brought out from it, it will lack neither food nor clothing, fire will not burn it. A king to whom this tale is told prior to battle or conflict will be victorious. This tale should be told at offering drinks, feeding princes, or taking over inherited land. The reward for reciting this tale is a white-speckled, red-eared cow, a shirt of new linen, a cloak of fleecy wool with brooch, from kings and queens, from married couples, from stewards, from princes, to the one who can recite it and tell it to them.

A SATIRE ON RHYS MEIGEN

Dafydd ap Gwilym will receive a fuller introduction in the next section. For now, suffice it to say that he flourished in the fourteenth century, after the loss of Welsh independence and at a time when English and continental influences in Welsh life were at a high level. As we shall see, his poetry reflects to a large extent those external influences. But Dafydd was a product of the Welsh bardic tradition, and he composed in metrical forms he inherited from that tradition and on inherited themes as well. Thus, in addition to the themes for which he is best remembered today, he composed poems of praise to his patrons in the old manner, and even satire.

Satire was a potent weapon in the hands of the Celtic poets; we see instances of this in the narratives that concern Dallán Forgaill, Senchán Torpéist, and the dreaded Athirne. There are fewer instances of it in early Welsh literature, but it is clear from the present case that a sense of the power of satire lasted well into the fourteenth century. The identity of Rhys Meigen is unknown. It is possible, of course, that he was a figment of Dafydd's fertile imagination. But a number of manuscripts refer to the tradition that Dafydd killed Rhys with a satire. The historical note that precedes the satire here is from Peniarth manuscript 49 (late sixteenth, early seventeenth century). The translation is based on the edition of Parry 1952.

Bibliography: Parry 1952

A Satire on Rhys Meigen

Dafydd ap Gwilym composed this satire on Rhys Meigen because Rhys himself composed the following satire on Dafydd's mother and on Dafydd himself:

> Stinking liar Dafydd, mangy dog,
> Son of many, many fathers;
> Just on impulse, I tickled your ma,
> Over her ass and in her hole.

The englyn was recited on Christmas day in the court of Llywelyn ap Gwilym Vychan ap Gwilym ap Gwrwared in Deheubarth,

at dinner. In response, Dafydd composed and recited this poem in Rhys
Meigen's presence. And if what they say is true, Rhys fell dead upon
hearing it:

> There's a half-mad dolt of many faults,
> > Not one of Gwalchmai's folk;
> > Dogs after him everywhere,
4 > He'd get neither gift nor honor.

> Rhys Meigen, blockhead, troublemaker,
> > Wherever he goes, a gloomy loser;
> > A boob, a mutt, a stray:
8 > Curdled milk in the month of May.

> Empty, beggarly brute, boasting
> > From Teifi to Menai;
> > Hoary old dwarf trusted by none,
12 > Bird-like beak, without granny or son.

> Shamefaced, when he tried seduction
> > He never found love, truth be told;
> > His songs are wormwood, bitter and vile;
16 > Face like a leprous ape, he's not my style.

> A grating tongue that wasn't good at words,
> > And a flatterer who spewed them out;
> > Pure, unadulterated buffoon who sings
20 > For a meal in his dirty underthings.

> Sneaky, bungling clod, though he'd try to keep up
> > With the swift, he couldn't;
> > On a shoddy saddle, in every race,
24 > Every fault mars his pace.

> Lewdest, sickest lover of diseased women;
> > Useless with weapons;
> > Hateful beggar, shitty cur,
28 > Legs like a gull, aging whore.

Clumsy scrap, his pants strips of coracle skin,
     Contemptible old hide;
  Never could learn strict meter,
32   Avoided fierce conflict and battle.

Filthy, foul versifying hack,
     Frothing, fat-lipped shit,
  A sullen, vain and surly lad
36   Amid a host of churning cockroaches.

Verse like the snarling of an ass-wiggling mutt,
     Slinking, pot-bellied wanderer;
  Cunning beggar, bony,
40   Hide like the skin of a boat.

Dirty-legged, clumsy, baggypants, scum;
     Blessed the man who'd hang him;
  Sucking begged soup into his belly,
44   Tough tomcat poking about nimbly.

Testy blabberer, drunken, slurring words,
     Grunting like a pig when he vomits;
  Lacking more sense than cockles to a carnivore,
48   Wild, ugly, untamed, drained of color.

Renegade vagrant, irritating parasite,
     Cramming food with a filthy hand;
  Hair the devil himself snips,
52   Cowardly cupbearer of minstrel piss.

Truly a body that needs help–he's no Sir Kay!
     Always late for the fray;
  Sucks on intestine fat,
56   Empty skin, gray and flat.

The dregs of the barrel will suit the creep,
     Wimpy lamb, unfit for a fight;

Big-titted beggar,
60   An ape has less hair.

He sings songs of abuse to all
            Not knowing what he's doing;
A mouse who lives in a privy's hole,
64   The worst, shittiest dolt of all.

Rhys Meigen, a noose under a strong tree
            will be your end, old man's hands;
Scared and grieved your teeth chatter,
68   Wondrous feast of bacon fat, squishy vermin ridden.
Loose-lipped, foul, friend of puppy puke,
            Rather feast on foul flesh than fine mead.
You lust after suet and marrow in the hollow of big bones,
72   Cockle-skinned before a drink, by Cyndeyrn!
The meat-skewer of a head like an iron stanchion is amazing,
            Red butt-holed bell of bards, chalk-white greasy boils.
As a soldier, a coward, a wonder in war,
76   Faint flicker of fire, he's not a second Dinbyrn.
Lying, louse-ridden, sly-eyed, shrivelled foetus,
            Shapeless, worthless hulk, like tubs of chopped meat.
Uncouth, ignoble, baggy pants, constipated,
80   Shrivelled old shadow, skin and bones.
Your lightless eyes always prying about,
            Vile, vain, pockmarked Rhys, a tomcat in trousers;
Licks the vile dregs of vats, bursting, swollen belly,
84   Big-bellied trail of shit, no noble he!
Since you, slimy, woeful-grunting caca-pants, know neither
            Awdl nor englyn, you tightfisted thief,
Run away, you croaking, surly, babbling fool,
88   Run away, go suck the drinks that others leave!

WELSH POEMS

Cyntefin: Summertime

At first, this poem from the Black Book of Carmarthen (mid-thirteenth century) seems to be very much in the vein of Finn's poem on summer ("The Boyhood Deeds of Finn"). But as it wears on we see something quite different. In his analysis of the work, Geraint Gruffydd finds in the opening englyn an example of the ancient Welsh tradition of gnomic and descriptive poetry about nature. The first line simply says, "summer is the finest time." The second presents impressions of the new season: bright voices of birds, budding greenery. The third line moves to man's activity, plowing with the yoked oxen. The fourth line returns to nature: the greenness of the sea.

The second englyn sounds a sad note with mention of the cuckoo. Here, as in the poems associated with Llywarch Hen, the cuckoo is a symbol of sadness and grief. In the third line in this stanza we have a nature gnome leading to (or validating) a human gnome: just as smoke stings the eyes, so is grief apparent on the fact of a person. In the last line we discover the cause of the grief: friends have passed away.

In the third englyn, Gruffydd finds the first clue that this might be a religious poem. He suggests that the hill and dale and island refer to burial places: places like Enlli Island in North Wales, where so many religious chose to die and be buried, or places like the deserted areas that were favored by the early Irish and Welsh anchorites. Christ here is depicted as a fearful figure from whom none can hide.

The next stanza presents Christ as "the architect of life" and a refuge for the weary soul after death. And we find that those who have been unable to hide in death from Christ have now joined the countless throng at the heavenly throne and now know no fear.

Finally, the poet moves from the plural to the singular asking that like those countless ones who have preceded him he too shall find peace at the heavenly throne. The poem moves from description of nature, to the theme of transitoriness of human existence, to the religious, to a final prayer.

There are other ways of interpreting the poem, especially in light of medieval European literary conventions. For example, there is often a thin line between the religious and the secular, as we shall see when we encounter the poetry of Dafydd ap Gwilym. The translation is based on the edition of Gruffydd 1969.

Meter: The poem consists of three different types of englyn, and a six-line stanza in awdl meter.

Bibliography: Jackson 1935; Gruffydd 1969

Summertime

Cyntefin, ceinaf amser;
Dyar adar, glas calledd,
Ereidr yn rhych, ych yng ngwedd;
Gwyrdd môr, brithotor tiredd.
Summertime, the finest time!
Birds boisterous, stalks freshening,
Plows in furrows, oxen yoked,
Sea's green, the land dappled.

When cuckoos on fair boughs call,
    Melancholy grows,
  Like sting of smoke, and no repose,
  Since death has claimed dear ones.

On hill, in dale, on islands at sea,
    Wherever one might be,
  Before Christ nothing stays unseen.

Our Beloved, our Path, we longed to pass
    to the land of the Heavenly Father:
Seven hundred, seven score and seven saints
    at the throne all together;
There, in the company of glorious Christ
    Fear would be nothing to nurture.

I ask a boon — let it not be denied me:
Between me and God, tranquility;
May I find the path to the gate of glory;
Christ, I'll not be sad beside your throne!

POEMS BY TALIESIN

In a work called *Historia Brittonum*, dated to about the year 800 A. D. and attributed to a Welsh monk by the name of 'Nennius,' we read that about the year 575 A. D. there were five poets especially famous among the British. Their names are given as Talhaearn Tad Awen, Aneirin, Taliesin, Blwchbardd, and Cian. Of these five, only the works of Aneirin and Taliesin survive. Talhaearn's epithet, Tad Awen, means 'father of poetic inspiration,' and he seems therefore to have been the chief of them; hence his place in the list. It is indeed a pity that we don't have any of his work. The word *awen* (Irish *ai*) 'poetic inspiration,' reminds us that the poet was in a sense a 'medium' and that poetry was something that came from without and was 'breathed into' men who had been properly trained and initiated (see Introduction).

The works of Taliesin have survived in a manuscript of around the middle of the thirteenth century known as The Book of Taliesin. This manuscript contains a number of poems, some of them on religious themes, some on themes of arcane knowledge that speak to what I would call the darker, or mystical side of poetry and the poetic experience. In one of these poems, "Cad Goddeu," (Ford 1977), the poet speaks of having been in many different shapes, including 'a bubble in beer.' In fact, as we see in "The Story of Gwion Bach, Who Became Taliesin," he undergoes a series of transformations before being reborn as the chief poet of the Western world. Finally, some of the poems in the Book of Taliesin are poems of praise in the conventional mode, addressed to real, historical persons such as Urien and his son Owain. Urien was ruler of the kingdom of Rheged (see map). We recall the words of the Greek and Roman ethnographers to the effect that the Celts were accustomed to have with them singers of praise, chanting to the accompaniment of the lyre the valiant deeds of men and of their ancestors.

Consistent with the ethos of this early medieval British warrior aristocracy, certain virtues are extolled again and again in the poetry (Jarman 1967, 1992). Principal among them are:

• Leadership: a ruler or chieftain attracts followers who will do his bidding.

• Bravery in battle: he overcomes his enemies, who flee from him in terror.

• Generosity: all the booty he acquires as a result of his victories he freely gives out to his followers, in particular to the poets who praise him; this is perhaps the greatest virtue of all.

• Pedigree: the chieftain is great because he is descended from great men. Often it is the ancestor's leadership, bravery, and generosity that are extolled, so that the patron, his descendant, basks in the reflected glow of his ancestor's fame.

The poems seldom provide a narrative account of a particular battle or event, rather they build an image of greatness through the piling up of images reflective of the virtues most highly prized. Thus we get an impression of the patron for whom the poem is intended, emphasizing the degree to which he possesses those virtues. The translations are based on the edition of Sir Ifor Williams in J. E. C. Williams 1968.

A Poem on Behalf of Cynan Garwyn son of Brochfael

The patron eulogized here is Cynan Garwyn, a king of Powys (see map) who flourished in the second half of the sixth century. This could very well be the earliest extant poem in the Welsh language.

Meter: as set out by Sir Ifor Williams, an awdl, with rhyming half lines of 5 or 6 syllables, each containing two stresses. The first nine lines begin with the sound [k], an example of *cymeriad*, or 'linking,' characteristic of much Welsh poetry. For an overview of the Taliesin meters, see Haycock 1988.

Cynan Garwyn Son of Brochfael

> *Cynan kad diffred*   *am arllofeis ced.*
> *Canyd geu gofyged*   *gwrthelgwn trefbred.*
> *Cant gorwydd kyfred*   *aryant eu tudded.*
> Cynan, host's defender, handed me gifts,
> Because the fame I gave him isn't false:
> A hundred swift horses, harnessed in silver,
> A hundred cloaks, purple, well-tailored,
> 5   A hundred bracelets, fifty brooches to hand,
> A sword with strong scabbard and the best gold band;
> All came from Cynan, with no trace of malice,
> Sprung from Cadell, an unwavering host.
> Battle begun on the Wye, spears galore,

10   Men of Gwent hewn with bloody sword;
       In Môn a great campaign, famed in song,
       The Menai was broached, then they were gone;
       Havoc on the hill of Dyfed, Aergol on the go,
       He's never seen his cattle driven by a foe.
15   Brochfael's son, his borders growing, eager;
       Let him set on Cornwall, leave them no honor,
       He'll cause them grief till he's appeased.
       Cynan, my support, master of conflicts,
       Broad flaming brow, stirring infernos;
20   Battle in Brychan, thunderous action,
       You pitiful princes, cringe before Cynan!
       His armor lashing, a Leviathan,
       Cyngen's kin, ward of broad lands.
       I heard praise, wherever men sing –
25   Throughout the world, thralls all to Cynan!

THE CELTIC POETS

THE BATTLE OF GWEN YSTRAD

This poem is in praise of Urien, lord of Rheged (see map; roughly modern Cumbria/Durham) and perhaps even additional lands. He is called the ruler of the men of Catraeth, which means that in his day Catraeth was still under the control of native British princes. In "The Gododdin," perhaps composed about the year 600 A.D., the British forces are attempting to retake Catraeth from the Anglo-Saxons. It is not clear exactly where Gwen Ystrad was.

The poem gives us a series of images rather than an account of the actual fighting and course of the battle. This is typical of the praise poetry of the period. The poet claims to have been an eye-witness to the events: he says several times, "I saw," and this is consistent with the idea that poets accompanied their patrons into battle, the better to record their valor and leadership (see Introduction and introductory note to "The Battle of Allen"). Finally, we note that seven of the eight poems addressed to Urien in The Book of Taliesin end with a coda similar to the one here. The poet insists that, so long as he is able, he will devote his energies entirely to praising his chieftain.

Meter: awdl, with rhyming lines of 8 to 10 syllables, and normally 4 stresses in each line.

Bibliography: Jarman 1981; Jarman 1992a; Morris-Jones 1918; Williams, I. 1961

The Battle of Gwen Ystrad

Arwyre gwyr Catraeth gan ddydd
Am wledig gweithfuddig gwarthegydd
Urien hwn anwawd einefydd.
Dawn, and the men of Catraeth rise
Around a cattle-rich ruler, victorious;
This is Urien, renowned chieftain
Who thwarts lords, cuts them down,
5   Warlike and rash, supreme sovereign–
Britain knows widespread destruction!
Reaper of hosts at Gwen Ystrad,
Neither field nor wood protected

164

Your enemy when they came, my lord,
10   Their screams flooded the land.
    I saw brave men marshalled,
    And after the attack, torn flesh;
    I saw the invading horde dead;
    A lusty and wrathful roar was heard;
15   In the fighting for Gwen Ystrad one saw
    Suffering and survivors exhausted;
    Before the ford I saw men blood-spattered
    Surrendering arms to the grizzled chieftain;
    Wanting peace as they wore down,
20   On the strand, hands crossed, pale and haggard;
    Hostages were left behind for warriors
    As waves washed over their horses;
    I saw men ragged and haggard,
    And clothing all stained with blood;
25   Against keen and penetrating cohorts –
    It wasn't retreat our defender intended,
    Lord of Rheged, I marvel at what he ventured!
    I saw splendid men around Urien
    When he fought his enemies at Llech Felen;
30   He revelled in the wrath of war,
    In men's shields borne to the fore –
    Urien, relishing battle more and more.

    And until old age and death
    And with my dying breath,
35   I'll not have satisfaction,
    Unless I'm praising Urien!

IN PRAISE OF LLWYFENYDD

Llwyfenydd was part of Urien's domain, perhaps well within the
kingdom of Rheged. Notice that the poet says at the outset that he's "here at
home, with Rheged's folk," in Llwyfenydd. The poet praises the liberality of his
patron, provider of mead and beer to supply the appetites of the men who will
fight for him. He provides for his poet too, giving him "fair furnishings."

Above all, the patron is a gift to the poets of the world: the virtues they celebrate are so strong in him that he is the perfect object of their art.

Meter: awdl, as set out by Sir Ifor Williams, with rhyming half lines of 3 to 5 syllables, and, normally, two stresses in each half line; a few half lines have a single stress. *Cymeriad* is employed frequently: the word that ends one line, or some form of it, begins the next line.   The translation illustrates this feature somewhat.

In Praise of Llwyfenydd

> *Yg gorffowys*   *can Rychedwys*
> *Parch a chynnwys*   *a medd meueddwys*
> *Meueddwys medd*   *y orfoledd*
> *A chein tiredd*   *imi yn rhyfedd*
> *A rhyfedd mawr*   *ac eur ac awr*
> *Ac awr a chet*   *a chyfrifedd*
> Here at home, with Rheged's folk,
> Honor and welcome and mead aplenty:
> Plenty of mead for revels,
> And fine estates for me as wealth.

5 Wealth galore, gilded and golden,
   Gold and gifts and esteem
   Inestimable, and granting of wishes,
   Wishing to grant them to please me.
   He kills, crucifies, nurtures, provides
10 Provident, nurturing, killing in glory!
   Glory he gives to the bards of the world,
   A world, to be sure, that submits
   To your will. God made kings groan
   Before you, for fear of destruction!
15 Inciter of battle, defender of the land,
   Land's defence, battle inciter,
   Around you always a restive crowd,
   Crowds restive and drinking beer;
   Beer for drinking, fine estates,
20 And fair furnishings he gave to me.

Beautiful Llwyfenydd and all of Eirch,
Great and small, in a single song,
Taliesin entertains you–
Of all known qualities, yours the best!
25   I praise your great gifts.

> And until old age and death
> And with my dying breath,
> I'll not have satisfaction,
> Unless I'm praising Urien!

THE CELTIC POETS

ANEIRIN: THE GODODDIN

A rubric at the beginning of this Welsh work reads, *Hwn yw e gododin. aneirin ae cant*, meaning 'this is the Gododdin; Aneirin sang (composed) it.' Aneirin is one of the five poets named by Nennius in his *Historia Brittonum* (see introductory note to "Poems by Taliesin"). "The Gododdin" consists of a series of heroic elegies, celebrating the virtues of North British warriors who took part in an ill-fated expedition against an Anglo-Saxon stronghold in Northumbria. From the elegies, we know that a band of 300 (or 363) engaged a host of 100,000. The odds were not conducive to victory, and of the men of Gododdin (the name of the district as well as its inhabitants), only one (or three elsewhere in the text) escaped, as well as the poet, Aneirin. "The Gododdin" consists of some thirteen hundred lines of which only a representative sample is presented here.

Many of the personal and place names cannot be identified unequivocally, and many of them may be descriptive epithets rather than actual names. The verse is characterized by a certain compactness, economy of expression, and a fondness for stark contrast, all of which conspires to reveal a richness of meaning. Throughout, the poet drums on what one might call the "comitatus" theme: the prince or leader retained a host of men whom he was obliged to feed and provide with drink, a relationship often characterized solely by the word 'mead' or 'wine.' The host in turn, in payment for their provisions and keep, were obliged by honor to fight bravely and without stint for the leader. Thus the mead/blood image persists, signifying the exchange of feasting for fighting, the ultimate payment for the mead or wine being death in battle. The translations are based on the edition of I. Williams 1961; the roman numerals refer to the numbering of the stanzas in that edition.

Meter: awdl, but for the most part in relatively short stanzas. The line lengths vary; shorter ones have 4 to 6 syllables and, normally, 2 stresses; longer ones contain lines of 9 to 11 syllables and 3 or 4 stresses. The line-end rhyme often changes through the poem. For a fairly full treatment, see Evans, D. Ellis 1978 and references given below. The first lines of each selection are given in italics, preceding the translation of that section.

Bibliography: Charles-Edwards 1978; Haycock 1988; Huws 1989; Jackson 1969; Jarman 1988; Koch 1997; Owen 1978; Roberts, B. 1988; Williams, I. 1961

Selections from the Gododdin

I   *Greddf gwr, oed gwas*
   Gwryd amddias
   A man's mettle, he was but a lad
   Fearless in the fray;
   Swift steeds with thick manes
   Beneath a bright lad;
   Broad light shield
   Across the crupper of a fine, swift one;
   Pure, bright swords,
   Gilded spurs.
   There is no emnity
   Between thee and me:
   Better that I make for you
   A song in praise of you.
   Sooner his blood to the ground
   Than he to his wedding feast;
   Sooner his flesh for ravens
   Than his proper burial.
   Beloved friend Owain,
   Miserable to be 'neath ravens!
   woeful to ponder where
   Marro's only son was slain.

II   *Caeog, cynhorog men ydd elai*
   Diffun ymlaen bun, medd a dalai
   Wearing a wreath, to the fore wherever he went,
   Breathless before a maid, he earned his mead.
   The boss of his shield picked to pieces wherever
   He answered the battle cry; and no quarter to those he
   chased.
   He stayed in the fray till the blood flowed;
   Those who did not flee he hewed down like hay.

The *Gododdin* recounts in stately courts
That when Madog returned
Not one in a hundred came with him.

III   *Caeog, cynifiad cywlad rwyd*
Rhuthr eryr yn ebyr pan llithiwyd
Wreathed warrior, enemies' snare,
Like an eagle in an estuary, feeding;
His contract a goal fulfilled,
He did not retreat from his purpose;
And so they fled before *Gododdin's* army
In mighty pursuit over Manawyd land.
He spared neither shape nor shield;
None could keep from Cadfan's blows,
He who was brought up bellicose.

IV   *Caeog, cynhorog blaidd ym maran*
Gwefrawr goddiwawdd torchawr am ran
Wearing a wreath, in the fore, a wolf in war,
A flame that tore torques from foes;
He was a valued flame, earned his ration of wine.
He repelled assault, a sea of gore cascading;
Though Gwynedd and the North both came,
Through counsel of Ysgyrran's son
Shields were in pieces.

V   *Caeog, cynhorog arfog yng ngawr*
Cyn no'i ddiwedd gwr gwrdd yng ngwriawr
Wearing a wreath, in the fore, armed in assault,
Before his time a mighty man in battle;
Prince in the front lines facing foes:
Deirans and Bernicians, two thousand and more,
Passed to perdition in a single hour.
Sooner his flesh a feast for wolves than he to his
wedding;
Sooner his body booty for ravens than he to the altar;
In exchange for mead in the hall with hosts,
Hyfaidd Hir will be praised as long as there are poets.

VI   *Gwyr a aeth Ododdin chwerthin ognaw*
     Chwerw yn nhrin â lläin yn ymddulliaw
     The men who went to Gododdin were laughter-loving,
     Savage in battle with spears at the ready;
     A short year in peace, then they fell silent.
     The son of Bogdad, his hand wrought slaughter.
     Though they went to churches to do penance,
     Old and young, mighty and slight,
     'Tis true, death came for them.

VII   *Gwyr a aeth Ododdin chwerthin wanar*
     Disgyniaid ym myddin trin ddiachar
     The men who went to Catraeth were laughing and
     intense,
     Attackers in a band eager for battle;
     They slaughtered with blades without much fanfare;
     Pillar of battle, Rhaithfyw delighted.

VIII   *Gwyr a aeth Gatraeth oedd ffraeth eu llu*
     Glasfedd eu hancwyn a gwenwyn fu
     The men who went to Catraeth were a spirited host;
     Bright mead their feast, but it turned to poison.
     Three-hundred under orders in battle;
     And after the rejoicing, there was silence.
     Though they went to churches to do penance,
     'Tis true, death came for them.

X   *Gwyr a aeth Gatraeth gan wawr*
     Trafodynt eu hedd eu hofnawr
     The men who went to Catraeth at dawn,
     Their fears stirred their tranquility;
     Three hundred charging a thousand hundred!
     Blood and gore staining blades;
     He stood most sternly in the fray,
     Before the host of Mynyddog Mwynfawr.

XI   *Gwyr a aeth Gatraeth gan wawr*

Dygymyrrws eu hoed eu hanianawr
The men who went to Catraeth at dawn,
Their temperaments cut short their lives;
They drank the yellow, sweet, ensnaring mead;
For a year, many a minstrel rejoiced;
Their swords red, blades unwiped,
White-faced shields and four-edged spears
Before the host of Mynyddog Mwynfawr.

XII *Gwr a aeth Gatraeth gan ddydd*
  Neus goreu o gadau gywilydd
  The men who went to Catraeth at daybreak
  Humiliated hosts;
  They made bier-bearers toil;
  With busy blades, nowhere to hide;
  This one, before any talk of truce,
  Made a blood bath and death for his foes.
  When he fought in the front of Gododdin's army,
  This doughty warrior worked his bold purpose.

XIII *Gwr a aeth Gatraeth gan ddydd*
  Neu llewes ef feddgwyn feinoethydd
  The man who went to Catraeth at daybreak
  Gulped mead-feasts through long nights;
  Pitiful were the screams of the host
  After that fiery striker's onslaught;
  No one set out for Catraeth
    With greater determination
      over mead.
    There was none
    From Eidin Fort
      Who so fully routed foes.
  Tudfwlch the Tall would drive the Saxon
  Out of his land and towns all week long;
  His bravery will long endure,
  Remembered by his fair comrades.
  When Tudfwlch, people's bulwark, came to fight,

Where the son of Cilydd stood there was blood all
around.

XIV   *Gwr a aeth Gatraeth gan wawr*
Yn ei fuddyn ysgorfa ysgwydawr
The man who went to Catraeth at dawn,
An enclosure of shields guarding him;
Savagely they attacked, gathering booty;
Like a crack of thunder the clash of shields.
A proud man, a prudent man, a champion:
He gouged, he stabbed with steel spikes;
Over blood he slew with blades;
Hard iron on heads in battle.
In courts the warrior was humble,
But armies groaned before Erthgi.

XV   *O freithell Gatraeth pan adroddir*
Maon dychiorant eu hoed bu hir
Of the battle of Catraeth it is told
That men fell; long were they lamented;
Whether easy or hard, they defended their land
From the sons of Godebog – a nasty lot;
A long line of biers bore bloodied bodies.
A sad fate – though it had to be –
That was fated to Tudfwlch and Cyfwlch the Tall;
Though we drank bright mead by candlelight,
And though its taste was good, its bitterness lasted long.

XXI   *Gwyr a aeth Gatraeth buant enwawg*
Gwin a medd o aur fu eu gwirawd
The men who went to Catraeth were famed,
Drank wine and mead from golden horns
For a year, according to honored custom:
Three, three score, and three hundred in gold torques.
Of those who set out after splendid mead
None save three escaped the maelstrom
Save the two war hounds of Aeron and steely Cynon,

173

And I too, streaming with blood, for the sake of my
song.

XXIII *Arf anghynnull anghyman ddull anghysgoged*
Trachywedd fawr treiglesyd llawr Lloegrwys giwed
(ll. 1-4 of trans.)
Arms scattered,
The invincible host in disarray,
Great destruction;
The warrior repelled the English folk,
Hurled javelins
In front ranks in a spear-throwing fray;
Flattened men and
Widowed women; before he died
The fiery son of Hoywgi made
Bloody carnage from spears.

XXIV *Arwr ardwy ysgwyd o dan –ei dalfrith*
Ac ail tith orwyddan
Bu trydar yn aerfre bu tân
Hero with a protective shield beneath his brindled brow
Lively as a colt;
There was tumult on the battlefield, there were sparks,
His spears were swift, were flashing;
There was food for ravens, booty for birds;
And before he had been left in the ash ford
As the dew descended,
Beside the spreading wave,
He was a graceful, soaring eagle;
Bards of the world judge men of valor.

XXX *Pan grysiai Garadog I gad*
Mal baedd coed trychwn drychiad
When Caradog roared into conflict,
Like a wild boar, a triple slayer,
Bull of battle, hewer in combat,
He would feed wild dogs from his hand;
As I am witness, Owain son of Eulad

174

And Gwrien, Gwyn and Gwriad,
From Catraeth and the killing,
From Hyddwn Hill before it was taken,
After fistfuls of bright mead,
Not one saw his father again.

XXXI *Gwyr a grysiasant buant gydnaid*
Hoedlfyrion meddwon uch medd hidlaid
The men who attacked rushed as one;
Short lives for drinkers of mellow mead,
The men of Mynyddog, famous in battle;
Their lives in exchange for their mead-feast:
Caradog, Madog, Pyll and Ieuan;
Gwgon, Gwion, Gwyn and Cynfan;
Peredur of stout spears, Gwawrdur and Aedan,
Attackers in the stir of strife –
But though they killed, they were killed;
None returned to his native land.

XXXII *Gwyr a grysiasant buant gydfaeth*
Blwyddyn odd uch medd mawr eu harfaeth
The men who attacked, they were nurtured
For a year over mead, proud of purpose;
How painful to speak of them, overwhelming longing;
Bitter their abodes, none bestowed care;
How long they are grieved and mourned,
Those lively men from the land of wine-feasts!
Gwlyged of Gododdin, getting ready,
Enjoyed the feast of famous Mynyddog –
And dearly he bought the battle of Catraeth.

XLI *Gwyr gormant aethant cennyn*
Gwinfaith a meddfaith oeddyn
Splendid men gone from our midst;
Men nurtured on wine and mead
From Mynyddog's feast;
I grieve
For the loss of a fierce fighter:

175

Like thunder from the skies
Shields clattered
      Before the onslaught of Eithinyn.

XLVIII *Nid wyf fynog blin*
Ni ddialaf orddin
Ni chwarddaf chwerthin
O dan droed rhonin
No weary lord am I;
I avenge no attack;
I laugh no laugh
Among maggots;
My knees stretched out
In an earthen abode;
An iron chain
Around my knees;
Of mead from drinking horns,
Of the army of Catraeth,
I – yet not I – (Taliesin
of the intricate utterance knows!)
I sang the Gododdin
Before dawn of the following day.

POEMS FROM THE LLYWARCH HEN CYCLE

Llywarch Hen appears in early Welsh genealogies as a first cousin to Urien, ruler of Rheged, and therefore he must have lived in the latter half of the sixth century. Most scholars agree that Llywarch did not write the poems associated with his name, rather it is believed that they represent the work of a professional poet of the ninth or tenth century who assumed the persona of the sixth-century figure. It was argued by Sir Ifor Williams (1935) that the poems are the verse remains of a saga, in verse and prose, about the fortunes of Llywarch. Whatever of the merits of that theory, there is no extant saga about Llywarch, and we are left to appreciate the poems on their own merits.

The metrical form is noticeably different from that of the poetry of Taliesin and Aneirin. These stanzas are written in the *englyn* (plural *englynion*) form. The englyn is intended to stand alone, as it were, with a complete thought or 'argument' in each three- or four-line englyn. As we see from the selection presented here, a series of these on the same or related theme may be strung together to form a longer 'poem,' but the englyn is still the basic unit.

That is the case with the poem "On Urien and the Gogledd." There we have a sequence of thirteen stanzas all given over to the theme of the grief the speaker experiences at having cut off the head of Urien son of Cynfarch, the ruler of Rheged we have already met in the Taliesin poems. The underlying assumption of these lines is that Urien has been killed in battle, and to keep his head from falling into the hands of the enemy, Llywarch, his cousin, has severed it from the body and taken it away with him. (For a discussion of the significance of the head in Celtic literature, see the introductory note to "Lomna, Finn's Fool".) The stanzas thus represent a traditional elegy framed by a dramatic situation. The poet's grief is enhanced by the immediacy of the situation, the dramatic frame, and the effect of this plaintive song is strengthened by the repetition of the same words at the beginning of each stanza. In the original of that poem, each englyn begins with the words, *pen a borthaf*, translated here 'the head I carry.' The lines convey the same elements of praise that we have seen constitute the ethos of this heroic age. Urien was a battler, was generous, a good ruler, protector of his land. Metaphor predominates: he was a shield, a wheel, a stave, a snare, a shepherd, a pillar, etc. In the last stanza of this group, the repeated phrase is not in the first line but the last: *pen a borthaf a'm porthes* 'the head I carry carried me.' The word-play is evident and intentional: multiple meanings of 'carry, support', and multiple meanings of 'head,' as in English.

These stanzas are followed by eight that focus on the subsequent burial of Urien's body, and notice that there is no praise of Urien here, no reference to the virtues that constitute the heroic ethos, only the grief experienced by the speaker over what he was compelled to do. In singing to Urien's head, the poet speaks of the head as if it were Urien himself; the body alone, however, is not so considered.

In "The Desolation of Erechwydd," we have a lament for the court of Urien, fallen into ruin after the death of that ruler. The poet reflects on the exuberance of the place when Urien was alive. One can easily imagine a milieu much like that of the men of "The Gododdin," feasting, jousting, entertainment and more, before going off to battle. We find a similar theme in Tadhg Dall Ó hUiginn's poem on "Enniskillen." Indeed, much of the Llywarch Hen poetry represents a longing for the past, and thus is a reverie on the transitoriness of human existence. "The Song of the Old Man" and "The Sick One of Aber Cuawg" are powerful evocations of this theme.

One of the most striking things about this poetry is its gnomic character. The poem entitled "Gnomes" combines human and nature gnomes in individual englynion, for example,

> Snow falls, mountain ridge white;
> Masts of ships without sails;
> A coward courts many counsels.

The first two lines state universal truths about winter; the last line states a truth about cowardice in humans. Whatever the precise signification of such an arrangement, one is struck by the pithy nature of the poetry and by its economy of expression: bright flashes of images rather than detailed description. The translation is based on the edition of Ford 1974.

Meter: englyn, mostly of two types. The *englyn milwr* (stanza 9) is a three-line stanza having, normally, 7 syllables in each line and end rhyme. The *englyn penfyr* (stanza 1) has a first line of 9 to 11 syllables, a second line of 5 or 6 syllables, and a third line of, normally, 7 syllables.

Bibliography: Ford 1974; Jarman 1992c; Rowland 1990; Williams, I. 1935, 1980;

The Sick One of Aber Cuawg

1   *Goreistedd ar fryn a erfyn fy mryd*
             A hefyd ni'm cychwyn;
         Byr fy nhaith; diffaith fy nhyddyn. (englyn penfyr)
      My mind seeks to sit on a hill
             and still it moves me not;
        short my journey, my dwelling desolate.

2   Brisk the wind, cowherds bare;
             while trees wear fair hues of summer,
        I remain gravely ill.

3   I am not agile, and I keep no host;
             I cannot rove;
        Let the cuckoo sing while he will.

4   The clamorous cuckoo sings at dawn
      lofty song in the dales of Cuawg;
             better generous than miserly.

5   In Aber Cuawg cuckoos sing
             on blooming branches;
        eloquent cuckoo, long let him sing.

6   In Aber Cuawg cuckoos sing
             on blooming branches;
        sad for the sick one who hears them constantly.

7   In Aber Cuawg do cuckoos sing;
             sad to think
        that those who heard them hear them no more.

8   I listened to a cuckoo on an ivy branch;
             my garb has gone slack

yet grief for what I loved grows.

9   *Yn y fan odduwch llon ddar*
Yd endewais i lais adar;
Cog fan cof gan bawb a gâr (englyn milwr)
From the top of a mighty oak
I listened to birds' banter;
lofty cuckoo, memory of a love lingers.

10   Singer of ceaseless song, longing in its voice,
        aloft, with hawk's haste,
      eloquent cuckoo in Aber Cuawg.

11   Birds raucous, streams in flood;
moon luminous, chill of dawn;
I feel raw, ravaged by disease.

12   White the hillcrest, streams in flood, dawn drawn out;
        the wise are respected;
      I earned a rest in old age.

13   Loud are birds, gravel wet;
leaves fall, the homeless fallen in spirit;
I cannot deny, I ail this night.

14   Loud are birds, the strand wet;
clear sky, the wave wide;
a heart broken from longing.

15   Loud are birds, the strand wet;
bright wave, its motion full;
the passion of youth –
I would love to have it again!

16   Loud are birds on Edrywy mound;
        the howl of hounds is desolate;
      the birds loud still.

17   May, and every living thing lovely!
        when warriors hustle to battle
        I do not go – a wound detains me.

18   Pale the mountaintop, tender the tips of ash;
            bright waves ebb from estuaries;
        laughter is far from my heart.

19   Today marks a month for me
        in the lodging he left;
        my spirit sad, fever grips me.

20   Clear the eye of a sentry;
        pride causes indolence;
        my spirit sad, disease wasting me.

21   Cattle sheltered, a bowl for mead;
        the content seek no conflict;
        patience is the crown of acquaintance.

22   Cattle sheltered, a bowl for beer;
        paths are slippery, fierce rain,
        the ford flooded; the mind brews treason.

23   Wicked work brews treason;
        there will be grief when it is atoned:
        selling little in exchange for much.

24   A cauldron for the wicked will be waiting
        when the Lord judges on judgment day;
        the false will be in despair, the true shining.

25   Cups on high, the warrior ragged;
            men merry over mead;
        reeds withered, cattle sheltered.

26   I heard the heavy thudding surf
        loud between sand and stone;

my spirits low from longing tonight.

27   Oak limbs like antlers, bitter the taste of ash;
pleasant the cow-parsnip, laughter of wave;
the cheek hides not the heartache.

28   Many a sigh overwhelms me,
          and I am used to that;
God endows not the luckless.

29   No good comes to the luckless –
only grief and anxiety;
God does not undo what he does.

30   The wasted one was noble once,
          a proud warrior in the court of a king;
May God be gracious to outcasts.

31   Whatever is done in an oratory,
Wretched is he who reads it:
abhorred by man here, God's hatred above.

The Song of the Old Man

1   Before my back was bent, I was a worker of words;
          my powers were praised;
the men of Argoed ever maintained me.

2   Before my back was bent, I was bold;
and I was welcomed in the courts of Powys,
paradise of Wales.

3   Before my back was bent, I was brilliant;
my spear to the fore in battle drew first blood;
Now I am bent over, weary, wretched.

4   Wooden crutch, 'tis autumn;

ferns ruddy, stalks yellowed;
I rejected what I love.

5   Wooden crutch, 'tis winter;
     men are boisterous over beer;
     no one speaks in my direction.

6   Wooden crutch, 'tis spring;
     cuckoos ruddy, their cries clear;
     no maiden loves me.

7   Wooden crutch, 'tis summertime;
     furrows ruddy, sprouts wrinkled;
     staring down at you saddens me.

8   Crutch of wood, steady staff,
     support the old wistful one –
     Llywarch of streaming words.

9   Wooden crutch, sturdy staff,
     God the protector welcomes me;
     the wooden one is a true fellow-traveler.

10   Wooden crutch, be kind
     and support me even better;
     I am Llywarch–babbling on.

11   Old age is mocking me
     from my hair to my teeth
     and the rod that young folk cherish.

12   Old age is mocking me
     from my hair to my teeth
     and the rod the women cherish.

13   Wild is the wind; white the tips of trees;
     bold the stag, hillside bare;
     the old one feeble, ambling slowly.

14   This leaf, the wind whips it about;
               alas for its fate:
      already old, though born this year.

15   What I loved as a lad I loathe:
               a new woman and a fresh horse;
      they no longer suit me.

16   The four most hated things
      befell me all at once:
      wheeze and age, pestilence and grief.

17   I am old and alone, disfigured and cold;
               descended from nobles,
      I am downcast now, bent over.

18   I am old and stooped, a wayward fool,
               simpleminded and quarrelsome;
      alas that death does not deliver me.

19   Neither rest nor joy comes to me
      since the deaths of Llawr and Gwen;
      I am mean, feeble and old.

20   Wretched the fate that was dealt to Llywarch
               since the night he was born:
      long labor, unrelenting pain.

On Urien and the Gogledd

1   Fierce Unhwch taught me,
               passion in praising –
      better to strike than sue for peace.

2   Fierce Unhwch taught me
               the plunder of conflict is pain;

I lead the hosts of Llwyfenydd.

3   Fierce Unhwch taught me –
          'twas said at Drws Llech:
      Dunod son of Pabo does not flee.

4   Fierce Unhwch taught me
          bitter and savage the sea's laugh;
      provoker of battle, prosperous lord.

5   Ardent Urien, Rheged's grasping eagle,
          enemy of Unhwch, bold and bountiful,
      battle's bane, prosperous chieftain.

6   Ardent Urien, Rheged's grasping eagle,
          enemy of Unhwch; autocrat of
      endless sea-streams of manly mead.

7   The head I carry at my side,
      it was busy between hosts:
      proud son of Cynfarch owned it.

8   The head I carry at my side,
      the head of Urien generous in governance of men;
      and on his blessed breast a villainous crow.

9   The head I carry in my tunic,
      the head of Urien generous in governance of courts;
      and on his blessed breast crows a-feeding.

10   The head I carry in my hand
      was shepherd of Erechwydd;
      noble breast, spender of spears.

11   The head I carry by my side
      was a shield over the land, a wheel in battle,
         a stave of battle, enemy's snare.

12   The head I carry at my left side,
      better alive than in the grave;
      he was a shelter for the old.

13   The head I carry from the plain of Pennog,
            far-reaching his forays;
         the head of Urien, easy of eloquent praise.

14   The head I carry on my shoulder,
      shame did not cover me:
      Alas my hand, striking my lord!

15   The head I carry on my arm,
      in the land of Bernicia he made
      many a bier in wake of battle.

16   The head I carry in the grip of
      my hand, generous lord in governance of the land;
      the head of the pillar of Britain has been snatched away.

17   The head I carry carried me;
      I know that it did me no good –
      alas my hand! – the harsh thing it did.

18   The head I carry from a hillside,
      its mouth a foaming, bloody wound;
      Woe to Rheged from now on.

19   My arm trembles, my breast throbs,
            my heart has surely broken:
         the head I carry carried me.

20   The fine, white body is buried today
            beneath earth and stone;
         alas my hand! striking Owain's father.

21   The fine, white body is buried today
            amid earth and oak;

186

alas my hand! striking my cousin.

22   The fine, white body is buried tonight –
             under stone he was left;
        alas my hand! destiny compelled me.

23   The fine, white body is buried tonight
             amid earth and sod;
        alas my hand! striking the son of Cynfarch.

24   The fine, white body is buried today
             under a marked grave;
        alas my hand! striking my lord.

25   The fine, white body is buried today
             under earth and sand;
        alas my hand! the wages of destiny.

26   The fair, white body is buried today
             under earth and nettle;
        alas my hand! destiny moved me.

27   The fair, white body is buried today
             under earth and gray stone;
        alas my hand! destiny empowered me.

The Desolation of Erechwydd

1   Erechwydd lies in need,
        anxious over a knight pierced through;
        Will there ever be another Urien?

2   My lord is a leader, strong and bold,
             warriors like not his wrath;
        many a chieftain has he chased.

3   Sad to think on Urien's passion –

he raged in every region
on the trail of Llofan law Ddifro.

4   Silent wind along the slope;
rare one worthy of praise –
save for Urien, tears do not come.

5   Many a bounding hound and spirited hawk
were nurtured here
before this spot was abandoned.

6   This hall, weeds overgrow it;
it was more used to entertain
mead and clamorous drinkers.

7   This hall, nettles cover it;
while its defender lived
it was more used to suppliants.

8   This hall, borage covers it;
in the days of Owain and Elphin
its caldron bubbled booty.

9   This hall, withered weeds cover it;
it was more used to earn its food
through persistent and fearless forays.

10   This hall, sharp briars cover it;
logs once blazed within –
Rheged was used to generosity.

11   This hall, thorns cover it;
its princelings were used to
the favor of Owain's fellowship.

12   This hall, ants cover it;
it was more used to bright candles
and loyal mead mates.

13   This hall, dock weed covers it;
        it was more used to entertain
        mead and clamorous drinkers.

14   This hall, a pig digs in it;
        it was more used to the rejoicing
        of men and companionship 'round cups.

15   This hearth, a chick scratches in it;
        need did not nestle there
        with Owain and Urien alive.

16   This pillar here and the one yonder
        were more used to
        the joy of men and constant giving.

Gnomes

1   Wind sharp, hill shorn, finding shelter fails;
        ford befouled, lake freezes,
        a man can stand atop a single stalk.

2   Wave upon wave covers the coast;
        powerful blasts against hilltops;
        hardly can stand up outside.

3   Marshland cold from winter's crunch;
        canes withered, broken reeds,
        warring wind, trees wearing bark.

4   Fishes' home cold in icy shadow;
        stag scrawny, bearded cane,
        afternoons short, trees sagging.

5   Snow falls, all white;
        warriors war not;

lakes cold, lacking warmth.

6   Snow falls, hoary white;
     shield on an old shoulder stands idle;
     wind gusty, grasses freeze.

7   Snow falls upon ice;
     breezes brush tips of thick twigs;
     shield on a bold shoulder stands strong.

8   Snow falls, roofing the vale;
     warriors rush to the fray;
     I do not go – hurt holds me back.

9   Snow falls along the hillside;
     steed disabled, cattle lean;
     today is not a summer's day.

10   Snow falls, mountain ridge white;
               masts of ships without sails;
     a coward courts many counsels.

11   Golden fists on goblets, gripped by all;
     seas cold, sky flashing;
     afternoons short, treetops atilt.

12   Bees in hives, birdcalls falter,
               dewless day;
     hillcrest cloaked in white, dawn crimson.

13   Bees under cover, ford's cover frigid:
               ice freezes to make it so;
     though one may dodge, death shall come.

14   Bees in bondage, the sea green;
               reeds withered, hill hard;
     cold and harsh the country here.

15   Bees kept from wetness of winter;
          grasses gray, hogweed hollow;
    cowardice in a man is an awful encumbrance.

16   Nights long, moor bare, hill brown;
    coast gray, seagull in spume;
    seas turbulent – will rain today.

17   Wind dry, the way wet, valley sly;
          growth is cold, stag lean;
    river smooth – it will be fair.

18   Foul in the mountains, rivers raging,
          the flow floods homes:
    it is the sea – seeing the world.

WELSH POETS OF THE PRINCES

Taliesin, Aneirin, and Llywarch Hen are referred to as *cynfeirdd* or 'early poets.' The poets under consideration here are known as *gogynfeirdd* or 'somewhat early poets.' These terms suggest that we are dealing with two distinct kinds of poetry, and, to a degree, that is true. But the poets of later medieval Wales were not unlike the early poets Taliesin and Aneirin, or the poets of medieval and later Ireland. Like their forebears, these poets sang poems of praise to their chieftains, enjoyed a special relationship with the patron, functioned as judges of valor, and were well rewarded for their poems.

The expression "Poets of the Princes" is nearly synonymous with the word *gogynfeirdd*, but it refers more explicitly to those poets who sang to Welsh princes, the last of whom, Llywelyn ap Gruffudd, was killed in 1282. With the loss of this great leader, Welsh independence was effectively lost as well, and the courts of independent chieftains ceased to exist. The poets had lost their patrons, even though poetry in this style continued to be composed by the *gogynfeirdd* beyond this date.

It is only an accident of the survival of manuscripts that we are able to account for the history of poetry in Wales. We have seen that the poetry of Taliesin and Aneirin, written in the awdl meters, belongs to the sixth century and the old northern British kingdoms (Rheged, Gododdin), in a kind of golden, heroic age. The poetry associated with Llywarch Hen, some of which is praise poetry and some of which is gnomic and/or personal and lyrical, is written in the englyn meters and belongs to the ninth or tenth century. The next body of poetry that has come down to us is that of the *gogynfeirdd*, composed mostly in the awdl meters, though the englyn was employed as well.

There can be no doubt that the history of Welsh poetry was a continuous one and that poems of praise and satire, eulogies and elegies, were composed and sung in the courts of rulers and other patrons in every period. The ideals expressed by Aneirin in "The Gododdin" or by Taliesin in his poems to Urien of Rheged and Urien's son Owain are to be found in the works of the *gogynfeirdd*. Indeed, these later poets were very conscious that they stood in a line of tradition that stretched back to Aneirin and Taliesin in the sixth century. This conformity is no doubt to be attributed to the powerful influence of the bardic schools on generation after generation of poets. Aneirin claimed that, "poets of the world judge men of valor." Echoing that claim, the Welsh poet Phylip Brydydd says to his patron in the thirteenth century: "I made fame for you." The central notion is unchanged: the poet is the judge of those ancient virtues that characterize the best chieftains or princes, and it is he who possesses the power to create reputation by celebrating those virtues in his song.

In the same century, we find the poet Dafydd Benfras praying for *awen*, 'poetic inspiration,' to be able to sing to his patron, Llywelyn ap Iorwerth, praises "like Aneirin of old on the day he sang the Gododdin." Even in the fifteenth century, when the period of the princes had passed, the poet Gutun Owain addresses a poem to an abbot in which he says, "Abbot John, I am like Taliesin; I come to ask for your horse." Clearly, he insisted on the same rights that his poetic forebears had enjoyed with their noble patrons.

The first of the thirty-one gogynfeirdd whom we know by name was Meilyr Brydydd (*prydydd* 'professional poet'; his principal work was poems of praise). Meilyr was chief poet to Gruffudd ap Cynan, and composed a *marwnad* or 'elegy' for him when he died in 1137. Gruffudd was raised in Ireland, in exile from his birthright, the throne of Gwynedd in North Wales (see map). In 1081 he returned to Wales with an army, overcame his enemies, and regained the lordship of North Wales. He also brought with him his court poet/musician, named Gellan, who was called a *telynyaur pencerdd* (*telynyaur* 'harpist'; *pencerdd* is the highest grade of poet).

At a bardic assembly held in the year 1523, a set of regulations governing the organization of poets was drawn up. It is traditionally known as "The Statute of Gruffudd ap Cynan." Thus Gruffudd ap Cynan seems to stand at the dawn of a new era in Welsh poetry. Gruffudd ap Cynan died in 1137. Two years earlier, Henry I, who had been a powerful and relentless enemy of the Welsh, died. His death brought on a period of renewed hope of independence, and a literary awakening as well, it would appear. One of the most influential works of the middle ages, Geoffrey of Monmouth's *History of the Kings of Britain*, appeared in 1137. It gave a tremendous boost to the popularity of the Arthurian cycle of romance that was to have currency from then down to the present day. The period of the ascendancy of Gruffudd ap Cynan, then, represents a literary renaissance in Wales. It is no wonder that we see a flourishing of the poetic art in the poets of the princes. Let us recall, however, that the poetry of this period, whatever of its indebtedness to the facts of Gruffudd ap Cynan's career, is aware of its debt to the past and is almost self-consciously traditional.

Bibliography: Lewis 1992; Lloyd 1992; Williams, J.E.C. 1978

ELEGY FOR GRUFFUDD AP CYNAN
BY MEILYR BRYDYDD

Meilyr's elegy for Gruffudd begins, as many of these poems do, with a prayer to God. Poets of this period were taught that their first obligation was to sing poems of praise to God, and after that, poems of praise to princes. But the poet soon moves on the the matter at hand. He reminds his audience of the value of poetry and of the generosity of Gruffudd: not one singer was ever refused a reward from him. Thus the poet/patron relationship is reaffirmed as one of exchange: poets give poems of praise to patrons who reward them with gifts of money and goods.

The enumeration of battles won by the patron is a commonplace of this poetry, quite naturally. In Irish bardic poetry there is a special term for this, *caithréim*, and it became a hallmark of the Irish bardic elegies (Simms 1989). Meilyr lists perhaps twelve of Gruffudd's battles. It may be that a contemporary audience would be reminded of the celebrated list of twelve battles fought by Arthur against the Saxons, as recounted by Nennius in the *Historia Brittonum*. If so, Gruffudd would be further praised by bringing him into orbit with the celebrated king of the Britons.

Toward the end of the poem, Meilyr takes care of his future by referring to Gruffudd's sons Owain and Cadwaladr. Then he ends with an exhortation for Gruffudd's soul, expressing also the hope that his elegy will keep alive the memory of this prince. The translation is based on the edition of J. E. C. Williams 1994.

Meter: a type of awdl called *cyhydedd naw ban*, meaning lines of nine syllables in length, with end rhyme. The end rhyme changes four times in this long poem. Additional ornamentation consists of alliteration, assonance, and internal rhyme.

Bibliography: Williams, J. E. C. 1994

Elegy for Gruffudd ap Cynan

Rhên nef mor rhyfedd Ei ryfeddawd,
Rhiau Rhwyf elfydd rhydd Ei folawd
Lord of heaven, His majesty supreme!
Sovereign, Ruler of the world, of endless praise,
King of consummate grace, have mercy,
5   When God comes on that day,
May the Lord receive me for judgment
That I may have with the holy a haven,
For the fear of death will come.
Most dire, too, the death of a mead-host,
10 A scourge in battle, his court the island's light;
Why are bards silent? will they not sing
For a fierce and ardent master of seamen?
Poems err not, tributes are no lies;
And no singer was ever rejected by him.
15 Through the gift of song I offer tribute
To a king generous to a fault.
Brave Gruffudd, grave in conquest–
Alas for those who shared his wine!
A leader in battle before he was laid low,
20 Bold conqueror in a cruel grave!
Waging war careless of the perils of predators,
Warden of warriors, possessor of all Britain;
Buoyant in battle, Anarawd's kin,
And Rhun's too, Rhun Hir, battle-hard.
25 Always to the fore, in the manner of Modred
And magnificent Urien in attack;
At the head of his host, this lord
Was not seeking the pleasures of court!
Cynan's son, before he was buried,
30 Bragget and mead were the mark of his hall.
And Cynan down in a crimson crypt –
I keen a great ruler – rue the day!
Before his ruin, a menace in weaponry –
He roared through hotheaded hosts;

35   May Rome grant him the gift of mercy,
        For the warrior lacked the love of no one.
        The people's prince, patron of the poor
        Brought down, brave and bold one dead:
        May God see to his end,
40   That he might not be lost through sin.

        O gyfranc brenhinedd brain foddawg
        Pan fai gyfluydd o wyr gwychawg
        When, with a host of bold followers,
        There were ravenous encounters with kings,
        The kings wound up subdued –
        In groups of four and five, grovelling.
45   They'd glance furtively, slip away stealthily
        From the stern son of Cynan.
        For him who dares the game of plunder
        He is run to the ground in splendor.
        Fierce and cruel fighter, proud, passionate,
50   Though they called him 'loner' he was never cowed,
        Always fought with a golden shield
        Before an army worthy of mighty Emrys;
        Steel-bladed destroyer in battle,
        Terrible the weight on his brittle body–
55   He who was celebrated in stately song
        From Ysgewin to the gates of York.
        England's king came with a host,
        But if he did he didn't leave wealthy:
        We in Eryri remained rich,
60   No easy prey in our pastures!
        Gruffudd, his vehemence evident,
        Protected his people avidly,
        Defended his right with a thousand knights
        and his battles resounded beyond Bannog!
65   Wrathful and cruel king of conflict,
        Never a derelict spear, above all kings,
        Stunning master of long-maned steeds,
        Ruler of the Welsh, daring warrior.
        Defender of countless in his court,

196

70   Rhodri's ilk, he poured out wealth;
       Before this wall of giving went dumb
       He paid me well, made me prosper.
       I drank with the prince from golden horns,
       In sumptuous servings from a willing hand;
75   In Aberffraw's court, brilliant in fame,
       I was beside the prince on his throne;
       Another time I was on the field of battle,
       Candle of conflict, a proper prince.
       The golden prince plied the seas in force
80   With a force that broke the enemy fleets;
       And after the green surging seas,
       Lively steeds bore his armor;
       But now, it's underground he lies –
       Alas for him who trusts the world's treasons!
85   Pompous, wandering bards don't know
       When an ardent defender will die:
       I keen, I will not be unprepared,
       In the manner I choose I will praise him.
       May Christ who is perfect have mercy
90   On Gruffudd of Gwynedd, a man of gentility.
       Let him come to his heavenly inheritance –
       Don't leave his fine soul lowly!

       Hael a ri a renni yn ei riydd,
       Ni chronnai na seirch na meirch gweilydd
       A generous king who shared his wealth,
       Amassed neither mounts nor arms in vain;
95   Hope of lands, hero of Gwynedd,
       A warrior before he met doom.
       Gruffudd, mountain of strength, like Mechydd:
       He on horse, his foes on biers!
       Head of the host, friends' defender,
100 Soldiers' shield, borderland sentry.
       Till the earth was his pillow,
       No peace for enemy folk;
       Lord of Môn, he battled their best at mid-day
       In Mynydd Carn, where Traehaearn fell.

105   Against two chieftains, kings of Powys
           And their men of Gwent, the rightful ruler
           And his loyal warriors retaliated,
           So he saved face and avoided disgrace.
           Enemies and their allies lay hidden,
110   Then were slain on a famous day,
           Deadly casts tearing towns' defenses,
           Breaking the bastion of Trenn's lands.
           In Tryffwn's land, as the prince attacked,
           Spearhead's withered before a wave of swords;
115   Prisoners cringed, crept from the field,
           While crows gnawed torn flesh –
           Fresh from the passion of a generous lord.
           His fields of battle fully owned by dawn,
           He doled out horses and cattle he'd taken;
           Weapons broken as each attacked,
120   And blood flowed as spears strayed.
           Those who survived to return home
           Brought new tales of his battles:
           The grievous battle of Castlemarch
           Against the armies of bold, meek Cynwrig;
125   The heavily armed battle of Meirionydd
           A bold lord bearing heavy iron:
           He gave no quarter in their confusion;
           In the battle of Gwaederw, a bitter bruiser;
           At Cardigan, the army fully arrayed
130   And afterwards widows trembled;
           The battle in Ireland of the pleasant dwellings
           Was not idle in the eyes of those who were there;
           The battle of North Britain, bold as Mechydd,
           Gruffudd won with a wrathful host;
135   The battle of Môn's castle, magnificent!
           A siege that saved civilized folk.
           For my gift I chose, truth be told,
           From among steeds of his household –
           May the Lord give him an eternal reward
140   In exchange for his gift to his poet.
           Lowly poets of little learning know not

Which of the people will prosper;
The golden prince, protector of his people,
Left courtly cubs of noble pedigree:

145   Owain will arise, England's bane,
Ruler who'll win the borderland;
The men of Powys will see his career
And fearing him will be second nature.
Noble Cadwaladr, foremost warrior,

150   Swift to horse, New Year's host;
Their bards will sing the proper songs –
In the crisis of conflict, they will succeed.
Gruffudd, mighty battler, never deprived me
Of his great wealth, never distance between us.

155   Until my haunt is an oaken box,
I'll never break with my beloved.

Cerennydd ysydd herwydd Trined
I Gristiawn ys iawn ei gyrhaedded
The love that the Trinity gives,
It is right for a Christian to achieve it:
Life with the Creator in honor

160   For glorious Gruffudd, gravebound.
Lest sin bring long lamentation
For this splendid and generous chieftain,
I sing forth in fullness an elegy
For a wall of strength worthy of the sea,

165   Strong as driven sleet – before his death.
I'm filled with dread for his arduous trek:
May Cynan's son, with great purpose, come
With Christ a happy journey to the blessed home,
Where the prince will have in bright anticipation

170   The joy of angels' ministration–
One with the Trinity as wished for,
With shining saints, at home in Heaven's halls.

ELEGY FOR LLYWELYN AP GRUFFUDD
BY BLEDDYN FARDD

Bleddyn Fardd or 'Bleddyn Poet' flourished in the latter half of the thirteenth century. Little is known of him except for what can be gleaned from his poetry. His surviving work is chiefly elegies for the grandsons of Llywelyn ap Iorwerth, Llywelyn the Great, who died in 1240, perhaps the greatest of all rulers of Wales. There are two elegies each to Owain Goch, Llywelyn, and Dafydd, and one elegy dedicated to the three of them, the sons of Llywelyn the Great's son Gruffudd. Bleddyn was clearly a court poet to the ruling Gwynedd dynasty, and it has been suggested that he succeeded his teacher Dafydd Benfras as *pencerdd* or 'chief poet' to Llywelyn ap Gruffudd, the prince to whom this elegy is addressed.

Llywelyn ap Gruffudd is known among the Welsh as *Ein Llyw Olaf* 'Our Last Prince.' He and his heirs were granted the title Prince of Wales by Henry III. Under Edward I, relations between Llywelyn and the English crown deteriorated, and on December 11, 1282, Llywelyn was killed by English troops in a chance encounter at a bridge near Builth. Llywelyn's head was cut off, taken to London and exhibited there. The translation is based on the edition of Andrews 1996a.

Meter: a chain of *englyn unodl union*. This englyn meter consists of a *toddaid byr*, that is, a line of normally 10 syllables followed by a line of normally 6 syllables, and a couplet, with seven syllables in each line. The chief rhyme occurs at the end of the 7th, 8th, or 9th syllable of the first line; a further rule says that in the couplet, an accented syllable must rhyme with an unaccented syllable.

Bibliography: Andrews 1996a; Gruffydd 1986; Roberts 1982

Elegy for Llywelyn ap Gruffudd

Lladd llew Ffraw; bu braw bryd addas –orchwyl
Erchwyniog teÿrnas;
Eithr Un Mab Mair, mawr lias
Duw nef, dyn mal ef ni las.
Ffraw's fearless leader dead! The mind recoils
Reflecting on our protector;

But for the grievous death of Mary's Son,
God of heaven, his like was never slain.

5 Slain was Bendigeidfran, familiar with trouble,
   and there too was terror;
  Llywelyn of the bloody blades slain,
  Arthur slain, the world's sovereign.

  World's woe, saddened at the violent theft of a leader,
10   Llywelyn ap Gruffudd,
  Defender of the South from shame,
  Lord of a host that gained from him.

  Bounty from a fine, proud hero – before he was felled
   by spears from every side.
15 A great effort by the lord of the host:
  In Morgannwg he was a powerful force.

  While our hero commanded men and arms,
   He was utter defense of his folk:
  The power of Arthur, a wall against seas,
20 In bloody battle, a pre-eminent chief.

  Know that catastrophe has wrapped
   Around our Welsh emperor!
  The world is ended, time to mourn;
  Pity those to whom it's still unknown.

25 Let the wretched know the awful fate, O God,
   For Llywelyn lives not;
  Sad is the lasting scar of longing:
  But for God, only grief for men.

  For noble and base, our leader's loss
30   Makes us utterly mad;
  Hawk and hero with Geraint's might,
  Hero worthy of any king's right.

May God, guardian of saints, tend to Llywelyn,
　　Taking him to Himself;
35　　　Hope of his hosts in far-flung wars,
　　Lion-like leader, fruitful force of Aber Ffraw.

ELEGY FOR LLYWELYN AP GRUFFUDD
BY GRUFFUDD AB YR YNAD COCH

Gruffudd ab yr Ynad Coch, 'son of the Red Judge,' seems to have sprung from a family of lawyers and may have been one himself. Little is known of him outside the few poems that have survived. There are six poems to God in the awdl meter (four of these are edited and translated in McKenna 1991), and two poems to Llywelyn ap Gruffudd – one an englyn the other an awdl, our present poem. The elegy has been translated many times and discussed often in the literature (see, e.g., Matonis 1979-80; Higley 1988). It is possibly the most famous poem in the Welsh language.

The elegy is remarkable in several ways. For one thing it personalizes Llywelyn in ways that are unconventional and untraditional. The poet says little of Llywelyn's lineage, a common theme in eulogies and elegies. And he says very little about the role of poets or about the poet-patron relationship, another commonplace in this poetry. Rather he concentrates on his intense feelings of loss: "How loudly I lament, alas for the lamenting!" (*uched y cwynaf, och o'r cwyno*); this is, literally, keening: *och* is the Welsh equivalent of the *ochone* of Irish keening.

The intensity is achieved in several ways, one of which is the repetition of a word or phrase at the beginning of a series of lines, such as "I grieve, I grieve;" "mine, mine;" "don't you see, don't you see." This is a powerful dramatic tool, drumming the themes of the poem into the ears of the hearers. Another way in which the intensity is achieved in this poem, though it cannot be reproduced in the translation, is the repetition of a single rhyme throughout the poem on the syllable *-aw*. Normally the line-end rhyme in an awdl will change a number of times throughout a given poem – but not here. One scholar summed up the effect this way:

> [The poem] is the most powerful expression in the language of dismay and unrelieved black despair. It is at the same time a miracle of art. The one main rhyme, *-aw, -aw, -aw*, like an unending wail occurs ninety-four times. (Lloyd 1992).

The translation is based on the edition of Andrews 1996b.

Meter: awdl, a tour-de-force combining several different awdl meters. The poem opens with a *toddaid*, lines of 10 and 9 syllables respectively. The final word in the first line rhymes internally with words in the second line. The penultimate word in the first line carries the chief rhyme, -*aw*, which is retained throughout the poem. The next two lines are *cyhydedd fer*, lines of 8 syllables each. There is much use of *cymeriad* 'linking,' where a series of lines begin with the same syllable or word.

Bibliography: Andrews 1996b; Lloyd 1992; McKenna 1991

Elegy for Llywelyn ap Gruffudd

> *Oer galon dan fron o fraw–allwynin*
> *Am frenin, dderwin ddôr Aberffraw,*
> *Aur dilyfn a delid o'i law,*
> *Aur dalaith oedd deilwng iddaw*
> The heart's gone cold within a breast of fear, grieving
> For a king, defender of Aberffraw;
> He gave out gold unstinting,
> Deserved his golden diadem –

5   Splendid prince and lavish! But I know no joy
For Llywelyn no longer wraps me in riches.
I grieve for my lord, noble and flawless,
 I grieve for the mishap that brought him down,
I grieve for the loss, for the terrible fate,

10   I grieve to hear he's been struck down.
Cadwaladr's kin, swordsman,
 Wielding a ruddy spear, but generous with gold.
He spread his wealth, endowed me each winter
 With his princely wraps.

15   A lively lord guides us no more,
Eternal life in store for him.
Mine, now, to hate the English for despoiling me,
Mine, having to keen in the face of death,
Mine, with good cause, accusing God

20   Who left me lonely;
Mine, praising him without end, never silent,
Mine, forever now, longing for him,
Mine, for as long as I live, grieving for him,
 And because I grieve, weeping.

25   I have lost my lord, and now enduring fear –
       A princely palace pulled down.
    Dear sweet God, hear me!
       Hear how loudly I lament, Alas!
          A masterful lord before he and his men fell,
30   A generous lord, hero now silenced,
       A brave lord, like a lion leading the land,
          A lord wading into war,
    A lord of the council, before he left Emrys
       The English didn't dare challenge him;
35   A lord of Wales, of the rightful rulers of Aberffraw,
       But now, beneath a stone slab.
          Lord Christ, Lord of true salvation,
          How grieved I am over him!
    From the heavy stroke that bit into him,
40   From the long blades drawing him down,
       From the gashes that gouged my prince,
       From feeling the pain of Bodfaeo's prince!
    A perfect man the enemy slew,
       Perfect the privilege of his lineage;
45   Princely beacon, bold lion of Gwynedd,
       Throne of honor, we needed him.
       From a death bewailed in all of Britain–
       Defender of Nancaw and Nantcol's lion–
    Many a tear overflowing cheeks,
50   Many a side rent and red,
       Many a foot bathed in blood,
       Many a widow wailing over him,
       Many a mind deep in gloom,
       Many a son bereft of father,
55   Many a town broken by war,
       And many a wasteland in ruin;
    Many a mournful cry, as at Camlan,
       Many a tear rolling on and on,
       Since the slaying of a gold-giving guardian.
60   Since the death of Llywelyn, my mind is gone,
       The heart chilly in a breast of fear,
       Passion dead and dry as kindling.

Don't you see the wind and rain raging?
The mighty oaks colliding?
65   Don't you see the sea eating at the shore?
Doomsday on the horizon?
Don't you see the sun sailing through the sky?
The stars falling from the heavens?
Don't you fools believe in God?
70   Don't you see the world in peril?
Alas, dear God, that the sea might drown us!
Why are we left to linger?
There's no place to hide from the irons of fear,
Nowhere to live – alas, that we must!
75   There's no help for it, no lock, no key,
No way out of a counsel of fear.
        Every retinue was worthy of him,
        Every warrior was loyal to him,
        Every fighter swore fealty to him,
80   Every lord and lordship was his;
Every district, every town now overrun,
Every family and clan in decline;
Weak and strong were under his sway,
The child in his crib cries out.
85   It's of little use – even a trick –
Keeping my head with his cut off:
        A head cut off, and welcome terror;
        A head cut off, better it hadn't been;
        Head of a soldier, honored henceforth;
90   Head of a prince and hero,
Fair Llywelyn's head, deep and universal dread
        Seeing it stuck on a steel pike;
Head of my lord, his fall fills me with grief;
Head of my soulmate, expressionless;
95   A head honored in hundreds of lordships
        And hundreds of feasts;
Head of a leader handy with spears,
Head of a proud, princely hawk, hacking,
Noble head of a keen and daring warrior;
100   May the Head of heaven's host have mercy on him!

Blessed prince, may the Keeper of heaven be kindly
toward him!
Ambitious as far as Brittany,
This rightful king of Aberffraw,
May the blessed land of heaven be home to him now.

HYWEL'S BOAST
BY HYWEL AB OWAIN GWYNEDD

Hywel ab Owain Gwynedd, son of Owain Gwynedd, was a nobleman who was also a trained poet. Hywel's martial and political career are well attested, and he is also survived by eight poems. Five of these are love poems, two celebrate his or his father's military accomplishments, and one is identified as a *gorhoffedd*. Only two poems in our manuscripts are identified there as *gorhoffedd*, a term that may be translated as 'exultation' or 'boasting.' One is our present poem, the other is by Gwalchmai ap Meilyr. In these poems we find mingled together expressions of military prowess, delight in nature, love of country, and love of women. All of these themes existed in the prior tradition, but it is the way they convene in a single poetic outburst that distinguishes the *gorhoffedd*. The poet abruptly turns his attention from one theme to another and back again. Hywel begins his poem with a lyrical expression of patriotism, dwells on the richness of the land and the landscape, then switches to the women he has loved. He is, in a sense, both poet and patron in one. Wales would have to wait nearly two hundred years for such lyrical passion to become established in the person of Dafydd ap Gwilym, poet supreme of love and nature. Like Dafydd after him, Hywel calls himself 'Ovid's man,' referring to the popularity of Ovid's treatises on love in the Middle Ages. The translation is based on the edition of Bramley 1994.

Meter: awdl; in the first part of the poem, through line 42, the awdl meter is *cyhydedd naw ban*, for the most part. This consists of lines of normally 9 syllables with four stresses in each line. The end rhyme changes at line 28. In the second part of the poem, the awdl meter is *byr a thoddaid*, which consists of *toddaid byr* (two lines of 10 and 6 syllables respectively) interspersed with *cyhydedd fer* (a couplet with 8 syllables in each line). In this second part, the end rhyme changes at line 67.

Bibliography: Bramley 1985-86, 1994; Lloyd 1992

Hywel's Boast

Ton wen orewyn a orwlych bedd,
Gwyddfa Rufawn Bybr, ben teÿrnedd

A white, foaming wave wets a grave –
The sepulchre of Rhufawn Befr, lord of princes.
I love what England hates–the bright land of the north,
And about the Lliw abundant growth.
5   I love who gave me my fill of mead
Where the seas reach, in long contention.
I love her hosts and her rife habitations,
And waging war at her ruler's pleasure.
I love her moors and her mountains,
10   And her fortress beside her forests and fair lands,
And her watered dales and valleys,
And her gleaming seagulls and her comely maidens.
I love her soldiers and her steadied steeds,
And her forests and strongholds and homesteads.
15   I love her fields and her wealth of tiny trefoils,
Where honor achieved true triumph.
I love its regions, known for boldness,
And her vast open spaces, and its opulence.
Son of God! It is a great wonder –
20   Such magnificent horses, so much wealth!
I battled brilliantly with spear thrusts.
In contest between comely Gwynedd and Powys;
And astride a silvery horse, with much toil,
May I win release from this exile.
25   I will not endure, until he comes to my side:
What I saw in a vision, God will provide.
A white foaming wave wets a grave.

A white foaming wave invades homes,
Glinting like silver as it floods;
30   I love the fens in Meirioneth,
Where a maid's arm was my pillow;
I love the nightingale on bended bough,
In Cymer, lovely river's vale.
Gwynedd's King, Lord of Heaven and earth,
35   How far is Carlisle from Ceri!
I rode from Maelienydd mounted on a bay,
All the way to Rheged, going night and day;

And may I, before I die, make a fresh conquest
In Tegeingl, the loveliest in her district!
40   Though I be a lover in the mold of Ovid,
May I at the end be cared for by God.
A white foaming wave invades homes.

Cyfarchaf I'r Dewin gwerthefin –gwyrthfawr,
    Gwrth ei fod yn Frenin,
    Cysylltu canu cysefin,
    Cerdd foliant, fal y cant Myrddin
I salute a most eminent sage,
    So precious, for he is king.
45   Composing pristine poetry,
A song of praise, like Merlin sang,
To maidens who own my poetic muse;
How terribly tedious they are about virtue,
Most of all in the west
50   From the gates of Caer to Porth Ysgewin.
One is the maid who is most of praise
    Gwenllian, bright as summer.
Then there's another failure; far are my lips
From her, because of her noble nature;
55 Fair Gweirful, my gift, my virtue, I did not have –
    None of my family had her;
By striking me with two-edged swords,
This wife of a king's kin broke my heart.
And fair Gwladus, shy young lass,
60   The hope of her folk;
I breathe a secret sigh
And I shall praise her with yellow gorse.
May I soon see (with my passion far from her man,
    And my weapon in my hand!)
65 Bright Lleucu, my love, laughing;
But her husband, outraged, won't laugh!
Heavy oppression engulfs me, torments me,
And longing, alas, is constant
For fair Nest, an apple blossom;
70   For Perweur, center of my sin;

For the virgin Generys, who does not relieve my passion;
    May her chastity not prevail!
    For Hunydd, enough there till Doomsday;
    For Hawis, my kind of morality!
75   I had an agreeable maid one day;
    I had two – the more their praise!
    I had three, and four, and fortune!
    I had five comely, fair-fleshed ones,
    I had six, not avoiding sin;
80   A beauty from a bright fort fell to my lot;
    I had seven, and it was almost too much;
I had eight in payment of a song I had sung;
    Better now to bite my tongue!

GWALCHMAI'S BOAST
BY GWALCHMAI AP MEILYR

Gwalchmai ap Meilyr (d. 1180) was a contemporary of Hywel ab Owain Gwynedd (d. 1170), author of the other poem identified as *gorhoffedd* or 'boasting poem.' His father was Meilyr Brydydd, the first of our Poets of the Princes, whose patron was Gruffudd ap Cynan. Gruffudd, in turn, was Hywel ab Owain's grandfather. Indeed, Gwalchmai was court poet to Owain Gwynedd. At least two of Gwalchmai's sons were professional poets as well.

Like Hywel in his *gorhoffedd*, Gwalchmai relishes nature, his bravery in battle, his patronage by Owain Gwynedd, women and love. He refers to himself twice by name in his poem, and otherwise speaks in the first person. The poem begins serenely enough with a beautiful day at the beginning of summer, reminiscent of other poems we have seen in celebration of summer time. But it quickly becomes personal as he sets himself firmly in this landscape. His eye seems to catch everything as he charges forward, his blades flashing, chasing down the Saxon foe. The images here are bright and clear, and the poem deserves the judgment of many that it is one of the finest poems in the Welsh language. The translation is based on the edition of J. E. C. Williams 1994.

Meter: The rhyme changes nine times in this awdl, breaking it into as many sections. Of the several awdl meters it employs, the great majority are *cyhydedd naw ban* and *cyhydedd hir*. In the former, we have rhyming lines of, normally, 9 syllables and 3 or 4 stresses. In the latter, we have lines broken into three rhyming phrases of, normally, 5 syllables each, with a final phrase of 4 syllables, which carries the chief rhyme. Gwalchmai frequently omits the requisite internal rhyming, as well as other features of this meter, though other ornamentation, such as alliteration, is plentiful.

Bibliography: Lloyd 1992; Stephens 1986; Williams, J.E.C. 1994

Gwalchmai's Boast

Mochddwyreawg huan haf dyffestin,
Maws llafar adar, mygr hear hin
Sun, an early riser as summer draws near,
birds sing sweetly, splendid weather;

I, a noble scion, bold in combat,
a lion leading troops, lightning attack;
5   nights I stood guard at the border,
where the fords of Dygen Freiddin murmur
'round green untrammeled reeds, glistening water;
nightingale sings out the familiar song.
Seagulls at sea circling around,
10   a screaming flock, feathers flashing;
my thoughts wander at summer's beginning,
all for the love of a beautiful maiden –
a chieftain far from the slim one of Môn,
my cozy one, secret seducer;
15   I listened to lips in pure pleasure,
to the strange, soft sounds of a girl;
And for bountiful, mighty Owain's sake,
cringe, you English, before my blade!

Llachar fy nghleddau, lluch ydd ardwy –glew,
Llewychedig aur ar fy nghylchwy
My sword flashes – the brave defend brilliantly,
20   the gold on my shield glows;
waters eddy and noise about, a warm day;
birds busy about their harmonies.
Impassioned am I in a distant land today,
penetrating into Efyrnwy;
25   apple trees bright with tight, white blossoms,
lovely blanket of trees; each thinks on the one he loves.
I love a beautiful girl of noble traits,
and hate those who hold back her praise;
Genilles showered me with gifts, and though she kill me
30   with a single word, my affliction seems paltry.
Happy the man, Dear God, whom a virgin favors,
with a maiden's gift of sweet release.
My sword flashes – brilliantly it performs in battle;
the gold on my shield glows;
35   scores crave me who've never seen me –
the girls of Gwent, eager to rave about me.
I saw before Owain, English lying dead;

and beside Rhibyll, a ruler embattled.
I am Gwalchmai, Saxons' foe,
40   for the ruler of Môn, I rushed into war,
      and to please a beauty bright as snow,
      I drew blood in the slaughter at Caer.

Fierce and bloody is my sword in battle –
against the English no hero cowers!
45   I saw hundreds of wretches, crushed in flight,
      pursued by warlike Owain, Gruffudd's heir.
The battle of Aberteifi, Owain's war,
      fair prince of Prydain, landed lord;
      hearing he was there, they avoided him,
50   from Iago's descendant, trouble and gore.
Gwalchmai am I, foe of Angles and Edwin,
      and in the midst of assault, how bloody my hand!
      I have witnesses whose lead I follow,
      descendants of Cynan, the lineage of Coel.
55 And to please those who greet me from Breiddin's proud
                                    heights,
      I shall not flee battle from fright.
      I love the nightingale of May who interrupts sleep,
      and the glances of the one with the smooth, white
      cheeks.
      I love fine horses, in long phalanxes,
60   a protective force in battle harness.
      I loathe the base with their cowardly fear,
      it's at the front where the fighting is fierce,
but not so they; and I so relentless for her sake,
      'tis a maid of royal status I contemplate,
65   nor do I disparage the splendid memory of her;
      the generous and beautiful girl will not deny me;
      maid as fair as the first rays of sun,
      and when it sets, her beauty shines on.

I led the attack at the head of the troop;
70   men go forth, fill the ford,
      in the narrow strait Owain moves forward,

after the tumult of battle,
the foe retreats in haste
the fleet smashed pitilessly.
75 My sword flashes; it won't pay to taunt me –
my hand will strike those who can't check it;
I saw the passion of a king at Craig Gwydyr,
when the fair lord of Môn went to war.
I saw in Rhuddlan Owain's fiery rush,
80 and corpses stiff, bloodied blades;
I saw those bodies, flesh torn,
fallen silent and reckless no more.
Carmarthen fell in heroic siege –
oppressive strike by the eagle of Emrys.
85 Let princes all do homage to him,
ruler of Aberffraw, Ynyr's realm.
I listened to a nightingale, longing for her,
A purple-clad maid owns my reverie.
It's long since my beauty has slept (and I know why!) –
90 when the apple blossoms begin to branch out;
at Porth Wygyr there'll be a foam-crested wave,
a lover will be passionate, a nobleman proud;
dreaming of a girl shiny as a dew drop –
rare is the night I'm spared the dream.
95 Be happy for the sake of the land I'm kept from:
I brandish weapons, spears tipped in gold!

I sorely tested the stamina of my horse
between Penwaedd and Porth Wygyr;
with a bold and ready force, I attacked
100 at Ceredigion; how long did I labor there?
I craved the company of generous Owain,
until I found him, bold, courageous lion.
In splendid Ystrad Meurig I saw
mighty Owain, resourceful and awesome;
105 ever a conqueror, the lion of Din Emrys
formed his troops before attacking the English;
I love the little bird, softly singing,
filling the wood with song, on the wing.

A girl wants me when she greets from afar,
110   she has in mind for me things I'd not dare!
        And I, as far as I remember, had a great one –
        I got into the habit at her place – she's steady!

        At Aberffraw a green wave lulls me,
        laps at the peaceful land, brings prosperity;
115   land where song of small birds echoes,
        where forests grow that harbor no shadow;
        a solitary spot to wait in quiet,
        a place for my foes to find adversity.
        My horse excelled in the battle of Caeo,
120   all for Cynan, of well-earned renown.
        'Gwynedd's famous son is ours,' all say,
        the hold on all of Prydain is his;
        I listened to an eagle feasting on a corpse –
        it was men of Gwynedd who provided the gore.
125   When lord Owain defended Denbigh,
        a day in Ystrad, destroying weapons,
        I hurried off with a host to England:
        bringing grief with the pass of my hand;
        my very nature merits my inclusion
130   in Cadell's line in the land of Tysilio.

        At Aber Dau a green wave lulls me,
        laps at the lovely shore in bright streams;
        from beaks of small birds song echoes,
        where enemies wait, the bravest oppose;
135   rich growth of reeds as the days pass,
        rich too the cover of trees, flowery canvas;
        I sipped mead, made in gold vats,
        in the court of Owain, man of substance;
        his wine, poured for me from his own noble hand,
140   in Caernarvon, in the hero Hiriell's land;
        to please me he demanded a gift
        from lords at the battle of Maes Carnedd;
        he gives gifts – a drove of kine,
        is famed through all of Prydain.

145　his hostages come from Din Alclud in the North,
　　　　yet he's a dragon in wars way off in the South.

　　　　Summertime, so lovely, days are fair,
　　　　the hillside soft and fertile in summer;
　　　　grasses rejoice as fresh waters flow through:
150　the Ogwen, Cegin, and Clywedog too.
　　　　the surging roar of the sea lulls me,
　　　　flowing often from Abermenai;
　　　　white waves pound the coast at Great Orme,
　　　　at Morfa Rhianedd, the marsh of king Maelgwn;
155　I crossed the Lliw to Lleuddinion in the Lothians,
　　　　rode to York's fort on a swift, sturdy mount;
　　　everywhere they asked, 'in all of this realm,
　　　　who is the most generous provider of all?'
　　　　And I declared, without any shame,
160　'None other than Owain, whom all owe allegiance!'
　　　　He shared a girl with me, a delightfully well-made one,
　　　　and it deepened into a long relationship;
　　　　she came to me all decked out, bursting with pride,
　　　　long, deep blue brows, and cheeks soft and high;
165　and at court I was lusted after mightily;
　　　　(tonight I'll be amazed, provided I get away at all!)
　　　　And if God of Heaven prospers me,
　　　　the girl will make heaven in bed for me!

IEUAN'S BOAST
BY IEUAN AP RHYDDERCH

This boasting poem was composed some three hundred years after the *gorhoffeddau* of Hywel and Gwalchmai. Ieuan ap Rhydderch flourished in the mid-fifteenth century. His father was a wealthy landowner who held office under the English king in the late fourteenth century. Ieuan himself was schooled, probably at Oxford, and there is evidence that he was a lawyer. In any case, he was closely familiar with the poetic tradition. He composed a prophetic poem (*cywydd brud*) on the War of the Roses, evocative of the prophecy poems of Taliesin and Myrddin (Merlin) of a far earlier time. He seems to have been familiar with the Welsh chronicles (*Brutiau y Tywysogion*), and no doubt with such manuscripts as The White Book of Rhydderch, which his father had owned. His boasting poem is fashioned after the *gorhoffedd* of Hywel ab Owain Gwynedd, though, as will be seen, he boasts about achievements quite different from those of the earlier warrior-bard. The translation is based on the edition of Lewis 1937.

Meter: cywydd; this meter consists of couplets of 7 syllables each, with the added requirement that a stressed syllable rhyme with an unstressed syllable. Each line must contain some form of *cynghanedd*, or 'harmony'; see section on Dafydd ap Gwilym.

Bibliography: Lewis 1937

Ieuan's Boast

>*Hywel a wnaeth, mab maeth medd,*
>*Awen gain, Owain Gwynedd*
>Hywel, nurtured on the mead of
>Sweet poetry, son of Owain Gwynedd, made
>A powerful poem of praise, splendid hero,
>Handsome champion, a prideful poem of fine form
>5 To exhibit, as a show-place of praise,
>His achievements as a powerful prince.
>I too shall compose, before forsaking mead,
>A scintillating song, a *gorhoffedd*.

I aim to show chief poets well
10   The subjects I have mastered and how I excel;
If anyone doubts what I have done,
It's all true, and I guarantee it.

First of all, O brilliant adventure,
When I was young, with a bright nature,
15   I studied extremely well and confidently
Fine learning, grammar and poetry;
Educated among thousands, I know
The weighty, complex civil law;
I studied the *trivium* for two trimesters,
20   On the rolls as a wise sophomore.
Familiar am I with Holy Bible –
The bold and lively need to know!
And I know the contents of every true chronicle,
For I have studied and read them through.

25   I studied French with great care:
Its traditions are learned, its language fair.
I understood, though I was amazed,
How good it was to find the unknown;
I studied closely, excellent instrument,
30   Clear orbits of the astrolabe;
That and the learning of the old disciple,
On orbits (ignoring the Bible),
The number and manner of true unity,
The white wheel of the mighty firmament,
35   And its luminous course and its qualities,
And the branches and grades of nature.

I studied, finally broke through,
Understanding the way of the Zodiac:
The seven planets, unbending fate,
40   Gentle mention of the twelve symbols,
Those that are called in general
By the genial term, the Twelve Signs,
Their names, all their splendid shapes,

219

Their exact courses and their natures.
45 I held forth, profoundly spoke
At great length on Ptolemy's book.
And somehow, wonder of wonders,
I spoke of the number of stars.
A lot of learning, like a real philosopher,
50 From a fine book taken from its coffer;
And if I knew the chapter, I'd speak a while
Of the amazing work of Aristotle.

I studied, I have strongly maintained,
For some time on the brass quadrant.
55 A fine thing it is, with its denticles,
Its checkered compasses and cycles,
Its files and bright plumb lines,
And the very bright pearl on it;
But all of the fine calculation
60 was the work of Augrim, mathematician.
This invention shows us precisely –
I didn't lose heart or grow weary –
The degree and the point as the seven parts move,
Where the sun and the bright sky are,
65 And the high point of every star,
And every sort of land, every copse,
And the lowest point of every depth
As far as the distant world of Annwn,
So that one can see (don't swoon!)
70 The most distant things through the lens;
The hours of the day, by the way,
Appear tidily on the two sides.
Attached to it, properly bound,
A brass clock, an horloge with sound.

75 I studied, at a desk learning,
Diligent, maintaining discipline;
A well-crafted tool of double scope
Is the computus, and I know it by rote.
I know well, could figure quickly,

80 The easy to use Dionysian Table;
   I know that I have, its fame assured,
   A valuable form and chart of the world
   That shows with a finger, without a doubt,
   The shape of the world – solid facts.
85 A wondrous thing that always appealed,
   'Tis splendid – though it does you no good –
   The Wheel of Fortune and its divisions,
   Necromancy and the Devil, or Ragman.
   What else might hold my interest?
90 Better be silent with much of the rest:
   They're not good for man, but it's right
   To treat of them, as I did one time.
   Let us turn now, ever so discreetly
   And wisely – for it's not anything ugly
95 To skillful, well made verse,
   And happy pastimes and crafts.
   I am a master, a dauntless power
   Of poetry, a revered tradition.
   I could make fine, strict verse,
100 Stinging satire, as thousands know!
   An accomplished and faultless *cywydd*
   Before that, and a smooth *englyn*;
   I composed a bright, lively, structured
   Awdl, every meter well remembered.
105 I learned to play my favorite two psalms
   On the harp, some time before that;
   I played splendidly, as you would think,
   For that's the way after strong drink.
   Played checkers, a great profession,
110 On a board shared with chessmen.
   I know actions requiring great skill –
   I can do them, too, and do them well.
   Taming a horse between two cinches,
   Under a strong, straight saddle;
115 Shooting, like a son of Southwark,
   Into a low hanging target;
   And with true and unerring aim,

Hitting the mark without fail;
Making a long cast of the javelin,
120   And heaving the stone fiercely before that.
Running strongly, boldly,
High-jumping, swimming gracefully.

I got from generous noblemen
Greetings of great reverence;
125   I got, for as long as I wanted them,
A lifetime of fine appointments;
I got much from those who welcomed me:
A pet dog, hounds, and horses;
I got from virtuous maidens
130   Mead and lovely love-making;
Love was mine, to honor me,
And I got my heart's desire.
I enjoyed wealth for a lifetime,
Fully refined, a pleasurable time;
135   In the end I'll come, full of grace,
And be admitted to the sublime feast;
At my life's end my body will suffer
A reminder of dust in a wooden coffer;
A conspicuous place in the chancel wall
140   Of Llanddewibrefi, fit for St. Doewan,
In the community of most innocent Mary,
In an adorned grave, an accessible temple,
And heaven, O happy place! will reach out
To succour my soul! Amen!

LLYWARCH AP LLYWELYN: PRYDYDD Y MOCH

Llywarch flourished as poet between about 1175 and 1220. During that period he composed many poems for his patrons, of which thirty, comprising 1,780 lines, have survived. This is more than has survived of any other of the thirty-two known Poets of the Princes, with the exception of Cynddelw Brydydd Mawr, an older contemporary of Llywarch. That is surely more than just an accident of survival, for Llywarch was well remembered by succeeding generations. In the very next generation, poet Dafydd Benfras puts Llywarch, Cynddelw, and the legendary Llefoed Wynepclawr in a class by themselves. Llywarch continues to be praised by the poets of the fourteenth century. His reputation as one of the finest of the Poets of the Princes, then, insured the survival of his works.

Llywarch ap Llywelyn is better known by his nickname, Prydydd y Moch. The name means 'Poet of the Pigs.' Why he was called that is by no means clear, though there have been a few attempts to explain the name. Perhaps the most viable explanation is that offered by Joseph Loth (1907). He thought that it derived from the lines in a poem to Owain Gwynedd's grandson, Gruffudd, in which he claims,

> Strewing my songs before you shall not be
> Like strewing pearls before swine.

A clear echo of Matthew vii.6. But we shall probably never know the real reason for the name.

Llywarch's surviving work consists almost entirely of praise poems to his patrons, as we would expect. But, as we shall see, praise needs to be broadly defined, for there is a good deal of variation in the work. His principal patrons were the House of Gwynedd, from the time of the sons of Owain Gwynedd (d. 1170) to the career of Llywelyn ap Iorwerth. Llywelyn ab Iorwerth Drwyndwn came to be known as 'Llywelyn the Great' because of his statesmanship and his success in unifying so much of Wales. It was his efforts that made it possible for his grandson, Llywelyn ap Gruffudd (d. 1282) to truly become Prince of Wales. Llywelyn ap Iorwerth became the principal patron of Llywarch, who composed six awdlau and three series of englynion to him, which represents more than a third of the surviving corpus.

Llywelyn was a generous patron. There were gifts of land – one hundred acres in one recorded instance; free use of land for farming; a gift of a mill, which would have been a lucrative source of fees from grinding grain; and in his poetry Llywarch speaks of gifts of gold and silver, horses, and so on. It is easily seen, then, that Llywarch ap Llywelyn, despite his rather pedestrian sounding nickname, Poet of the Pigs, represented the highest standing obtainable by a professional poet during this period. He praised his patrons in the traditional manner, validating their valor, generosity, lineage, sovereignty over many lands, and the ability to defend those possessions. Praise very much in the mold of the *cynfeirdd*, themes that would have been familiar to Taliesin and no doubt even to the Celtic poets about whom Posidonius and Caesar wrote. And in return for creating and maintaining the patron's fame, he received rich rewards.

Because of his productivity and his enduring reputation as a poet of high achievement among the Poets of the Princes, we have chosen to present a number of his poems here. This brief introduction and the introductory notes to each selection are deeply indebted to Jones, Elin M. 1991.

A SONG FOR GWENLLIANT

As noted earlier, the poems by Hywel and Gwalchmai are the only medieval Welsh poems identified as *gorhoffedd*. But as T. Gwynn Jones (1915) claimed, Prydydd y Moch's poem to Gwenlliant daughter of Hywel belongs to the same tradition as that of Gwalchmai and Hywel. The basic elements of nature, war, and love are all present. And Jones goes on to show how these poets treat those themes in similar ways. D. Myrddin Lloyd disagreed to some extent. In Prydydd y Moch's poem he finds simplicity of pattern with fewer of the peculiarities that characterize the other *gorhoffedd* poems. In particular he finds a rarity of compound words that normally characterize Prydydd y Moch's work. It has all of the hallmarks of the *gorhoffedd*, he claimed, but not much else. However true that judgment may be, the poem to Gwenlliant is a sophisticated and well-wrought poem.

The sun, its rising, its equivalence with Gwenllian, the fervor of the poet as lover, his sexuality, his poetic inspiration, are all subtly woven together, with words in the original Welsh text that describe a surging up and outwards, a bubbling up, literally an exultation. These are effects we cannot reproduce in translation. But, nonetheless, the warmth of feeling and drama is apparent there and we can experience the exuberance that characterizes the poem. The translation is based on the edition of Elin Jones 1991.

Meter: awdl, primarily of *cyhydedd naw ban*; the poem opens with a *toddaid*, which is employed in two other places in the poem. The former meter consists of lines of, normally, 9 syllables with four stresses; the latter has lines of 10 and 9 syllables respectively. The final word in the first line rhymes or alliterates internally with words in the second line. The penultimate word in the first line carries the chief rhyme, *-e*, which is retained throughout the poem.

Bibliography: Jones, Elin 1991; Jones, Nerys 1992; Jones, T. Gwynn 1915; Lloyd 1937

A Song for Gwenlliant

Duw Sulgwyn yw hyn, hynt gyfwyre – glyw,
Hynt a ddyco glew, gloyw ddyddwyre;
Dygychwyn, olwyn, elwaf mangre,
Dygymer hwyl ffêr, haul neud ffofre!

Whitsuntide! the right time for rising up in arms!
 Let the bold sally forth in bright rising!
 Set out, my steed, for the choicest spot,
 Set a lively pace, for the sun is ascending!
5 Be bold and follow the road there
 Sweaty, rangy, prancing,
 Past the place of Tudur, Elise's land,
 Lamented famous one of Cyfeiliog,
Past Cynfelyn's daughter, foe of beaux,
10 Though she's a princess, she's impossible!
 Nest told me she won't rise to the bait –
 Like a warp that's left unwoven.

I am Llywarch, among the legions,
 England's bane, invincible, implacable!
15 They've seen my shield on the field
 And wear my spears in their bellies.
Wherever I go, crows caw grimly,
 Because a man of fury is among them.
 Many a groan comes of my grit,
20 My lust sending screams to the sky.

Waters wear, in their watery way,
 Cloaks of bright leaves on branches, like bird-flocks;
 Trees branching out in shelter for cuckoos;
 And I know a maid who makes me go pale.
25 Usk of a hundred streams carries
 The leaves of uplands to Caerlleon;
 Just as a splendid and lusty mount carries me
 Along in the cause of praise – for one like the sun –
 To the halls of Gwenllian, who hails from Gwynllwg,
30 Loveable and lovely, light of the land.
 Alas, she favors me not, and I, afire
 For a maid radiant as the rising sun,
 Feel my heart consumed like a fire
 Burning for her all ablaze.
35 Perfect her appearance in golden garb,
 And silver mounts will sally forth,

Carrying her claim: her fame will spread
Where sets the sun and also where it rises.

A THREAT TO DAFYDD AB OWAIN GWYNEDD

Was the 'threat,' Welsh *bygwth*, a distinct genre among the poems of the *gogynfeirdd*? It seems possible, for, as we have abundantly seen, the Celtic poets were well aware of their power in society, and it would not at all be far-fetched to imagine them chastising their patrons for not providing for them properly. It is also possible to read the 'threat' as friendly admonition, a set of precepts, as it were, about how to treat one's poet. Others (Elin Jones 1991, p. 23) see the overall effect of the poem as being quite different. The poet has displeased his patron in some way and is asking for reconciliation. That sort of poem is well known in the Welsh tradition, and the name for it is *dehuddiant* 'consolation; reconciliation.'

This poem, like so many others, has a seasonal opening. Its purpose is to enhance the theme of the poem, for October is the time of year when decay begins to set in, reflecting the state of turmoil between himself and his patron. Llywarch then speaks of his poetic genius, of which he claims Dafydd has been neglectful. And then comes the threat: the poet has been patient up till now, but don't count on such patience continuing. He even threatens satire. Above all, he reminds his patron how valuable he is to him, in words that evoke Taliesin's consolation of Elphin in "The Story of Gwion Bach, Who Became Taliesin." Then he begins to cajole him, advising him how he should treat his court poet. But the poem is also full of conventional praise for Dafydd, even if, in this context, those lines may be read as ironical.

Meter: awdl, primarily of *cyhydedd naw ban* and *toddaid*. The former meter consists of lines of, normally, 9 syllables with four stresses; the latter has lines of 10 and 9 syllables respectively. The final word in the first line rhymes or alliterates internally with words in the second line. The penultimate word in the first line carries the chief rhyme, *-i*, which is retained throughout the poem. *Cyhydedd hir* is employed twice in the poem, at lines 43-44 and 55-56. Here the line is broken into three rhyming phrases of, normally, 5 syllables, with a final phrase of 4 syllables, which carries the chief rhyme.

Bibliography: Jones, Elin M. 1991

A Threat to Dafydd ab Owain Gwynedd

Calan hyddfref, tymp dydd yn edwi,
Calaf gan lloer fan llwrw fynegi
October, a time when day dwindles,
Stalks white, the moon high lighting the path;
Tides in turmoil, Llyr flooding;
The far-travelled sea a wintry frontier;
5   The Lord's poetic arts have been dealt to me
As they were not dealt to my forebears.
News has reached me of a mighty, proud prince –
One as fine as my own gift – at debasing me!
Fiercely does he steal the bride-price of my song;
10   Violent his cruel anger toward it.
I have been patient, O wall of wrath,
Renowned overlord, in remaining silent.
But I no longer promise, O generous scion of Beli,
That I won't burn from such long chafing.
15   I know that where I stab, so poisonous will be
The tongue's course that salve will not heal.
My gift rages under siege–
Roars in contention, battle, and tumult!
Calm your passion, O haven of bards,
20   Whose passion sparkles from poetry.
Be wary, generous Dafydd, who explodes in battle,
    Bountiful one, in warding off my spears.
Fierce one of Teyrnon, people's protector,
Dragon of dragons, fire of Eryri,
25   Prince of the West, succour me:
Rejecting my song riles me!
    I'm better for you, generous ruler, than the herds
Horsemen need to join you on campaigns.
Admired lord! you're better than the proverbial three –
30   Mordaf, Nudd, Rhydderch – in the custom of giving.
Prosperous lord, master of the mighty,
Endow me with wealth in return for praise,
Giver of the grace of gold, heir of Rhodri,
    And know that I am still furious!

229

35   Don't drive me from you, don't repulse me,
        Don't leave me on the threshhold of silence.
        Happy prince of Britain, try to nurture me
        With your red gold, your gain, your gentility.
        Your fame glitters from dramatic declamation
40   Through my zeal, my song, and my contention.
        I saw bards hoarse – and they weren't toying,
        With very great effort, rehearsing your boldness:
        I sang your praise as they never could,
           Powerful warrior, mighty king.
45   The wise know that it is not fear of poverty:
        Pre-eminent skilful song is what I am in engaged in.
        I know that God, Prince of prophets,
        Will not, of his goodness, lessen my gift.
        And know, Dafydd, Elifri's ilk,
50   Regulating me will not be without cost.
        If you devise, generous lord, to harness my muse,
        With counsels of miserliness to silence me,
        It will not be concealed that there is penury,
        That I am besieged so you can build wealth.
55   Princely son of Owain, carnage of princes,
           Splendid realm, fury of Benlli,
        Eagle among men, don't become lazy
        In dealing with me, lord who turns tides of battle.
        Don't trample your mantle, I am your gain,
60   Don't trod on me despite any pressure.
        Don't sell me for gold to other lords,
           No other delights me no matter how he honors me.
        Dignity befits me, endow me with it
        As does a knight with his betrothed.
65   The day has come, esteemed Dafydd,
        Generous lord, to receive me or lose me.
        Before there's war between you and me,
        Let an angel of accord bring lasting peace.
        May I have, bountiful lord, concord with you:
70   And may you prosper in long life!

A THREAT TO GRUFFUDD AP CYNAN

This is the earliest of the four poems which Llywarch ap Llywelyn composed to Gruffudd ap Cynan ab Owain Gwynedd. There are two surviving praise poems and an elegy (see below) upon Gruffudd's death in the year 1200. Like the threat (*bygwth*) to Gruffudd's uncle, Dafydd ab Owain Gwynedd, the poet is warning the patron of his failings in his relationship with his poet. Llywarch claims first of all that his poetic gift, his *awen*, comes from God. He claims, as if it were proverbial, that the generous shall find fame from the poet's efforts, but the miserly will find only shame and disgrace. There is a suggestion that Gruffudd has been content to hire inferior poets (perhaps to save money, as in the "Threat to Dafydd ab Owain"), and the poet urges him to drive them off. There is a veiled reference to poetic contention here, of the sort that Taliesin relishes as he challenges the bards of the court of Maelgwn Gwynedd. Llwyarch goes on to recount the generosity of famous men of the past, challenging his patron, as it were, to emulate them. It is in this poem that we find the reference to swine, prompting some to claim it as the source for the poet's nickname, 'Poet of the Pigs.'

Meter: awdl, *byr a thoddaid*, which consists of *toddaid byr* (two lines of, normally, 10 and 6 syllables respectively) interspersed with *cyhydedd fer* (a couplet with 8 syllables in each line).

Bibliography: Elin Jones 1991

A Threat to Gruffudd ap Cynan

Arddaly nef arddunia fy nlid,
Arglwydd Dduw yn ddyn y'th enid
Lord of heaven, glorify my gift,
Lord God, born as man,
Hear my plea for generosity,
If my song emanates from Your grace.
5   Don't go from me, or let me from you;
Generosity marks your Divineness;
With my words, which came as your gift,
Someone's glory will endure;

For a generous and brave one, his fame will endure,
10 For a miser, his satire and grief ensured.
And you, wrathful weapon of war,
Merciless, song-loving, splendid,
Strewing my songs before you shall not be
Like strewing pearls before swine.
15 And consider, chief lord, how dear
The gold of Arabia – if one were to ask for it.
Base men don't consider the brilliance in my song,
　Drive them from you lest shame befall you!
And if you don't, I will bring such a blush
20 To your cheeks to prosecute your deep shame,
That your grandson and his son will feel its effect,
To avenge my misfortune and my anger.
And here is your freedom of choice:
Let there be blame or fame from my coming.
25 Reproach and regret have come to me,
For the loss of lords who gave and gave:
Bold Iorwerth killed, giver of gold to his friend,
　No wonder I sigh for him;
Madog's son, fierce and famous arm,
30 During his grand life great poets earned land;
Dead is Einion, immeasurably wealthy,
His custom to attack thousands;
Son of generous Tegwared, proven champion,
　Opposition was not suffered by him:
35 A wolf does not kill a warlord,
And a thief does not steal my brilliant song;
Gain is less, gifts more base,
　For Cadwgan son of Llywarch,
Vigorous manhood, has been taken away;
40 May the power of the Heavenly Son of God free him!
He does not renege on what he embraced:
He makes gifts – not promises.
And as for me, may my virtue earn me favor
With God and purity of life.
45 'Twas against the faults of kings where wealth is divided
　That I sought to warn you, Gruffudd!

IN PRAISE OF GRUFFUDD AP CYNAN

There are four surviving poems by Llywarch to Gruffudd ap Cynan ap Owain Gwynedd. Gruffudd and his brother Maredudd defeated their uncle Rhodri ab Owain Gwynedd in 1194, after which Gruffudd ruled at least a part of Gwynedd until his death in 1200 (see the Elegy to Gruffudd below). Rhodri himself was the subject of four praise poems by Llywarch, though in no way did that prevent him from being rewarded for practicing his art for the benefit of Gruffudd.

Meter: awdl, a mixture of *toddaid, toddaid byr, cyhydedd naw ban, cyhydedd fer.* The single end rhyme in – *e* unites the poem.

Bibliography: Jones, Elin M. 1991

In Praise of Gruffudd ap Cynan

Rhag rhyw Dygannwy dygynwyre – glyw,
O Fôn hyd Fynwy llyw llu angdde
Before the lord of Degannwy an army rises up
   From Môn to Menevia; leader of a teeming host,
He provides the many with lusty mounts
   As far as a bright dawn lights the land.
5   He stirs swift slaughter in the clash of shields,
   Rising up with his blazing sword and his fame;
   Reaper who mows down arms and war trumpets;
   Gruffudd, lordly prince of Elise's people.
Sprung from brave leaders, he musters the best,
10   Like his grandfather, because of his generous gifts.
   Worthy of praise in battle and on blazing hill;
   His mount winged, in woven, torn harness;
   Praiseworthy giver of gifts in the morning;
   Noble descendant who cares not for gold.
15   I praised the free-wheeling ruler of Cemais,
   Attacking encampments, fierce and fiery.
   Praising a lord's generosity is proper,

233

Gentle lord, giver of well-bred horses.
When his angry, onward rush routs foes,
20   A spoiler of spoilers,
Before the hosts of the genial son of Nwyfre,
Before Bernicians' foe, ravens scream.
Not an object of praise in the outback of Britain,
          This champion of poets:
25   He to the pinnacle of success painlessly,
He who will make it his fine land;
He who'll push fearlessly to Buddugre court,
He who produces mounts of many hues,
He flood-like strikes, destroying Saxons,
30   Defender of the minions of Môn, gory lord.
May a place of peace be his end,
Protector of petitioners seeking peace,
In the encounter of praise by a company of poets,
In glorious reception by God in heaven.

AN ELEGY FOR GRUFFUDD AP CYNAN

Gruffudd ap Cynan ab Owain Gwynedd died in 1200, having ruled parts of Gwynedd. He is well remembered in this elegy. The poet praises his exploits on the field of battle, comparing him to Achilles, to Bran (i.e., Bendigeidfran) son of Llyr, the hero of the second branch of the Mabinogi, and to Arthur. His favor with poets is stressed, as is his generosity to poets. In the last englyn, he is said to be even more generous than four leaders whose generosity was proverbial.

Meter: a chain of *englyn unodl union*. This englyn meter consists of a *toddaid byr*, that is, a line of normally 10 syllables followed by a line of normally 6 syllables, and a couplet, with seven syllables in each line. The chief rhyme occurs at the end of the 7th, 8th, or 9th syllable of the first line; a further rule says that in the couplet, an accented syllable must rhyme with an unaccented syllable.

Bibliography: Jones, Elin M. 1991

An Elegy for Gruffudd ap Cynan

Hael Ruffudd ddiludd ddilawch –teÿrnedd
Teÿrnfeirdd neus gwddawch,
Periglew glew a glywsawch,
Pair Prydain pryd nad oedd rhawch.
Generous Gruffudd, undaunted defense of lords,
Lordly bards, you know him:
A lion, you've heard, and brazen,
Caldron of Britain before this pain.

5   Poets mourn the piteous loss of a lord,
Princely bards of the whole of Wales;
As they grieve, so they feel pain:
A hundred breasts, bruised and broken.

He battered his foes, kept them at bay,
10   On battlefield and wild waste;
Fearless, powerful and quick with a stroke,
With battle and booty, as far as Chester.

I praise the prince of thousands, golden-lord of legions,
    Wall in defence of warriors;
15   Bound and bowing to poets, generous fosterer,
    Refined and wise, strong, silent, and tender.

Tender to many, to the world entirely
    Stead of strangers, path of pleasure,
    An Achilles in fury was our dear ally,
20   Lofty guardian of the lovely host of Gwynedd.

Gwynedd's surging hero, bold man at the border;
    Responsive to poets and people,
    All of whom feel the loss of their prince,
    Noble Gruffudd, courtly lord.

25   Courteous to praise, to warriors he was strong,
    But oppressive to aliens,
    Mighty manhood like Bran fab Llyr,
    Bountiful but raging eagle.

Eagle of princes, princely hero of Britain,
30   Poets in great consternation –
    Gone the prince, profit of armies,
    Generous lord, to the bosom of the earth.

Generous Gruffudd, companion of many a guest,
    Many more for whom you are not;
35   Since you have gone, poets have gone
    Without horses, gold harness, or food.

Feeder of wolves, fierce, a dragon was Gruffudd,
    Eminent lord, might of Maig,
    Mainstay of multitudes, brilliant in battle,
40   And leader among a sea of men.

An ocean gentle and fierce for folk high and low;
    Poets hastened to his side;

Great hero, Britain's whole recourse,
Fellow of fortune, contender, Cynan's son.

45   A Cynan, divined one of druids, will come;
        He too was one of the Britons;
        But songsters grieve for the loss of wealth
        Of one who was better: Môn's munificent lord.

Noble and excellent, elevating bards,
50   Many a bard with full support,
        A mass of song in the wake of his might:
        Cruel in war, free with streams of gold.

Generous Arthur, leader, world renowned for giving;
        Generous Rhydderch, for gains in gold;
55   Generous Mordaf, generous and splendid Nudd,
        Generous still more – and mightier – Gruffudd!

IN PRAISE OF LYWELYN AP IORWERTH: 1

Llywelyn ap Iorwerth, known to the Welsh as Llywelyn the Great, was born in 1173, the son of Iorwerth ab Owain Gwynedd. In 1194 he defeated his uncles, Dafydd ab Owain and Rhodri ab Owain and thus succeeded to the rule of Gwynedd. He married Joan (in Welsh, Siwan or Sioned), daughter of King John of England in 1205. By 1215, through both military and diplomatic means, he had become ruler of nearly all of Wales. The subsequent course of events was uneven, but there is no question that Llywelyn was indeed a 'great' leader of Wales. He died in 1240.

Llywarch ap Llywelyn was his poet for nearly thirty years, and there are nine surviving poems in praise of Llywelyn. This one would appear to have been written early on, when Llywelyn was around fifteen years of age. Perhaps he was just beginning his career, for while the poet does praise his exploits as a warrior, he also instructs him about his relationship with poets.

Meter: awdl, *byr a thoddaid*, which consists of *toddaid byr* (two lines of 10 and 6 syllables respectively) alternating regularly with *cyhydedd fer* (a couplet with 8 syllables in each line) to the very end, where *cyhydedd fer* concludes the poem.

Bibliography: Jones, Elin M. 1991

In Praise of Lywelyn ap Iorwerth: 1

A'th fendicwy Dwy Dëyrn, werlin – hael
  Hil Fleddynt fab Cynfyn,
  Arf eryr gwyr llewyr llewyn;
  Aergymid gyndlid Cynfelyn
May the Lord God bless you, noble prince!
  Bred of Bleddyn ap Cynfyn,
  Armored eagle of many a man,
  In war, worthy of Cynfelyn.

5   Raging, wrathful reaper of chieftains,
        Chief of Britain's compass;
        Similar your shield, host's fury,

238

To the swift, destructive shield of Cuhelyn.

The word I speak is from the caldron; it belongs to all
10   Who hasten hither;
        Mine, red gold among my gifts –
        I am Llywarch, you Llywelyn!

Great lord of warriors, battle-hewing, weapons red,
        Gold galore, glorious in war.
15   Swirling about you, hewer of shields,
        A sea of blood as you sue for lands.

Your enemy ravaged – alas for him!
        Clamor and country behind you;
        When barely fifteen, you went to his border
20   Fifteen times – may you grow much older!

First principle for you is spending freely
        On the bards who cluster about you;
        We trust your long hand won't tremble
        As it pays out red gold and yellow.

25   God made you marvelously, most generous of men
        As far as the sun has travelled;
        Like your father before you, grace adorns you,
        You're the bounty of Heilyn reborn.

Grandson of Owain, daunting dread of foes;
30   Enemy-tamer of Merfyn's line;
        Grandson of Madog, heir of eminent ancestors;
        Son of Iorwerth; well-born this noble one!

I greet you, a prince who doesn't thwart poets,
        As a bard on poetic rounds:
35   Unswerving in purpose, generous, undaunted,
        Noble, most gentle, open-handed Llywelyn,
        May I prosper from you, as you merit song,
        And may God and man prosper you!

239

IN PRAISE OF LLYWELYN AP IORWERTH: 2

The similarity of this poem to the *gorhoffedd* poems of Gwalchmai and Hywel is apparent in the opening lines as well as in the lines toward the end where Llywelyn's reputation as a lover is recounted. The poem is a praise poem, to be sure, but the poet begins by celebrating the land, the figure he cuts as he rides about Gwynedd. But then the boasting turns to Llywelyn: his vigor in battle, his wide-ranging campaigns, his virility in love. Finally, he hopes that Llywelyn will be around for a long time, not only for a hundred years but for an impossible three ages of the world and more.

Meter: awdl, a mixture of *toddaid, toddaid byr, cyhydedd naw ban, cyhydedd fer*, and, to close, *englyn unodl union*. The chief rhyme, which occurs throughout the poem, is on the syllable – *wy*.

Bibliography: Jones, Elin M. 1991

In Praise of Llywelyn ap Iorwerth: 2

Neu'm bu dydd cer elfydd Elwy,
Eiliwn wawd â defawd, a dwy
I was, one day, in the district of Elwy,
I plaited a verse or two, as usual;
Another day, I roamed freely
About the harbor of fair Conwy;
5   I rode around Llyn,
     On my gold trimmed saddle,
     And golden Arfon and Ardudwy,
     Land of deep, swirling waters–and double pay!
     I loved what I saw at Dinsylwy,
10   A sitting of seagulls, maidens that is, and many;
Whitewashed, the ramparts 'round Maelgyning,
     Swift as hounds their men as they move.
     No need to pursue the question who
     Or what keeps this land safe from harm:
15   Llywelyn does, lion in a lair,
     Governs Gwynedd as far as Mawddwy,

A forceful hand that rules the sea lanes,
Sending England back to Loch Lomond.
Grandson of Madog of growing honor,
20   Grandson of Owain, great destroyer.
His long lance leading, his levies heavy
In the land of Mechydd and Machawy;
From Brittany yonder, across to Severn Sea –
Shattered shafts in Porthaethwy –
25   From Dyfnaint, from Naint, from Nanheudwy,
From the land defined by the Efyrnwy,
Spirited, proud Llywelyn prepares his pursuit;
He'll not cower behind the waters of the Dee!
A lover since youth, your virility like Garwy,
30   Loving a fair maid, comely and graceful,
With a large, gold ring and flowing mantle;
A maid doesn't stray from the one she loves.
A century easily ruling Wales,
       and your regard growing ever:
35   May God in his wisdom allow you
Three ages of the world and longer!

A PRAYER FOR THE HEALTH OF MADOG AP GRUFFUDD

Madog ap Gruffudd Maelor was ruler of Powys Fadog and a cousin to Llywelyn ap Iorwerth. Except for a brief period, he was a loyal follower of Llywelyn until his death in 1236. It is surely due to this relationship that Llywelyn's poet, Llywarch ap Llywelyn, composed this poem and prayer for Madog's recovery from illness. This is a most unusual theme in the *gogynfeirdd* poetry, though we must always remember that there may have been good reasons why such poems would not have been recorded. The poet touches on many of the same elements one would find in a *marwnad* or 'elegy,' but death has not yet occurred and, with the help of God (and the power of the poet's song!), the patron may yet be spared and the dire consequences of his death avoided.

Meter: *englyn unodl union* (see "Elegy for Llywelyn ap Gruffud" by Bleddyn Fardd for description of this meter).

Bibliography: Jones, Elin M. 1991

A Prayer for the Health of Madog ap Gruffudd

> *Am unig treisig y trawsiolaf–Dduw*
> *A ddigawn iach o glaf,*
> *Milwr milwyr fodrydaf,*
> *Madawg lawddëawg lary naf.*
> On behalf of a hero, I boldly beseech God,
>   That he may make hale from ill
> A leader of men, mighty
> Madog, zealous, generous lord.

5   Lord God, spare the sad burden of pain;
        Assured for me, his red gold;
    Celestial Son of God, shelter my lord,
    Gruffudd's son, resolute and bold.

    For the ardent eagle of Maelor's men, I plead
10   With the Protector of heaven and earth;

242

For an unfailing lord, refuge of warriors,
Flawless and noble, his mother's only son.

O sole Son of God Himself, do not take the life
Of a man whose wane will ruin poets;
15   Snare of foes, but friend of saints,
Leader of Powys, pride of the land.

Death, and the quiet he brings (Powys knows
That he chooses from the best),
Leaves kings that are evil and base,
20   And those that are noble he takes.

He took fair Owain, left me no peace from grief,
Stabbing pain to think of his life;
Offspring of Gruffudd, fierce, fiery threat,
Yours, O Death, the dire deed!

25   Lively battles were waged by the world's princes
before they were thine;
Mighty Christ! from the fetters of Death
Keep noble Madog mine!

Mine, great grief; my cheeks scored;
In my prime I'm not,
For…[here the poem breaks off in the mss.]

THE CELTIC POETS

THE WHITE-HOT IRON

This is an important poem in that it provides evidence for ordeal by hot iron in medieval Wales. Ordeals of one sort and another have been common throughout the world. They were means of determining guilt or innocence by appealing to the judgment of God. The guilty would be burned by iron, boiling oil, hot coals, or whatever, whereas the innocent would be safe. According to our poem, Llywarch ap Llywelyn was accused of the murder of a certain Madog. He seems on the point of taking up the white-hot piece of iron to prove his innocence. One can understand the fervidness of his prayer: he would have been required to take several steps with the bar in his hand before letting it fall to the ground!

Meter: awdl, *byr a thoddaid*, which consists of *toddaid byr* (two lines of 10 and 6 syllables respectively) interspersed with *cyhydedd fer*.

Bibliography: Jones, Elin M. 1991; Jones, Nerys 1992

The White-Hot Iron

> *Creawdr nef crededun I'I was,*
> *Credwn I hwn fal y credwn I Ionas;*
> *Dur ynad deddf rad rhyswynas –Dofydd*
> *Dof wyf it yn wanas.*
> Creator of heaven, true to His servant,
> I believe this as I believe the gospel of John;
> Steely judge, rite by grace of God,
> Humbly I take hold of you.
> 5   Your truth shimmers white-hot,
> Your fervor is no threat to my integrity;
> Consider, when you judge my noble lineage,
> Creature of sizzling torment, who created you.
> I petition Peter, kin of Christ,
> 10   Who carried the Cross in dignity,
> Entreat, implore and pray to Thomas
> And Philip and Paul and Andreas.
> By taking in hand the white-hot bar,

To avoid the crime of homicide,

15 I testify, good iron, that when Madog was murdered,

Not by my hand was it accomplished,

Any more than Cain and his clan

Merit heaven and its nine kingdoms.

As for me, I long for fellowship –

20 God's good will, and escape from his wrath!

DAFYDD AP GWILYM

Dafydd ap Gwilym was born around 1320, most probably at Brogynin near Aberystwyth (see Map). We know something of his family, which claimed descent from a certain Gwynfardd Dyfed and his son Cuhelyn Fardd. This was a noble, aristocratric family, for there is a twelfth-century praise poem addressed to Cuhelyn Fardd in The Black Book of Carmarthen. These names, which include the word *Bardd*, along with additional evidence indicate that this family of noblemen were also gifted, perhaps amateur, poets. We have seen evidence of the practice of poetry by a non-professional in the person of Hywel ap Owain Gwynedd, who belongs to the period of the *gogynfeirdd*

Dafydd's uncle was Llywelyn ap Gwilym, who, like earlier members of his family, was in service of the English crown. Llywelyn was an educated man who apparently followed in the footsteps of his poetizing ancestors. Dafydd, in an elegy addressed to the uncle, calls him a poet and a linguist, and one who possessed all knowledge. He also says that Llywelyn was learned in the book of Donatus, a reference to grammars of the sort that were used in the bardic schools. Dafydd himself was a professionally trained poet, more than likely trained by his uncle. Given the family's connection with the English government, it is almost certain that they had English and French in addition to the native Welsh language. And so literary influences from beyond Wales, those of England and the continent were open to them, as was, in part, a new vocabulary.

The work of a great poet can be said to transcend any quest for sources and perhaps literary history in general. But in surveying the literature of a people, we would like to know what is traditional (continuity) and what is innovative in the work of any one period or any one poet. This book stresses the continuity of Celtic poetry across time and across geographical boundaries, of course, so let us see how Dafydd fits onto that continuum.

Dafydd's earliest poems, some twenty of them, were written in the older meters of englyn and awdl, which we have seen exemplified in the work of The Poets of the Princes. But he also composed poems on traditional themes using the cywydd meter. These early poems are conventional in that they deal with themes articulated by the official court poets: eulogy and elegy addressed to noble patrons, and also some religious poems. Such poems show Dafydd to be in the mainstream of the traditions continued by the Poets of the Princes, for the *pencerdd*, highest grade of poet, was expected to sing songs of praise to God as well as to the patron.

Among Dafydd's religious poems is an awdl-cywydd on the passion of Christ, a sequence of englynion on a part of the liturgy of the mass, a cywydd to the Trinity, etc. Among his conventional praise poems is an awdl to one of his most important patrons, Ifor Hael, or Ifor the Generous. This man was apparently a successful merchant; the poet calls him,

> Merchant, maker of treasure and praise,
> Whose wealth makes Normans wince, essence of praise

Though the style is conventional, the content is strikingly different. The poet refers to Ifor's business skills being the envy of the English, a neat contrast to the usual praise of a patron for being bolder in battle than his enemies–Ifor's a better merchant!

Dafydd's use of another metrical form for eulogy, the cywydd, would seem to be a break with tradition. Dafydd did not invent the cywydd. It was surely in use before his time, but it seems to have been the medium of a lower order of poets or, to put it another way, it was normally used for less elevated purposes and themes. In Wales, as in Ireland, the poetic orders were ranked. In Ireland the laws stipulated the payment a *fili* received for his poems, but a *bard* was said to have to be content with whatever he could get. In Wales, the principal divisions of poets were the *pencerdd* at the top, then the *teuluwr* or poet of the household or retinue, and finally the *clerwr*, who was a kind of travelling entertainer and who sang scurrilous, satirical, and other less noble forms of verse. The cywydd was no doubt a traditional form, but Dafydd is innovative in turning it to new purpose.

Dafydd was thoroughly rooted in Welsh poetic tradition, sprung from the same soil as the *cynfeirdd* and the *gogynfeirdd*. The difference is that circumstances of the fourteenth century did not permit Dafydd to practice poetry as his forebears had. As Dr. Rachel Bromwich has said, "The traditional bonds of poetic patronage became loosened at the very time that ideas and influences from the outside world were flooding into Wales as never before" (1979, p. 112).

The innovative themes for which Dafydd is best known, and those which modern audiences in particular find most appealing, are the ones associated with what is generally called courtly love. The conventions of courtly love originated in Provence in the eleventh century and developed further in France, whence they spread to England. It is important to remember that after the Norman conquest of England in 1066, French was the language of the upper classes in England. Libraries consisted of books mostly written in French, and French literature was the literature in vogue among those classes. This situation persisted right down to the fourteenth century, Dafydd's own time, when Chaucer, going against the literary tide of his time, asserted the right of English as a suitable vehicle for literature. Even then French standards were applied. Chaucer "defended and illustrated the mother tongue by transmitting to it a French lexicon, French courtly style, rhetoric, and, of course, rhyme and meter" (Calin 1994, p. 13).

The source for many of the elements in courtly love was the work of the Roman poet Ovid, whose very popular work, *Ars Amatoria*, proposed love as an art or science that could be taught by precepts and practiced according to rules. Love could be a kind of warfare; it could also be a kind of sickness. According to some scholars, the troubadours exalted Love as an idealized form of service by analogy with the feudal relationship between lord and knightly retainer. The beloved was often a married woman and inaccessible. The lover thus suffered extreme torments in his attempts to get near to, get a glimpse of, or, heaven forbid, obtain favors from his beloved.

But Dafydd didn't simply adopt these new themes. What sets his work apart is the very special way he presents the situations of lovers. In Dafydd, love and nature are virtually inseparable, and it is the combination of the two that distinguishes his poetry. Dafydd is an acute observer of nature, and that is another thing that puts him squarely in the tradition of the Celtic poets. Finn and Marbán have an eye for all that nature has to offer, and the gnomic poetry of the *cynfeirdd* demonstrates a clear eye too. In the *gorhoffedd* type of poem (Hywel, Gwalchmai, Prydydd y Moch) we begin to glimpse a more personal involvement with nature – no longer simply nature description. Much of Dafydd's poetry takes this involvement further. In those poems, nature and love are intertwined, and nature is often personified – in particular as it is called upon to assist Dafydd in his lovemaking.

Some of Dafydd's most entertaining poems recount his frolicking failures to achieve the object of his love. In these poems we find mostly the innovative side of Dafydd, the side that is bringing to Welsh poetry popular themes of the time from England and the Continent. But even at his most innovative, the tradition out of which Dafydd developed may be glimpsed in his work. The translations are based on the edition of Parry 1952.

Meter: Except as otherwise noted, Dafydd's poems are all in the cywydd meter. Of the four types of cywydd, the most common, and the one we find here, is *cywydd deuair hirion*, consisting of rhyming couplets with 7 syllables in each line. The end rhyme must be between a stressed syllable and an unstressed syllable. The lines are characterized by *cynghanedd*, or 'harmony,' a complex system of alliteration and internal rhyme. For details, see Parry 1970, Rowlands 1976, Bromwich 1982.

Bibliography: Bromwich 1979, 1982, 1986; Fulton 1996; Loomis 1982; Parry 1952

AN AWDL TO IFOR HAEL

Ifor ap Llywelyn, nicknamed *Hael* 'Generous,' was the principal patron of Dafydd ap Gwilym. Dafydd addressed two praise poems in the awdl meter (of which this is one), one in the englyn meter, and four in the newer cywydd meter. In subject matter as well as meter, this is a traditional praise poem, very much the sort that Dafydd's bardic predecessors, the *gogynfeirdd*, would have recognized. Ifor is praised for his generosity, is called a bulwark, a pillar, ruthless in battle, victorious foe of the Deirans. Now this last is openly anachronistic. Deira was one of the old Anglo-Saxon kingdoms; along with Bernicia it formed what came to be known as Northumbria. It belongs to the era of the Gododdin, not fourteenth-century Britain! On another occasion, he refers to his patron as 'putting the men of Deira on biers,' a line nearly identical with that employed by Llywarch Hen for Urien. Nothing could show Dafydd's debt to and knowledge of the old poetry better than this conscious hearkening back to that heroic age. As in the poetry of the *gogynfeirdd*, classical comparisons are adduced: Ifor is as stout as Hector and Hercules. His comely appearance is praised, as is his pedigree. All of these are conventional and are characteristic of gogynfeirdd poetry. A more vivid example of the traditional element in Dafydd's poetry would be hard to find; Dafydd shows himself to be a master of the techniques characteristic of his bardic forebears.

Meter: the poem opens with four stanzas of *englyn unodl union*, followed by eight stanzas of *toddaid*. Though the meter changes, the end rhyme is on the syllable – *or* throughout, and each of the four-line stanzas ends on the word *Ifor*.

Bibliography: Parry 1952

To Ifor Hael

Da y rhed ar waered, arw oror –olwyn,
Neu wylan ar ryd fôr
Deuwell y rhed, buddged bôr,
Diwyd wyf, dy wawd Ifor.
Well does a wheel roll downhill, O border's scourge,
Or seagull strut on estuaries;

But better still, O liberal lord,
4   Does your praise proceed, for I persevere.

Well do the waves of the sea weave, ever wetting
       The anchor rope of a privateer;
But better still do I weave, O bravest bulwark,
8   Songs of praise for you, Ifor.

Your prosperity comes from me, my well-born lord,
       And a precious blessing;
Armed for battle, steely bulwark,
12   Feared by the mighty, mightier Ifor.

The sea-spume of a torrential tide does not swell,
       O mighty Arthur or Hector,
Glorious protector, proverbial pillar,
16   Like praise swells for you, Ifor.

Ruler of nations of the four corners of the world
       And Prince of heaven's bright compass,
May He sustain, on sea and on land,
20   Ruler of the firmament, resolute Ifor.

Merchant, maker of treasure and praise,
       Wealth that Normans envy, essence of fame;
Hewing arms of conflict, afflicting angry English,
24   Ruling the seas; may Mary give Ifor protection!

Like unto mighty Hercules, comely in shiny crimson,
       As open-handed as generous Nudd;
Well-wrought and strong like a ship's anchor:
28   Noble Ifor was not begot basely.

No place could be without him for long,
       Nor will I be without this generous lord;
No giver of gifts excels or betters him,
32   Nor even equals Ifor.

Handsome heir of free flowing mead
      Of fair-helmed Llywelyn, akin to radiance;
Today no guileless, fair-browed lord
36   Has the good fortune, no question, of Ifor.

Happy day for me when he gives good counsel;
      Happy night of peace and bright surroundings;
Happy chatter at table, good fortune each night;
40   Happy world when dear friends bow to Ifor.

Easy of praise like lofty Hector in turmoil,
      Easily he scatters Deirans, with his thick mail;
I sought and found, with a vigorous host,
44   Unstinting feasting with fair and generous Ifor.

Splendid and faultless, protector of poets, ornate shield,
      Agile warrior of the battle of Severn shore,
Prince of splendid defence; long-lived was Noah,
48   May Ifor's life, elegant company, be longer still.

ENGLYNION TO IFOR HAEL

This poem in praise of Dafydd's patron is in the englyn meter, which we have seen exemplified in the work of the *gogynfeirdd*. Generosity is mentioned at the outset, where the poet calls his patron his 'Nudd'; Nudd was one of a triad of heroes of old, renowned for their generosity. Ifor is a bold and daring warrior, of noble pedigree. He is virile, has the eloquence of Ovid – perhaps a reference to his familiarity with the language of love, though he is also called a poet. Though these englynion do indeed stand on their own, individually, with respect to their content, they are skillfully joined together by comparing Ifor with an ever-increasing number of men.

Meter: *englyn unodl union.* This englyn meter consists of a *toddaid byr,* that is, a line of normally 10 syllables followed by a line of normally 6 syllables, followed by a couplet, with seven syllables in each line. The chief rhyme occurs at the end of the 7th, 8th, or 9th syllable of the first line; a further rule says that in the couplet, an accented syllable must rhyme with an unaccented syllable. There is frequent use of *cymeriad,* or 'linking'; every stanza begins with the preposition *O,* and in all but one stanza, the 4th line begins with the word *Ofer.*

Bibliography: Parry 1952.

To Ifor Hael

> *O haelder fy nêr, fy Nudd–a'm eurgaer,*
>   *A'm eurgarw hael am fudd,*
>   *Afar yw, gaethryw gythrudd,*
>   *Ofer un wrth Ifor udd.*
> In generosity, my lord, my Nudd, my golden fort,
>   My splendid stag, generous to a fault,
>   Sad it is, grievous afflicter,
> 4   One is nothing compared to prince Ifor.

> In valor, a flashing sword, easily told,
>   Able to shorten battle
>   By swift onslaught, my golden fort;
> 8   Two are nothing compared to ardent Ifor.

In wisdom, no Norman is nearer to him
    Than France is to the Isle of Man
    For quick resolution of conflict;
12   Three are nothing compared to our Ifor.

In gentility, fortune, faith and generosity,
    And love for his poet,
    Four are nothing, for free and easy giving,
16   Compared to Ifor, eloquent as Ovid.

In nobility and lineage, true his spear,
    Full and unfailing passion,
    Descended from illustrious hawks,
20   Five are nothing compared with Ifor, ever.

In strength, my forceful, firm-fisted, fair prince,
    Bearing gilded weapons,
    Master of warfare who defies warriors;
24   Six are nothing compared to the vigor of Ifor.

In beauty, most dignified, stateliest, great leader,
    A prince of bold nature;
    His poet am I, of deep complexity;
28   Seven are nothing compared with wise Ifor.

In dignity of duty, composer and poet,
    Soul of bards and their protector,
    Bitter in battle to vanquish a traitor,
32   Eight are nothing compared with virile Ifor.

In virtues I love most in a man,
    An eagle among men I deem him;
    In frequent and flowing gifts,
36   Nine are nothing compared with lord Ifor.

In excellence my lord is lively as Fulke,
    Defensive wall of Glamorgan;

In besting a man, fierce in purpose,
40   Ten are nothing compared with towering Ifor.

THE CELTIC POETS

BASALEG

Ifor Hael, Dafydd's patron, had his court at Gwern-y-clepa, near Basaleg in Morgannwg in south Wales. The poem begins rather like a *llatai* or 'love-messenger' poem, except that we don't know who the messenger is. But the message this time is to tell the 'lively choice one' that he won't be coming, because he has another love, his patron Ifor Hael. The notion that the patron was the poet's beloved ('greater than the love for a mistress') is an old one in Celtic poetry. In the case of early Irish poetry the subject was taken up in detail by Professor James Carney (1955, chap. 7). The conceit is that the poet is the patron's 'bedfellow' and lover or spouse. Upon his death, the poet considers himself the patron's widow (Simms 1989). Here, Dafydd sends a message to one of his many girl friends that he cannot come to her because of his love for another, Ifor. Ifor is described then, in traditional terms, including his success against the Deirans (actually, the traditional enemies of the Britons in the age of Taliesin and Aneirin). The poet then goes on to praise the quality of life in Ifor's court, Basaleg. There the poet enjoys hunting, drinking, falconry, music, board games. He concludes by saying again that he will not leave Ifor, and will remain forever faithful to him.

Bibliography: Bowen, D. J. 1966-67; Carney 1955; Mac Cana 1988; Parry 1952; Simms 1989

Basaleg

Cerdda, was, câr ddewiswyrdd,
Ceinfyd gwymp, uwch ceinfedw gwyrdd
Go, lad, and love a lively, choice one,
My handsome universe, above the fair green birch;
From Morgannwg bring tidings
4   To Gwynedd, land of flowing mead,
Where I, the most passionate, am loved,
And bring back a greeting from Môn.

Say that I have not been let from my land,
8   God knows, guiltless you are,
That for some time, Song of Solomon,

256

I have loved one from above Cardiff.
My case is neither base nor evil;
12   'Tis not love for a smooth-lipped, slender maid –
Rather great love for Ifor has overcome me,
And greater than the love for a mistress it is.
Love of Ifor whom I have praised,
16   Not like the mule-ish love of the English.
And I will not go, this most perfect lord,
If he asks, because of my love for Ifor,
Neither a single day to wretched towns
20   Nor a single night from Morgannwg.

Sprung from the finest heroes is he,
A true wolf, gold-helmed, great and generous.
Wealthy, highly regarded hawk,
24   A man splendidly mounted on horse.
Swift and fierce feller of foes, refined,
Everywhere in battle, a wise and deft hawk.
Lively stag whom the Deirans cannot endure;
28   Men find him very loyal.
Obedient and good is his will;
Man is nothing save fair Ifor.

High honor has come to me:
32   If I survive, I shall have all these:
Hunting with dogs – there's no more generous lord –
And drinking with Ifor,
And shooting stags on well-worn trails,
36   And sending hawks to sky and wind,
And fair songs on tips of tongues,
And beguilement in Basaleg.
Is it not fun in the company of many,
40   Object of poets, aiming high,
To play backgammon and chess
On a par with the handsome man?
If one should get, in reasoned agreement,
44   Victory over his worthy opponent,
'Tis in eloquent song I compose for him

That victory is mine over Ifor.

No generous one can compare with him,
48   None is as brave; is he not a prince?
I will not depart from his court, bold lord,
Obedient to none save Ifor.

ELEGY FOR IFOR AND NEST

Ifor and Nest apparently died at the same time, or nearly so, and thus we have this joint elegy. It is possible that the cause of their death may have been the Black Death, which was raging in the mid-fourteenth century (Bromwich 1986, p. 24). But whatever the cause, the poem suggests that they were in their prime when they died – unless the language is pure convention: Ifor is 'ramrod straight' and Nest has 'the fair bloom of summer' on her face. The opening line suggests that the poet is advanced in age when he is composing the elegy. But I think it wise not to try to read history from conventional poetry; the poet may only be saying that 'inept old age' is just one of the feelings he is experiencing at the loss of these cherished patrons. There is reference here, too, to Ifor and Nest's court at Basaleg.

Meter: The poem opens with four stanzas of *englyn unodl union*; the remainder of the poem is *toddaid*. The end rhyme throughout the *toddaid* section is on the syllable – *aint*, the poem ending with the word *henaint* 'old age,' the word which also opens the poem. Thus the word *haint* 'deadly plague' lurks in the poem, though it doesn't actually occur, and lends support to the tradition that Ifor and Nest died from plague (Bromwich 1986, p. 24).

Bibliography: Bromwich 1986; Parry 1952

Elegy for Ifor and Nest

Henaint anghywraint a hiraeth –a phoen
A phenyd fal blaen saeth,
Marw Ifor, nid rhagoriaeth,
Marw Nest, y mae Cymry'n waeth
Inept old age, longing, pain
      And anguish like an arrow's point,
      The death of Ifor marks decline,
4   The death of Nest makes Wales pine.

It's worse for fosterage: a door between us
      Sealed before the sanctuary.
      With Nest gone, my string is full

8   For heaven's maiden; gone indeed is Ifor.

     Ifor, ramrod straight, our regent, impaling Deirans
      On darts, was the best of
     Those that were, beloved lineage,
12   Those that are, those that will ever be.

     Never again will I fly impassioned to a traveler
      Who traversed the world;
     My fingers will not play for a while,
16   Neither will I find nor have happiness.

     Hawdd fyd a gyfyd digofaint –calon,
      A hiraeth I'r fron hon, a henaint
     Happiness brings on an anguished heart
      And longing in this breast, and aging.
     From a torrent of weeping, awash with tears
20   For Ifor and Nest, rivers are swollen.
     Generous God! a tide of grief engulfs me
      Seeing Nest, beloved one, without a winsome word.
     Like the onslaught of battle or anguished pain,
24   Her face the fair bloom of summer, smooth-skinned,
     To see the bounteous, beloved of saints for blessings,
      And a thoughtful, dear one whom they maintained.
     Fair, refined, knowing Nest, pearly smile, and Ifor:
28   With more than enough they endowed me.
     They indulged me with goblets of bright wine at feasts,
      And mead from horns faultlessly flowed.
     And fine, red gold they gave me at every turn,
32   And honored me with fabulous falcons.
     Lofty virtues in these two, of late they went, hidden
      Together, withdrawing within their retreat.
     And a pair are they who did not delay rewards for me,
36   And as one will they lay claim to their reward.
     He a destructive lord in war, they were not slow to act;
      He challenged nine thousand in tournament.
     To the fair court of Basaleg they brought good fortune,
40   And the glow of her golden floor, a palace,

A place of eloquence, a tide of wine vessels:
  A shining lord and she of the slender brow.
Broken blades, like Lear, chasing English;
44   Battle-bruised lion, worthy of the multitude.
Pillar of people, of prosperous kin, widely beloved;
  May the lord guide heavenly sleep for the aged.

IN PRAISE OF SUMMER

In this poem, and many of the ones that follow, we see Dafydd as poet of nature, celebrating summertime in particular. The chief reason for the pleasure Dafydd derives from this season is that fair weather abets his love-making, which typically takes place in the out-of-doors. The present poem is an address to summer, which is personified here. After praising the fellow and recounting all the fine things summer is responsible for, Dafydd sounds a sad note: the course of summer, enjoyable as it is, leads to 'long decay' and the advent of winter. And so Dafydd wonders where summer goes. His question is met with a mild rebuke from summer, who explains that he comes to do his job, and when that is done he escapes winter's rawness by going off to Annwfn (or Annwn). Annwfn is a name for the Welsh otherworld, the well-provisioned land of beauty and wealth visited by Pwyll in the first branch of the Mabinogi, and raided by Arthur and his men in the poem *Preiddeu Annwfn* in The Book of Taliesin.

Bibliography: Parry 1952

In Praise of Summer

> *Tydi'r Haf, tad y rhyfyg,*
> *Tadwys coed brwys caead brig*
> 'Ah, Summer! sire of the stalwart,
> Father of lush, close forest growth,
> Fair woodward, ward of the wide, wooded slope,
> 4   You're above all, a roof over every rise.
> You're the sovereign of bold salutation,
> Perfect pilot, world's energizer;
> You're the source of solemn promise,
> 8   Farmstead of flourishing herbs
> Nurturing growth to twice its size,
> Bathing the assembly of woods.
>
> By the beloved God, your hand knows well
> 12   How to weave a tree's fresh branches.
> Lovely spirit of the world,

Because of you, too,
Birds flourish, and earth's fruits,
16 And flocks aloft,
Moorland hay and lush meadows,
Honey, hives, and hardy swarms.
You're a fosterer, prophet of broad paths,
20 Sanctuary of verdant harvest.
You bring buds to my fair abode,
Handsome buds for a tenant of leaves.
And the approach of August, night and day,
24 Is an eternal evil,
Knowing that through long decay
Gilded temple, you'll go away.

Tell me, Summer, for this is unfair,
28 I have to ask you, where?
Where, or to what realm,
To what land do you go, by Peter!'

'Silence, poet of careful craft,
32 Silence your masterful, charming pride.
My fate, a mighty feat –
For I am a leader – is to bring them warmth,
To come for three months and cause to thrive
36 The material of all men's toils;
And when roof and leaves have ceased
To grow, and weaving branches,
To escape winter's awful winds
40 To Annwfn from Earth I go.'

'May the blessings of the world's bards
And their song of farewell go with you.
Farewell, climate's king!
44 Farewell, our leader and lord!
Farewell, little cuckoos!
Farewell, June's air!
Farewell, lofty sun
48 And broad sky, bright with clouds.

Lord of hosts, 'tis true you'll not be
This high, mountain of snow aloft,
Until Summer, with its fair and fertile open fields,
52   And splendid slopes come again.'

MAY

May, the onset of summer, is the turning point in the poet's year. For him, May is a gift of God, sent from heaven. The world begins to turn green with rich, new growth, and the poet benefits from having his wooded retreat at hand once again. It's there that he 'tames' a maid, where his love trysts take place. May is the foster-father of poets – and of lovers as well. This poem is one of only two poems extant in which Dafydd uses a single rhyme throughout. As the cywydd is a rhyming couplet, the rhyme may change with each couplet throughout a poem, but here the rhyming syllable remains unchanged through the poem. The effect of this is quite striking. The cywydd meter requires that a stressed syllable rhyme with an unstressed one. For Welsh this means that the word rhyming with May (*Mai*) must be a word of more than one syllable, and so it is that all but four of those words in this poem are third person, singular verbs in the imperfect tense (ending in – *ai*). That imparts to the poem as a whole a sense of reflection and longing.

The poet wishes that winter would never come, that May would last forever, and he regrets that the advent of summer has trammeled it. May is a patron as well. In language that echoes traditional praise of a chieftain, Dafydd says that May is an 'open-handed, great generous man' who gave him money, the leaves of the treetops being likened to florins, the coins of the day, stamped with a *fleur de lys* on one side.

Bibliography: Ford 1996a; Parry 1952; Rowlands 1958

May

> *Duw gwyddiad mai da y gweddai*
> *Dechreuad mwyn dyfiad Mai*
> God knew that a gentle beginning
> Well befit the growth of May.
> Fresh-stalks would grow without delay
> 4   On the first of the fair month of May.
> Freshening tips of trees yesterday,
> Delayed me, as God presented May.
> The gem of poets did not deceive me,
> 8   The good life came with the coming of May.

The fair, splendid lad brought me gifts,
A great and liberal noble is May.
He sent to me proper money:
12   Fine green leaves of the hazels of May.
Florins of treetops brought me no pain,
Fleur-de-lis wealth of the month of May.
He kept me safe from treachery,
16   Under the leafy mantels of May.
How sad I am that he would not stay,
So much to me is the month of May.

I tamed a maid who met me one day,
20   A lovely thing, under the mantle of May.
The fosterer of fair poets honored me,
Fosterer of tender lovers is May.
Godson of the faultless Lord,
24   Great the dignity of bright green May.
From heaven came the one who refined me
To the world; my life is May.

Green is the hillside, happy the love-messenger,
28   Day is long in the green wood of May.
It would not conceal the greenery,
Of hills and tips of shrubs of May.
Night is short, travel not tedious;
32   Splendid the hawks and blackbirds of May.
The nightingale is happy where it flits;
Voluble the tiny birds of May.
Swift energy he taught me,
36   There's no great glory save May.

Green-winged peacock of townhouses,
Which one out of a thousand? The best is May!
Who built it of leaves
40   In the space of a month but May?
It fostered bright green battlements,
Brilliant green-hazels of the tiny leaves of May.

Puddly, and best if it faded away,
44   Is winter; loveliest is May.

Spring has ended, it did not concern me;
Gentle, refined gold is the gold wealth of May;
The beginning of bright summer trampled it,
48   It brings tears, for lovely is May.
Hazel-leaves of green-bark dressed me;
Good life for me is the coming of May.
Wise and powerful God decided,
52   In league with Mary, to sustain May.

SUMMER

This is the only other poem, along with "May," that sustains a single rhyme throughout. Here the stressed rhyming word in each couplet is *Haf* 'summer.' That allows for a large number of rhymes in the other half of the couplet in first person, singular verbs in the present tense; the ending of such verbs is – *af.* It also allows the poet to use the superlative degree of adjectives, whose ending is also – *af.* Thus 'summer' rhymes with 'the best' and with the speaker of the poem, 'I.' The speaker of the poem, then, is fully engaged not only emotionally but morphologically with the season of love, the best season.

The poem is another excellent example of Dafydd's praise of the seasons. Summer, like May, is a gift. The earth is at peace after winter, and summer's job is to bring back the lush growth, growth that enables Dafydd to dwell in his woodland 'homes.' After praising the season, Dafydd turns his attention to his girl. He calls himself *dyn Ofydd* 'Ovid's man,' meaning that he follows the practices and precepts of love. We meet a stock figure here, the jealous husband, who in the courtly love conceit, is usually depicted as an old man, married to a young wife, and constantly worried about being cuckolded. "The Jealous One," says Dafydd, "Doesn't matter till summer comes." Summer is the season for lovers, and that's when the jealous one has to watch out.

The poem begins and ends on a melancholy note. Summer is a great blessing, but its arrival bears a sad reality: it's short, and therefore painful that it comes at all. At the end of the poem, Dafydd says that if the change of seasons drives off summer, then he's going to ask Christ where it has gone.

Bibliography: Ford 1996a; Parry 1952

Summer

> *Gwae ni, hil eiddil Addaf,*
> *Fordwy rhad, fyrred yr haf*
> Pity us, poor, feeble Adam's race,
> How short the surge of summer's grace!
> By God, hateful is the coming of summer,
> 4 Because its days are already numbered!
> But the lovely sky is at its clearest,

And a merry sun wearing summer's dress,
And the air slow and unhurried;
8   In summertime the world is splendid.

In summer, out of the old sod,
Comes fine growth, unblemished,
Summer was given to make trees green,
12   To make them grow with a sparkling sheen;
It makes me laugh to see the splendor
Of the fuzzy tips of a birch in summer;
And who wouldn't smile amid such beauty –
16   It's Paradise I sing my song to.
And I praise it with my native vigour,
Contentedly; O what a gift is summer!

Brighter than a waterfall is my lover,
20   Lying in the wood, bold as summer;
If I ask, the cuckoo will sing soulfully
As summer begins to brighten;
I'll kindly let this pretty, gray bird
24   Sound the vesper bell at midsummer;
The sweetest nightingale, in fine voice,
Sleek and bold in summer's penthouse;
And the thrush, I gladly give way before him,
28   Sassy, flattering song of summer.
I'm Ovid's man in these fine, long days,
Going here and there with a bold phrase;
The Jealous One, disowned by Adam,
32   Doesn't matter till summer comes;
Winter was made for the likes of him,
But summertime is lovers' time.

Under the birch, my home in the grove,
36   I want nothing but summer's own cover;
Wearing about me like new woven finery
A splendid cloak of summer's fair greenery;
I'll reweave the leaves of ivy
40   So there'll be no cold about me;

269

And if then I should greet a meek maiden,
She'll be closely attended this season!

It's harsh business, and satire won't work,
44 Taking summer from a flourishing bard;
Though I can dress warm, the wind won't leave
Trees in good shape – poor summer yesterday!
I don't apologize for the longing I feel
48 For summer's fair weather here in my soul.
If autumn comes, yes, and winter,
With ice and snow to drive off summer,
Woe is me! if He drives it off so soon,
52 'Christ!' I'll say, 'Where's my season?'

THE HOLLY GROVE

Dafydd ap Gwilym has been called a close observer of nature, and this is demonstrable in almost any of his poems that deal with the subject. Here a grove of holly has his attention. It is commonplace that Dafydd prefers the woodland for his lovemaking. In a famous line, often quoted, he says, "A house is better if it grows!" His house of choice, then, is a house whose walls and roof are trees and branches, and his neighbors are often the birds that inhabit those trees. In that respect, we are reminded of the seventh-century Irishman, Marbán, who preferred the solitude and beauty of nature to the trappings of a royal court. But of course Dafydd has something in mind other than meditation. As we learn from several of his poems, structures built by man are usually inimical to Dafydd's amorous purposes. If Dafydd dwells in the woodland in his house of leaves, then that's another reason why May and summertime are the poet's seasons of choice and why the end of summer is viewed with alarm. In this poem, however, Dafydd shows his ingenuity. Holly is an evergreen, so that even in winter he has found May! He has a mansion, made by God, brightly painted, with good defense-works (the sharp spines of holly) to keep out unwanted visitors. The place is watertight, because dense, unlikely to ever be uprooted (dense root structure), and is ornamented with coral-red berries. What better place to bring his girl in winter! Dafydd even seems to be aware of the fact that holly leaves tend to get dry and wrinkle as well as spot, but such blight doesn't mar his mansion.

Bibliography: Bromwich 1982; Parry 1952

The Holly Grove

> *Y celynllwyn coel iawnllwyth,*
> *Caer araul ffriw, cwrel ffrwyth*
> Densely clustered holly grove,
> Bright-faced fortress, coral fruited,
> Seemly sanctuary safe from man,
> 4   Snug bower, a home for two.
> Tower of spiny, spur-like leaves
> For a maiden to attend to me.

Strolling along the slope
8   'Neath trees, fair leafy wood,
An exquisite arbor kept by grace,
I wandered in wood, dales and leaves.
Who ever found May in winter
12 Dressed in such fine attire?
I'll tell you who, for today I found
A holly grove on hill's crest.
The same bower of love, same thicket,
16 Same mantel as May was mine.
Woodland chair for poet's sweet sounds,
Fine, green trunk opening to a handsome vault.
Poetry's pantry, safe from deep snow's siege;
20 A penthouse, painted by God's hand.

Gracious God could make a lovely thing
Twice as well as the lordly Robert.
Hywel Fychan of noble mien
24 And steeped in song, a man who chooses well,
He praised, and not in peasant's terms,
A forest angel in fair recline.
Beautiful branches beside the road,
28 Dense and grizzled lad in flowing green gown.
Bastion of birds of paradise,
Arched temple of shiny green leaves.
Not like an old hovel beloved of rain,
32 But cozy and dry for a two-nights' stay.
Leaves seldom sere or wrinkled,
Holly has spines of steel.
Neither nanny nor billy
36 Makes a meal out of this, wherever!
Like an iron halter, when the nights are long
And frost in every glen and moor,
The fair wood keeps its crop
40 Despite the blast of the cold vernal wind,
A true camelot of verdant leaves
Enveloping the hillside branches.

THE WOODLAND MASS

Dafydd is in his familiar surroundings in this poem, but not with a lover. Rather he is in the company of birds who are celebrating mass. It's a daring conceit, though not without antecedents in the contemporary European literary tradition. It is also a reversal of the *llatai* or 'love-messenger' theme, whereby Dafydd calls upon some creature or element to deliver a message to his beloved. Here, it is the beloved, Morfudd, who sends the thrush as *llatai* to Dafydd. Morfudd is the most frequently mentioned (in some thirty poems) of Dafydd's loves. The message, a celebration of the ecstasy of love, is not direct but is encoded in the liturgy of the mass. The thrush, who is the celebrant, is dressed in priestly garments: an alb and chasuble consisting of flowers and leaves. The altar's roof is of gold, perhaps the brilliant sun, the preaching and reading of the gospel are in the thrush's clear voice, not the mumbling that clerics were often accused of in the Middle Ages. The host is an ash-leaf, and the chalice is filled with bliss and love. Some have considered the poem blasphemous, others have thought it a hymn to the Creator. It is worth noting that just as Dafydd prefers "a house that grows" to man-made dwellings, so does he seem much more comfortable at the woodland mass than he does at church on Sunday ("The Girls of Llanbadarn").

Bibliography: Gruffydd 1977; Parry 1952

The Woodland Mass

> *Lle digrif y bûm heddiw,*
> *Dan fentyll y gwyrddgyll gwiw*
> Ah, where I was today!
> All cloaked in hazel,
> Listening at break of day
> 4   To a gifted bird, a thrush,
> Singing in measured verse
> Of miracles and holy homilies.
>
> Not a native, but knowing –
> 8   A far-travelled pilgrim,
> Arrived from fair Caer

Commissioned by her, my beauty,
Ready with words he had no right to,
12   And lit at the head of the glen.
Morfudd sent him,
This fosterson of May and songster.
He wore an alb
16   Fashioned from the blooms of May,
And his chasuble
A wind-blown green mantle.

The altar's roof was
20   All of gold, by God,
And I could hear in language clear
Powerful preaching,
And reading the gospel
24   Effortlessly.
Then he raised on high
A luminous, ash-leaf host,
As an eloquent acolyte of a nightingale,
28   Kneeling beside him,
Tenor of the glen, chimed for all to hear
The chime of offering in tones true.
The host raised
32   To the heavens above,
In honor of our heavenly father,
And a chalice of bliss and love.

That liturgy pleases me:
36   A gift of the grove of loving birch.

A House All of Leaves

Love and nature are the abiding themes of Dafydd's cywydd poetry, and these two are frequently blended. The milieu in which Dafydd pursues his amorous impulses is not in human dwellings but in nature, in the woodland setting. In fact, Dafydd has his worst luck in man-made structures – be it church, tavern, or house. His great success comes in structures made by God, made by nature, made by the month of May, by Summer. The present poem illustrates this well. For Dafydd, the woodland setting is like a court, a citadel, and just as carefully constructed. Its walls are the trees, the leaves form the roof. It is to this dwelling he would bring his beloved. Birch and hazel are the furniture of his remote court, and it is in this poem that he insists that a room is better if it grows!

Unlike ordinary residences built by ordinary craftsmen, Dafydd's house is made by God. And therefore there can be no architectural flaw: "nothing extravagant", "no soot in the house." In the houses of the noblemen of Dafydd's time, one was accustomed to hear poets and music (for Ireland, compare "Enniskillen" and "Christmas in Creeve"). Dafydd's woodland court is no exception: here, he and his beloved can listen to the birds, who are the woodland poets, and hear the *songs* of these fledgling minstrels.

If God himself was the architect of the place, it was May who built it. In his poem "May," Dafydd asks rhetorically, "Who could build it out of leaves within the month but only May?" Here, Dafydd details the work of May and his helpers: his plumb-line the calm Cuckoo, his spirit level the woodland Nightingale, the house-timbers are the long summer day, and the whole is framed by the pangs of love-sickness. Finally, Dafydd claims that he's "the axe that executes it," insisting that he himself is the tool with which May fashions the wooded love nest.

At the end of the poem, Dafydd tells us that it is now the beginning of the year, and he no longer has the house, implying that it is a sunken hovel and that he has abandoned it, leaving us to wait – along with him – for May to return and the construction to begin anew. As always, Dafydd laments the passing of the season of love.

Bibliography: Bromwich 1982; Parry 1952

A House All of Leaves

Heirdd feirdd, f'eurddyn diledryw,
Hawddamor, hoen goror gwiw
My friends! a blessing on the beauty,
On the gorgeous girl who embraced me
In a grove of birch and hazel,
4   Those feathery garments of May
Draped along a hillside;
What a place for love,
Like real furniture in a real house–
8   But a room is better if it grows!

If my shy and shapely love comes
To the leaf-hut hewn by God,
Then the well-wrought wood is a reward –
12   A house free of soot and dust,
Nothing extravagant beneath the roof;
God's tenant am I, and nothing more.
My girl and I have a common goal,
16   And there in the wood we can hear
The birds babbling;
She loves the leafy laureates
Whistling songs like the weaving of branches
20   Among the leaves where they live,
Sweet-singing clan,
Minstrels of oak manor.
St. David endowed the spot,
24   And May's own two hands shaped it,
Using the tranquil cuckoo as plumb,
And the nightingale as spirit level;
Its sheathing comes from summer's day,
28   Framed from the pain of a lovesick lad;
The grove is truly an altar of love,
And I the axe that executes it.

In the course of a year,
32   I get the house no longer than this;

I wouldn't dream of paying rent
To a pile of thatch from some old retreat,
And I wouldn't return, I can tell you for sure,
36   To a flat that I left for good.

THE RUIN

This poem has received a good deal of critical attention. It would seem to belong to a genre of poetry common enough to the European Middle Ages in which the transitoriness of life is proclaimed or lamented. In the Celtic poetic tradition it is equally well known. The Llywarch Hen poems are filled with laments for the abandoned hall of a fallen chieftain, for the speaker's own glorious past, whereas now he can barely move about. The Welsh and Irish elegies express the same longing, a longing and regret so well encapsulated in the Latin phrases *ubi sunt* 'where are they' and *sic transit gloria mundi* 'so goes the world's glory.'

Indeed, Rachel Bromwich (1982) places this poem in a section entitled "The Poet's Meditations." But I think we do well to keep an open mind in considering Dafydd's poetry and not be overly influenced in our readings by contemporary analytic categories. The present poem expresses Dafydd's sorrow over a 'house' torn apart, perhaps by the wind as well as by time. As Summer says in "In Praise of Summer," "When roof and leaves have ceased/To grow, and weaving branches,/To escape winter's awful winds/To Annwfn from Earth I go." An alternative reading, then, would see the poem as one that expresses at length, perhaps in mock elegy, his lament for the loss of the house of leaves, the structures built and maintained by May and Summer, lovely retreats where he has found pleasure and love with his maids. But however we read the poem, the closing lines are, to say the least, enigmatic.

Bibliography: Bromwich 1982; Gruffydd 1979; Parry 1952

The Ruin

> *Tydi, y bwth tinrhwth twn,*
> *Yrhwng gweundir a gwyndwn*
> 'You, broken-down hut full of holes,
> Between meadow and unploughed land,
> Alas for those who saw you, and they have suffered,
> 4   As a place of past companionship
> And who see you now with broken branches
> Beneath your roof, O bruised and broken house!
> And also beside your lively wall

8   There was a day, pain of anguish,
        In you when you were lovelier
        Than you are, old rotting rafters,
        When I saw – I brought her fame –
12   In your corner a beauty there,
        A maiden, and noble and gentle she was;
        Handsome we were, twined together,
        Each one's arm, embrace of a docile maid,
16   Knotted around the other;
        Long and slender arm, like fine snow,
        Under the ear of the best lad of song;
        And my own arm, a facile ploy,
20   Under the ear of the comely, fine lass.
        A good life, and light-hearted in your bright wood,
        But today is not that day.'

        'Lament is mine, charm of refuge,
24   Over the path the wild wind took.
        A storm out of the east
        Wreaked havoc along the slender wall.
        South wind's sigh, a wrathful course,
28   Ripped off my roof.'

        'Is it the wind that made this mess just now?
        How well it winnowed your roof last night.
        How harshly it snapped your laths;
32   The world is ever deceptive and perilous.
        Your corner, mine a breath of sighs,
        Was a bed for me, not a pig sty.
        Yesterday you were in fine fettle,
36   A shelter over my lovely life;
        There's no question, today you are,
        By Peter! without beam or rafter.
        Many a subject is often madness;
40   Is that what this broken hut is – a kind of trick?'

        The family went, some time ago,
        Dafydd, with the cross; good custom it was.

SECRET LOVE

The idea of secret love, or of maintaining secrecy during an affair, is certainly a familiar one to modern audiences, though it is by no means a new one. And indeed it was among the precepts of *amour courtois* or 'courtly love,' whose ideas were so much in vogue (among the literati at least) during the Middle Ages. The Roman poet Ovid's *Ars Amatoria* enjoyed great popularity at that time, and there were translations of it into French in the twelfth and thirteenth centuries. Many of Ovid's doctrines about the conduct of love were incorporated into another important work, *Roman de la Rose* or 'The Romance of the Rose' (Dunn 1962). This was composed in the early thirteenth century by Guillaume de Lorris, but left to be completed toward the end of the century by Jean de Meun. A copy of this allegorical poem on love, with its stock characters, such as The Slanderer, was in South Wales in the early part of the fourteenth century. It is entirely possible, then, though one must add that it is undemonstrable, that Dafydd was familiar with some of the doctrines of courtly love through direct contact with one or more of these works.

The last eighteen lines of the original of this poem all begin with the letter *C* and most of those begin the syllable *Cyd-* 'together.' Thus the poet and his lover, in their secrecy, stay together, walk together, talk together, and so on. This is a clever way for the poet to isolate them as a pair, to reinforce the need for secrecy, to alienate them from the rest of society. But the verb formed from this root, *cyd-io* means both 'to join together, come together,' and 'to have sexual intercourse.' So the use of this element not only suggests togetherness but also bears on their lovemaking.

Bibliography: Bromwich 1982; Parry 1952

Secret Love

Dysgais ddwyn cariad esgud,
Diwladaidd, lledradaidd, drud
I learned to practice lively love,
Urbane, clandestine, gallant.
The best form of the words that work
4   Is to speak love in secrecy.

Such grief comes of a soul mate,
That secret love is best for man;
While we were in a crowd,
8   I and the lass, a frivolous pair,
No one spoke spitefully
Or suspected our signals.

Because of our trust, we had a long time
12   When we used to dally together.
Now, we have a more restricted mode:
Sharing few words, for fear of reproach;
Devil take the evil-tongued one
16   Through a knot of torment and misfortune,
Instead of casting slanderous words
On us, faultless reputation that we had.
It would have been nice if we'd had warning,
20   While we had purpose in secret.

I went to my sweet love's home,
Devoted to leaves while they were green;
It was lovely, girl, for a moment
24   Leading our lives beneath the birch.
Fondling each other, more pleasurable it was,
sheltered together in the secluded wood,
co-mingling like sands of the sea,
28   Hanging together at the edge of the wood,
Planting birch – blessed work!
Weaving wisps of wood;
Sharing words of love with the slender maid,
32   Gazing on secluded fields.
Nothing wrong with that for a girl!
Woodland and lover go together,
Keeping a straight face, smirking,
36   Laughing lip to lip,
Tumbling together beside the brush,
Avoiding people, moaning together,
Gentle coexistence, drinking mead,
40   Making love, lying together,

Keeping true love secret,
True, no more is said!

THE SEAGULL

The *llatai*, or 'love-messenger,' is a frequent figure in Dafydd's poetry. It does the poet's beckoning, especially in carrying messages to his beloved. The messenger may be a creature such as a lark, thrush, stag, or, as here, a seagull. It may be an element in nature, such as the wind. The *llatai* type of poem would seem to be unique to Dafydd's time, and is unparalleled in European literature of the day. Rachel Bromwich describes its principal elements as follows:

> an initial greeting, followed by a full description of the messenger; a request to carry a message, to give an assurance of love, or to ask for a kiss; an account of the proposed journey and a warning to avoid its hazards; a brief mention of the girl and of the journey's object. (1986, p. 37).

The description of the messenger often occupies a large portion of the poem; it takes up the first one-third of the present poem. The description is managed through the device of *dyfalu*, which we might translate as 'imagining.' Dafydd describes the messenger through a series of images, in metaphor and simile, to the point that it becomes almost completely abstracted. And this penchant for abstracting seems to me to be a governing force in Dafydd's poetry. We have already seen how he 'deconstructs' nature, personifying it. May is not a month but rather "a generous prodigal nobleman," the "fosterfather of poets...and of gentle lovers"; birds are poets; Summer is a "woodward, master of the thick forest," with whom Dafydd carries on a conversation in "In Praise of Summer."

Through the use of *dyfalu*, Dafydd goes beyond mere personification. Using a series of similes, metaphors, and other rhetorical devices, Dafydd disassembles some object in nature, usually an animal, in order to create a new persona with whom he can communicate. A seagull may be just a seagull in nature, but in Dafydd's hands it becomes a series of vivid images – anything but a seagull. By this means, Dafydd gains a helpmate.

With the mention of Myrddin (Merlin) and Taliesin we see Dafydd invoking two of the *cynfeirdd*, poets from the sixth century and the dawn of the Welsh literary tradition. Here they serve as points of comparison: however good those two were with words, neither loved a woman fairer than Dafydd's love.

Finally, let us recall that in Welsh poetic diction, seagull is a euphemism for 'girl, maiden' (see "Song to Gwenlliant" by Prydydd y Moch).

Why this should be so is uncertain, but the word for seagull, *gwylan* (feminine in gender) could easily be parsed as *gwyl* 'modest, bashful,' plus the diminutive suffix – *an*. *Gwyl* is an adjective used by Dafydd to describe the girl he loves; thus, *gwylan* could be understood as 'little bashful one.'

Bibliography: Parry 1952

The Seagull

> *Yr wylan deg ar lanw dioer,*
> *Unlliw ag eiry neu wenlloer*
> Lovely seagull on surging flow,
> White as a bright moon or snow,
> Unblighted is your beauty,
> 4   Ray of sun, gauntlet of the sea.
> Light upon the wave you are
> Swift, proud fisher.
> Close to the anchor you ride,
> 8   A sea lily, close by my side.
> Bright as a sheet of paper,
> A nun riding the wave you are.
>
> A beauty, her fame afar would tell;
> 12   Search out palace and castle,
> See if you could see, gull,
> One like Eigr atop the citadel.
> Say my harmonious words,
> 16   Let it be me, if it's in the cards.
> If she's alone, dare to greet her,
> She's refined, so do take care
> To win the day, and say I shall perish
> 20   My lad, if I don't get my wish.
>
> I love her, consumed by passion;
> True it is, that smooth-talking Merlin
> And Taliesin never
> 24   Loved one who was lovelier.

Copper-haired and shapely,
Delicate one for whom men vie.

Alas, if you should see, dear gull,
28 The fairest cheek in all the world,
And I don't get the noblest nod,
The girl will be my end.

THE STAR

In place of the *llatai*, the love messenger, Dafydd is doing his own business in this poem. He says specifically at the outset that he'd never send a human messenger to do his business, and here again we see that tension between nature and culture in Dafydd's poetry. It's all right to send a creature or the elements as a messenger, but it will not do to hire a *person* to carry a message. This is analogous to the opposition we see in the 'house that grows' and a house constructed by humans, or the woodland mass and Sunday at Llanbadarn church. So Dafydd sets out on his own. But here he has, instead of a messenger, a guide, and the guide is an element of nature, a star. As in the case of the *llatai*, Dafydd cannot deputize the star until he has re-imagined it through the use of *dyfalu*. The star is not simply a star, it is a candle that cannot be doused, a brilliant coin, even the sacred host of the mass itself. This is the torch that will accompany Dafydd as he goes in search of his beloved Morfudd. Note that there is a kind of merging of Morfudd and the star in that both are jewels, she a bright jewel, the star a glittering jewel. The ambiguity is compounded in that the Welsh word here, *seren* 'star' is feminine in grammatical gender, so that when it is referred to by pronoun, it is 'she.' We see a more ambitious exercise of the metaphysical in "The Sunshine Girl."

Bibliography: Bromwich 1982; Parry 1952

The Star

> *Digio 'dd wyf am liw ewyn,*
> *Duw a wyr meddwl pob dyn*
> I'm full of passion, God knows,
> For a pure-white maid.
> If love should nudge me
> 4   To seek my dear heart's home,
> I'd never send a messenger,
> Pay to find her door,
> Nor send some ugly hag
> 8   On an embassy of love;
> Nor light my way with fire-pots,
> Nor wax tapers at dusk;

No, I'll sleep at home by day,
12   Travelling only at night;
No one sees or knows me;
Mad am I till morning.

Rather I shall have for certain,
16   To keep me this night from straying,
The candles of the world's Landlord,
To guide me to my bright jewel.
Bless the Lord of creation,
20   Who so constructed the stars,
That nothing outshines
The glow of a tiny, white star.
Radiance from Heaven on high,
24   Clear, luminous candle
Whose features will not fade,
Nor will be stolen away.
Autumn's wind will not snuff
28   This fiery wafer in heaven's loft.
No faint flood will douse her,
Heavenly watcher, saints' platter,
Nor thief pluck her,
32   From the Trinity's canopy aloft;
It's not man's place to chase
The pearl of Mary away.

She shines in every place,
36   A brilliant, golden coin;
A glowing shield of light,
Like the sun, sky's brilliance, is she.
She will guide me without fail
40   To Morfudd's place, my glittering jewel.
Then Christ, from his place aloft,
Will darken this pure white loaf,
And send it for a time
44   To heaven's shadows to sleep.

UNDER THE EAVES

As we see from other of his poems, Dafydd's efforts at lovemaking and wooing are frustrated in man-made structures. The present poem is a fine example of this, for here we see not only the deprivation and misery the lover will endure for the sake of his beloved but the hostility of nature and houses built by man. The door of the house is locked – perhaps a metaphor for the woman's love being locked away from him. In contrast, Dafydd's "leafy hut" is never locked against him. He hammers on the door and the latch breaks (faulty construction, unlike the craftsmanship of "May"), but still no one seems to have heard him. So he suffers outside a human structure in the cold of winter, a time when he could be snug and warm in nature, as in "The Holly Grove."

"The night is dark, knows deceit," he says. Dafydd seems to prefer making love in the daylight, within his leafy bower. Secret lovers would revel in the night, considering daybreak a rough intrusion. Indeed, songs lamenting the need to depart from one's lover as the dawn approached formed a distinct genre in the courtly love tradition, known to the troubadours as *aubade*, from *aube* 'dawn.' For Dafydd, though, "Secret Love" could take place in broad daylight, in the open air – so long as it was away from human habitation.

Similarly, the lover's evening petition to his beloved, outside her gate or wherever, was known on the continent as *sérénade*. Our poem parodies that sort of song, for while Dafydd would like to court his lover this evening, he cannot even sing to her from without, rather he stands there beset by cold, rain and snow. He feels his contract with her has been abrogated. What is this contract? Perhaps it is that articulated in lines 29-36, the contract a courtly lover makes with the object of his affections. Since he had endured all this, he's entitled to her embraces. She fails to appear, reminiscent of the way that Morfudd disappears at night in "The Sunshine Girl." The night would not appear to be a good time for Dafydd unless, as in "The Star," he succeeds in enlisting the aid of the elements.

Bibliography: Bromwich 1982; Johnston 1983; Parry 1952

Under the Eaves

Clo a roed ar ddrws y ty
Claf wyf, fy chwaer, clyw fyfy

There's a lock on the door of the house –
I'm sick, sister, listen to me!
I've come to see your splendid self,
4   For God's sake, show yourself!
Why would you play me false?
By Mary, I'm driven to distraction!

I hammered three times, hard,
8   And broke the locked latch;
Wasn't it loud? Didn't you all hear it?
A horrendous sound it was!
Morfudd, my pure treasure,
12   Princess of perfidy,
Here, outside the wall from you –
I have to shout for you to hear!
Pity this poor sleepless one,
16   The night is dark, knows deceit.
See how sorry is my state –
Stung by the weather this night!
The eaves spewing streams,
20   Cascading, drenching my skin.
Sleet no less than rain –
I'm under it all, bruised.
This shivering is no fun,
24   No mortal ever suffered more
Than I have with all this woe;
Never a worse sty than this, by God!
No worse jail in Caernarvon
28   Than this sad habitation.
I wouldn't be out all night long
Nor grouse but because of you.
I wouldn't suffer constant pain,
32   That's for sure, if I didn't love you.
And I wouldn't suffer rain and sleet,
Not a bit, were it not for you,
Nor forsake the whole world,
36   I suffer so, were it not for you.

Here am I in the cold,
Lucky you, you're inside.
My spirit's there with you,
40   My empty shell here outside.
Anyone who heard about me
Would doubt I'd be alive, my love.
My mind won't let me leave –
44   Madness brought me here.

You made a date with me –
I'm here, where are you?

THE GIRLS OF LLANBADARN

The church of Llanbadarn Fawr looks pretty much today as it did when it was built in the early thirteenth century. At that time, the parish of Llanbadarn Fawr was perhaps the largest in either England or Wales and would certainly have been the parish of Dafydd ap Gwilym, born in Brogynin, nearby. In the eleventh century, under the leadership of Bishop Sulien, Llanbadarn became a center of learning, and it has been suggested that the Latin original of the *Brut y Tywysogion* or 'Chronicle of the Princes' was kept there. Sulien's son, Rhygyfarch, composed a Latin life of St David, patron saint of Wales. The church, then, was a large structure, the center of the largest parish in Wales, and an establishment with a reputation for learning and scholarship. It is certainly significant that Dafydd chose this church as the scene of his irreverent behavior: for Dafydd's audience, the effect of the bufoonery is greatly enhanced. It's as if one went to the Guggenheim Museum not to look at paintings but to ogle women. Or to Carnegie Hall, not for the music and wonderful acoustics but to pick up a date.

And that's exactly what Dafydd did do. In his *Ars Amatoria*, Ovid told readers that the best place to meet girls was at the theatre or at the race course. Twelfth century French versions of Ovid translated these Roman locales to clerical mystery plays and the church. Dafydd would have been familiar with such exhortations and so we find him doing just that, going to church to inspect the girls.

This poem, like "Trouble at a Tavern," is a fabliau, a work of comedy rooted in the lives of everyday people. Dafydd presents himself as the world's greatest lover, with more charm than the likes of the legendary lover, Garwy (whoever he was). But even so he can't make headway with the women of this parish. His estimation of himself, as persona, is seriously undercut by the words he, the poet, puts in the mouths of the two women: he's nothing but a leering fool, foppishly dressed. At the end, he appears resigned to concede his failure as a lover and take up the austere life of a hermit.

Bibliography: Bromwich 1982, 1986; Parry 1952

The Girls of Llanbadarn

Plygu rhag lid yr ydwyf,
Pla ar holl ferched y plwyf
Furious and indignant am I!
A plague on the women of this parish,
For I never had one of them, ever,
4   Nothing but failed endeavor,
Not a prayer with a tender maid,
Nor girl, or wife or hag!

What's the problem? What villainy?
8   What is wrong that they don't want me?
What harm for a smooth-browed gal
To have me there in the deep wood;
It were no shame for her
12   To see me there among the leaves.

There never was a time I didn't love
One or maybe even two every day;
Never was there charm as sure as mine,
16   Even among men of Garwy's line.
But despite that I'm no nearer one
Than if she were my sworn foe.
There wasn't a Sunday in Llanbadarn church –
20   And those who wish may judge –
That I didn't sit facing some beauty
With my neck turned to God Almighty.
And when I have searched the congregation,
24   Hiding behind the feathers of my cap,
Some lovely, beautiful girl will say
To her vivacious, clever mate:

'That pale-faced, affected flirt,
28   Wearing his sister's wig –
He's got sex on his mind,
He's a bad one – look at his eye!'

'Is that what he's after!'
32   Says the other one to her,
        'He'll get no answer in this world;
        To hell with him, stupid churl!'

        I thought the bright girl's curse was harsh,
36   Poor payment for the thrill of love;
        I must try to stop this habit,
        Which fills me with anxious dreams;
        I guess I'll have to become a hermit –
40   A job for a man with no options.
        From too much looking over my shoulder,
        A look of misery and a very hard lesson,
        I, poetry's best friend, have been left
44   With a crick in my neck and without a mate.

THE MIRROR

Dafydd often presents his persona as an irresistible, handsome lover, with a very high opinion of himself. It is characteristic of the fabliau nature of some of his poems that this opinion is unsubstantiated, either because some unforeseen intervention foils his plans for lovemaking or because of the response of his intended prey. In the present poem it is the simple act of looking in a mirror that bursts his balloon. Here, as in numerous other poems, Dafydd himself is the butt of the joke. It seems that, following the precepts of courtly love, he has doted on his girl for too long, and has languished. A classic case of love-sickness! His cheeks are pale, his eyes sunken, his hair falling out. As usual, Dafydd seems to be the last to know. Just as in "The Girls of Llanbadarn" he always thought himself a great lover, here he has always imagined himself to be handsome. He would like to blame the mirror – it may be lying, it was made by magicians and so presents him with an illusion only. But in the end he seems resigned and ready to blame his loss of looks on love.

Bibliography: Bromwich 1982; Parry 1952

The Mirror

Ni thybiais, ddewrdrais ddirdra,
Na bai deg f'wyneb a da
I never imagined – a needless ache –
I wasn't fair and handsome of face,
Until on one ominous occasion
4   I held a mirror – a miserable one!
The mirror told me, looking back,
That my looks lacked allure.

Sallow cheeks from too much love
8   For one like Enid – gone the blush;
Cheeks pale from pining,
Entirely yellow and blotchy.
Amazingly, that long nose:
12   Could be a razor – more woes!
Isn't it sad that once flashing eyes

Have dimmed to hollow holes?
And the mane of pretty curls
16   Falling out in handfuls.

It's a sorry state I'm in:
One or the other in my opinion,
Either I'm a gloomy Gus
20   Or the glass isn't telling the truth.
If the problem's mine, horny so long,
Then let death undo the wrong;
But if it's the mirror's blemished face
24   That failed, then damn that piece of glass!

Round, silver moon, circular,
Bewitching, a sort of seducer;
Wretched fake, deceptive gem,
28   Men of magic made him;
Most fleeting sort of fantasy,
Cruel betrayer, aloof and icy.
Most cunning and odious creature,
32   Throw the damn thing in the fire!

No one made me look so drawn –
If indeed the mirror's not wrong –
But that girl in Gwynedd there,
36   Who's left me looking not so fair.

THE CELTIC POETS

THE SUNSHINE GIRL

In this poem, which most anthologies call "Morfudd like the Sun," after the name given it by Parry (1952), we see a side of Dafydd that is strongly evocative of the much later English Metaphysical Poets. Obviously, Dafydd ap Gwilym precedes John Donne by over two hundred years, but 'metaphysical' might be a useful term for critics of Dafydd's poetry to adopt. Metaphysical was a term applied by Dryden specifically to John Donne, criticizing him for transcending the physical or natural in his poetry, and thus for indulging in the abstract. Here's what Dryden said of Donne:

> He affects the metaphysics, not only in his satires, but in his amorous verses, where nature only should reign; and perplexes the minds of the fair sex with nice speculations of philosophy, when he should engage their hearts, and entertain them with the softnesses of love. (Gardner 1957, p. 15).

In other words, love poetry should be amorous and not transcend those themes by philosophical speculation. He had in mind a poem like Donne's "The Sunne Rising." It begins with the poet addressing the sun and asking why he has to come in through the window and disturb his lovemaking. Why should you think that your beams are so reverend and strong, he asks:

> I could eclipse and cloud them with a winke
> But that I would not lose her sight so long:
> If her eyes have not blinded thine,
> Looke, and to morrow late, tell mee,
> Whether both the India's of spice and Myne
> Be where thou leftst them, or lie here with mee.
> Thou sunne art halfe as happy as wee,
> In that the world's contracted thus;
> Thine age askes ease, and since thy duties bee
> To warme the world, that's done in warming us.
> Shine here to us, and thou art every where;
> This bed thy center is, these walls, thy spheare.

The sun is nothing, for it can be eclipsed by a blink of the eye. But in doing so he would lose sight of his beloved. She is so radiant that her eyes may well

296

blind the sun's eye. And what the sun has seen on its daily travels in fact are gathered there in the poet's bed – the sun and the poet's lover are interchangeable. Therefore, the sun need not depart on its rounds.

Dafydd anticipates the 'metaphysics' of Donne's poem in the way he merges his beloved Morfudd and the sun in such a way that we are not always certain which he is speaking of. In early Welsh, the word for sun, *haul*, is sometimes feminine in grammatical gender and sometimes masculine. In this poem it is feminine, so that when a pronoun is used to refer to the sun, it is 'she,' and thus often ambiguous as to its noun referent. In the final section, Dafydd suggests that, since these two suns are equal in warmth and brilliance, why not have them take turns? Let one preside over night, the other over day. Taking turns thus, as long as Morfudd lives, Night will never be. The implication being that Morfudd would always be in view, for in the end there is no difference at all between Morfudd and the sun.

The comparison with Donne and the Metaphysical poets may seem fortuitous, but as Gwyn Williams (1956) has said, "It is the suddenness and success of this linking of the previously held to be incongruous that makes metaphysical poetry and distinguishes Dafydd ap Gwilym from Chaucer, John Donne from Ben Jonson, Dylan Thomas from W. H. Auden."

Bibliography: Bromwich 1982; Parry 1952; Rowlands, John 1971

The Sunshine Girl

Gorllwyn ydd wyf, ddyn geirllaes,
Gorlliw eiry mân marian maes
I, a man of shifty words, sit waiting
For one bright as a field of fine snow;
Beauty ordained by God,
4   And more brilliant than sea's spume,
Frothy-white, like the surging sea,
Shining like the sun, O she's a love!
She knows how good my songs are –
8   This brightest sun in the sky,
Like daybreak wrapped in a scarlet cloak –
And she knows too the posturing of a poetaster!
Lovely, gorgeous Morfudd:

12   Woe to the rimester who loves her:
For such a web of gold, the poor man
Can only cry out in pain.

Her ways are devious and foxy,
16   Crafty too, yet she is my love.
There are times when this glittering light
Illumines church and court,
Then again, like someone passing
20   Behind a parapet,
The brilliant Morfudd disappears.
So too, the lively, radiant rays of the sun,
Patron of the province of warmth –
24   A ward worthy of praise;
Merchant of May's majesty.
How eagerly I wait for radiant Morfudd,
Mirror of magnificent Mary.

28   The sun, like a spirited lass,
Handsome in her day's dress,
Roams the far corners of earth,
Shepherd of the vast firmament.
32   But when, like the menacing force of war,
A heavy cloud darkens her face,
We feel a great sorrow,
For she exhausts our eye
36   And escapes into a wall of dark –
A painful feeling when night falls.
The blue-black sky is full,
And a feeling of loss in the open air.
40   No one knows where this ball of God's
Goes, nor what way she wends.
Can't take hold of her
Nor soak up her warmth;
44   But tomorrow she'll rise again,
Afire in heaven's distant roof.

It's the same painful feeling

When Morfudd is hidden from me:

48 Having come from the brightness above
She sails along under the sun
Then sets, looking smug,
Behind the door of her miserable mate.

52 I pursued my passion in a glade
In Penrhyn, a place of love.
Every day I see the radiant one there,
And every night she flees.

56 And I'm no nearer to holding her hand
In court – and it kills me –
Than anyone is to holding the sun.
The brilliant and blazing orb

60 Has nothing on her.
If one of them is fairest this year,
Then, by Heaven, it's *my* sun.

Here's a brilliant suggestion:

64 Why doesn't one of them take charge of the night
And the other, with her fine warmth
And light, brighten the day?
Should these two beauties

68 Take turns around the earth,
Then while my sweetheart lived
Night would be as rare
As a book with straight pages!

TROUBLE IN A TAVERN

Here is another poem in the fabliau style by Dafydd. Typically, Dafydd begins on a high note: he's come to a fine city, is accompanied by a squire, registers at an upscale inn, and settles down to a fine meal. He's feeling expansive, so when he espies a pretty girl in the place, he invites her over, and orders wine and roast for the two of them. He succeeds in getting her to agree to receive him when all the company have gone to sleep, and that's the start of the trouble. The poem is certainly entertaining, especially so since the poet is not only narrator but principal. As Dr. Bromwich says in comparing the fabliaux of Chaucer, "Dafydd's treatment of such anecdotes is unique in that he tells them in the first person, and is invariably an actor in his *fabliaux* (1982, p. 158).

It is implicit from Dafydd's poem that the sleeping accomodations at this inn were common. There may have been bulkheads or partitions separating parts of the dormitory, but the impression we get is of a rather open space. It is also clear that the girl was at some distance from Dafydd, whether because men and women were kept apart is not clear. But Dafydd does seem to know the moment when everyone is asleep, for it is then that he rises and attempts to get to her bed. The attempt is disastrous.

Nearby, three Englishmen, described in less than complimentary terms, hear the ruckus first. One of them, whose breath is described as being like the residue of the process of brewing beer, swill usually fed to pigs (Welsh *soeg* 'draff'), says there's a Welshman loose, a thief. This was a common item of prejudice leveled against the Welsh by English, a racist slur.

One thing that makes the poem an artistic success is the frequent use of *sangiad* or 'poetic aside' which gives a kind of jerky movement to the narration, reflecting the jerky moves of Dafydd as he attempts, unsuccessfully, to carry out his scheme. Lines 21-46 show the effective use of this device very well, where the argument of the poem practically proceeds in the first half of each line, the interruptions filling out the second half line.

Bibliography: Bromwich 1982; Parry 1952

Trouble in a Tavern

Deuthum I ddinas dethol,
A'm hardd wreangyn i'm hôl

300

I went to a fine city one day,
My handsome yeoman in tow,
To an elegant place, with excellent food.
4   I, being an uppity youth,
Took lodgings in a fine inn
And I drank some wine.

I noticed a shapely lass
8   In the place, my sweet inspiration!
Bright as the rising sun! I set
My heart on reaching that slender world.
I bought a roast, though not to boast,
12   And some red wine, for me and the girl.
Playing the game that young lads like,
I called to the maid, a shy lass, to join me.
I whispered, I was a true hustler,
16   That's for sure, a couple of hypnotic words.
I set a time, no lazy lust here,
To come to the lovely lass,
After the patrons had gone
20   To sleep; dark-browed she was.

When all were asleep – O sad journey! –
Save me and the maid,
I tried, proceeding cautiously,
24   To reach the girl's bed; but it was not to be.
I stumbled and made a noise there;
Didn't move with sufficient care.
Costly mistake! 'Tis easier to rise
28   Clumsily than nimbly.
I hit my shin – no smooth move,
Poor leg! –
Against the side of some stupid stool –
32   Hosteler's fault! – just above the ankle.
Trying to get up – it's a
Sad tale, O Welshmen who love me!
Haste makes waste! –
36   I struck – and there it was, not an easy step –

An unwise move often betrays –
My forehead on the table's edge,
Where there was a loose basin
40 and a loud brass bowl.
The boards fell – O vile vessels! –
And the trestles and all the stuff on top.
The basin screamed at me
44 And was heard for miles.
The bowl clanged – Oh, I was so stupid! –
And the dogs began to bark.

Beside the stout partitions,
48 There were three English in a stinky pad,
Busying about their packs:
Hickin and Jenkin and Jack.
One of them, with breath like swill,
52 Whispered angrily to the others:

'There's a Welshman, a troublemaker,
Prowling about here;
He's a thief, I know,
56 Watch out for him now!'

The hosteler roused a crowd
And a sad tale it was.
They threatened me all about,
60 Searching all over for me;
And I, bedeviled creature,
Sat silent in the dark there.
I prayed, not fearlessly,
64 Silently, like one filled with fear.
And by virtue of dear, powerful prayer,
And by the grace of the true Jesus,
I got back – O knot of sleeplessness! –
68 Without penalty, to my own pad.
I escaped – O saints attending me! –
I ask forgiveness of God.

A RELUCTANT GIRL

Dafydd fairs no better than he usually does in this encounter with a young girl. The interest for us here is that, rather than meeting the woman in church or at a mystery play or at a tavern, he meets her in the countryside, out in the open. And that's usually a good sign for Dafydd. The scene of the encounter has encouraged some to compare the poem with the French *pastourelle*. That was a narrative poem in which a knight, often, riding through the country encounters a shepherdess to whom he makes advances. The outcomes differ, but sometimes she outwits him by some clever stratagem or other. Here the girl is referred to as being of high station, and Dafydd is called a lad from the region or neighborhood, hardly a knight. Still, the girl manages to outwit Dafydd, promising (emptily as it turns out) that she'll meet him either at Llanbadarn church on Sunday or at the tavern to arrange a date. We know what success Dafydd has with "The Girls of Llanbadarn," and we also know that he had nothing but "Trouble in a Tavern."

Bibliography: Bromwich 1982; Parry 1952

A Reluctant Girl

Fal yr oeddwn yn myned
Dros fynydd, gwyr crefydd Cred
As I was walking across the hills,
I tell you now my fellow men,
Wrapped in my bright cloak,
4   Like a ploughman longing for summer,
Suddenly, a maiden on the moor
Was in my path.
I greeted her, thinking her a swan,
8   Shapely and fine.
She answered her poet,
An answer of love–or so it seemed.

We walked together like children of May,
12   And not without warmth did she walk.
Patient was I toward the pure miss,

Not straining for a kiss.
I praised her shining eyes,
16   Things fine poets praise.
I asked her, before contention could arise,
If she desired me, she was so heavenly.

'You won't get an answer, neighbor,'
20   She said, 'for I don't know.
Let's go to Llanbadarn on Sunday
Or to the tavern, you fresh thing,
And there, in the woods
24   Or in heaven we'll make a date.
I don't want it known, for fear of scandal,
That I've been lolling among the birches.'

'I'm branded a coward for loving you,
28   Yet your lover is a brave man.
Don't hold back, my noble one,
Despite an old woman's reservations.
I know a lovely wooded place,
32   One she has never known of;
And no snooping nose will find it,
While wood and willow shield.
Accept my offer, girl,
36   You'll either make or break the grove.

The perverse wench didn't keep her word –
Fickle, just like the cuckoo;
The promise that made me happy,
40   Was but a promise made in wine.

LOOKING FOR A NUN

In this poem we find Dafydd including nuns in his pool of prospective visitors to the woodland retreat. In early Welsh bardic practice, among the *gogynfeirdd*, it was stipulated that poets were to sing poems of praise to religious men and women just as they were to sing poems of praise to noble men and women. The emphasis here is on 'praise': religious women were to be praised for their holiness, the purity of their lives, love of God, and other spiritual virtues as in the case of religious men. There are only a few of these poems as compared with poems to religious men, for the reason that there were very few nunneries in Wales in the Middle Ages. One of them was located at Llanllugan, which is mentioned in line 9 of the present poem.

There were poems addressed to nuns in English and continental literature of the time as well, but they were definitely not like our poem. The nuns Dafydd addresses are treated no differently than the other girls and women to whom he sends love messengers or whom he invites to meet him for a tryst in the brush. This may well strike some as sacrilegious, as there were severe penalties for women leaving nunneries and severe penalties for both parties in the case of a man seducing a nun. How might these poems have gone over with Dafydd's audiences? And who were these audiences? We are not likely to find sure answers to these questions, but it is suggested (Fulton 1991) that these poems functioned as eulogy, praise poems, just as were love poems that were addressed to noble women. I would add another point, relevant to Dafydd's diction, his metaphors, and *dyfalu*. Dafydd uses many words for 'girl' in his poems; one of these is *chwaer*. The basic meaning is 'female sibling,' but is attested as early as the thirteenth century in the meaning 'nun.' Its English counterpart, *sister* is attested in the meaning 'nun' even earlier. The word *chwaer* occurs once in our poem, in the plural (*chwiorydd*). So *chwaer* for Dafydd can mean both 'nun' and 'girlfriend.' In the "Song to Gwenlliant" by Prydydd y Moch, the poet states explicitly that 'seagull' is a euphemism for 'girl.' I suggest a reason why this might be so in the introductory note to Dafydd ap Gwilym's poem "The Seagull." And in that poem, in the passage of *dyfalu* or 'imagining,' Dafydd calls the seagull a *lleian* 'nun.' So we have a collection of terms here that blurs the differences between 'nun,' 'sister,' 'seagull,' 'lover.' There is, therefore, a delightful ambiguity in the subject of this poem: Dafydd is looking for a willing nun, that is, a sister, a seagull, a lover. This sort of ambiguity, which would surely not have been lost on his audiences, is a hallmark of Dafydd's poetry.

Bibliography: Bromwich 1982; Fulton 1991, 1996; Parry 1952

Looking for a Nun

Dadlitia'r diwyd latai,
Hwnt o'r Mars dwg hynt er Mai
Kindle your passions, lackey of love,
Come back from the Marches – it's May!
You left, Heavens! deserted me!
4   But I need now your gentle urgings,
Innocent affairs, like last time;
You were good – and you know where!

You got me a girl with a single word,
8   Now help me get Mary's girls.
Go to stately Llanllugan and choose
From those with lime-white skin.

Go to the church, greet the jailer
12   Who keeps the girls in check.
Tell her the poet's true claim,
Our psalm, our sacred song;
Say how much I ache,
16   And get me some nuns!

I'm stopped by saints everywhere,
Saints in their splendid bedrooms,
Snowy white and gossamer-like,
20   Graceful convent swallows,
Foster-sisters, every one,
To gentle Morfudd, my golden girl.

You've a good pair of feet,
24   Bring a fair one to the forest,
To our bower – one will do –
A black-robed beauty to the leafy lair.

O! I'll have from convent's cares
28   A maid with a clear bright brow,
One of some sixty such loves.
Try for the chantress herself!
If that bright snowy one won't come
32   To win fame, despite your work,
Then try your tricks on the abbess
Before the fair moon of summer warms.

THE CELTIC POETS

THE MAGPIE'S ADVICE

This is one of several poems in which Dafydd has a conversation with someone who advises him to give over his foolish love poetry and turn to more serious considerations. Usually when Dafydd speaks to a bird it's with the intention to send it with a message (as *llatai* 'love-messenger') to his beloved. But here it is the bird, the magpie, who accosts Dafydd first, telling him he's behaving foolishly. The magpie has shiny, black feathers on its head and body, white inner wings, and a long, irridescent purple-black tail. Its nest is a complicated structure and well defended. It is an industrious creature, and it seems to have no patience with the dallying of the lovesick poet, piddling away his time making verse and waiting for his girl. So Dafydd finds himself here in an unusual situation: nature, in particular a bird (the creature whom Dafydd elsewhere calls 'poet of the woodland') has turned against him. Here again Dafydd holds his persona up to ridicule, this time by what might have been one of his co-conspirators in the practice of love.

Bibliography: Bromwich 1982; Parry 1952

The Magpie's Advice

A mi'n glaf er mwyn gloywferch,
Mewn llwyn yn prydu swyn serch
There I was, sick with love for a merry maid,
In a grove, weaving words of love,
Bright snatches of song, one day
4   In April's infancy, under a mellow sky;
And the nightingale, too, on a verdant twig,
And a handsome blackbird in a batch of leaves
(Nature's poet in nature dwells!),
8   And a thrush atop a green branch
Before the rain, whistling clear
Golden-toned tunes on a leafy cushion;
And a lark, lonesome voiced,
12   Lovely, gray-cowled warbler,
Soaring with his song
At full speed straight into the sky

From the open field (pendant prince!),
16   Mounting in circles as he climbs.

I, a graceful maid's poet,
Full of bliss in a lush grove,
My broken heart remembering
20   But the soul in me awakened,
Stirred by the sight of the wood
Dressed afresh, a splendid feeling;
And sprouts of vine and wheat
24   Bright and dewy after a rain,
And bright leaves along the glen,
And the blackthorn alive in white blossoms.
And by Heaven, there was also
28   The magpie, wiliest bird in the world,
Building with skilful subtlety
A bold abode from leaves and clay
In the midst of a thorny thicket,
32   And her mate was helping her.

The magpie whispered an anguished complaint –
Proud, pointed beak from the thornbush:

'Much do you jabber in vain and pitiful poetry
36   To yourself, old man.
You'd be better off, praise Mary,
Beside the fire, you gray old thing,
Than here in the dew and wet
40   Of a green grove during a cold rain.'

'Cease your chatter and leave me alone
For a moment before my date.
Passionate love for a fine, chaste maid
44   Makes me wax poetic here.'

'It's foolish for you to serve sin,
You gray-haired, crazy, decrepit old man!
Raving about a merry maid

309

48   Is a silly sign of the folly of love.'

        'You, you black-beaked magpie,
        Hellish and villanous bird,
        Unwelcome visitor, yours is
52   Tedious business and even longer labor,
        Your nest like a mound of gorse,
        Thick, a weir of brittle twigs.
        And you, my dear friend, a pitiful appearance!
56   Dappled feathers, a crow's head,
        You're motley, people curse you;
        Your abode is ugly, your voice hoarse
        With every clear and foreign tongue
60   You learn, black-spotted wing.
        You, you black-headed magpie,
        Help me out if you're so handy.
        Give me the best advice you know
64   For my miserable state.'

        'I've got great advice for you–
        And if you'll do it, do it before May comes.
        You don't deserve a pretty maid, rhymer,
68   For you there is but one counsel:
        Serious song – become a hermit,
        You silly man, and never love again!'

        This is my oath, and may Heaven witness it:
72   If ever I see a magpie's nest,
        From this moment on, it shall have
        Neither egg nor chick, I swear.

THE POET AND THE GRAY FRIAR

This poem is one of three poetic altercations Dafydd has with friars, or members of the mendicant orders. Friars had come under attack widely in the thirteenth and subsequent centuries for such things as rejection of ecclesiastical authority, usurpation of the duties of the secular priests, such as confession and burial, attacks on the sinfulness of women, and, not least, poets' preoccupation with matters of the flesh ("Your music, minstrel, produces naught/Save vanity and silly ditties,/And urging men and women/To sin and iniquity"). Dafydd's debate with the friar (gray friars are Franciscans) has usually been discussed in the context of fourteenth-century anti-clericalism, but Davies (1995a) cautions us to consider the poem in the broader context of the corpus of Dafydd's poetry. Dafydd is insisting on the propriety of the things of this world. The friar has it all wrong: God is not as cruel as men (like the friar) say. And women are the fairest bloom in heaven except God, progenitors of us all. Secular song is as right as prayer, in its own place, and here Dafydd quotes from Ecclesiastes 3, the well-known passage that includes "a time to weep, and a time to laugh; a time to mourn, and a time to dance;" etc. Dafydd is not so much anti-mendicant as he is defender of the celebration of the passing things of this world. Indeed, as Davies argues, Dafydd's attitude that transience, and therefore transient pleasures, are proper to life in the world, is an essential part of Dafydd's poetics and may be seen at the most fundamental levels in his poetry.

It is to be expected that the friar would counsel Dafydd to give up poetry and the transitory things of this world in exchange for the reward of permanence in the hereafter. But, as we have seen, the magpie gives Dafydd similar advice. Dafydd is, of course, the composer of these lines, but whether he is the persona as well is unclear. Still, he uses his poetry to explore the tensions between the transitory and the eternal, the secular and the sublime.

Bibliography: Bromwich 1982; Davies 1995a; Parry 1952

The Poet and the Gray Friar

Gwae fi na wyr y forwyn
Glodfrys, â'i llys yn y llwyn
Alas for me that the praiseworthy
Maid who holds court in the wood

Knows not the mousy mendicant's
4   Mention of her today.

I went to the Friar
To confess my sin:
I confessed to him, indeed,
8   That I was a sort of poet,
And that I had ever been in love
With a black-browed beauty,
And that I had neither queenly gain
12   Nor favor from my slayer,
Yet I loved her still,
And pined mightily because of it,
And carried her name throughout Wales;
16   Yet despite that, I was still without her,
Longing to feel her in bed
Between me and the wall.

The Friar then said to me,
20   'I'll give you good counsel:
Since you have loved one like foam,
The color of paper, for a long time till now,
Lessen the pain of the day to come;
24   Far better for your soul to cease –
Silence your songs,
And practice your *paternoster*.
Not for the *cywydd* or *englyn*
28   Did God redeem man.
Your music, minstrel, produces naught
Save vanity and silly ditties,
And urging men and women
32   To sin and iniquity.
No good is praise of the flesh
That leads a soul to Satan!'

I then replied to the Friar
36   And gave him back word for word:
'God is not as cruel

As old men claim.
God doesn't damn the soul of a man
40 For loving a woman or maid.
Three things are loved all over the earth:
Women, fair weather, and good health.
A girl is the fairest bloom
44 In the world, save God himself.
From woman was born every one
Of all men save three,
And in that regard, no wonder
48 Women and maids are loved!
Every pleasure comes from heaven,
And every sorrow hails from hell.

Song brings solace to old
52 And young, to ill and hale.
I have to compose poems
Just as you have to preach,
And as proper for me to rove with my singing
56 As for you to wander about begging.
Aren't hymns and sequences
Kinds of *englyn* and *awdl*?
And the psalms of the prophet David
60 Are *cywyddau* to Holy God.

Not on a single food and taste
Does God nourish man.
A time was given for food,
64 And a time for worship;
A time to preach,
And a time to make merry.
Song is sung in every revelry
68 To amuse maidens–
And the *pater* in church
To find paradise.

It's true what Ystudfach said
72 To his bards in attendance:

"Happy face, full house;
Sad face, evil waits."
While some may love piety,
76   Others long for revelry.
Rare the one who knows sweet *cywydd*,
But everyone knows *paternoster*;
Therefore, pious Friar,
80   Song is not the greatest sin.

When everyone thinks it as pleasing
To listen to a harp-strummed *pater*
As it is for the maidens of Gwynedd
84   To listen to frivolous ditties,
I swear I will sing
Pater ceaselessly.
Until then, shame on Dafydd
88   If he sings a *pater* and not a *cywydd*!

THE POET'S SHADOW

Here is yet another dialogue poem where Dafydd is accused of leading a frivolous life. In that respect, the poem resembles "The Bard and the Gray Friar" and "The Magpie's Advice." But the poem also parodies a widely-known genre, popular in the Middle Ages, the debate between the body and the soul. The earliest examples of this in Welsh (one complete poem and a fragment of another) are to be found in the thirteenth-century Black Book of Carmarthen (Jarman 1982). The theme is expressed in various forms, usually with the soul chastising the body for leading a dissolute life and therefore pulling the innocent soul into Hell with it. In our poem the soul is played by the shadow, and of course Dafydd (or the persona created by him) is the body. The parallel to soul and body is clear, and allows for the dialogue to take place in the here and now rather than at the point of death, as is generally the case in the soul/body dialogues.

The shadow comes in second best in the encounter. Dafydd claims innocence: he was only doing what he always does, standing in the wood waiting for his girl. The shadow says he has come to confront Dafydd for his carnal ways. Thereupon Dafydd employs *dyfalu* 'imagining' to unleash a string of harsh epithets. Most notable among these are the comparisons to a monk, a black friar (Dominican) and a palmer or pilgrim. In his response to the admonitions of the gray friar, Dafydd justifies his life by claiming that the things of this world are worthy pursuits, that there is a place for everything. Here he seems more defensive and his response to the shadow is cast in negative terms. The list of things he says he has not done are, it seems, secular parallels to some of the ten commandments. But Dafydd is being a bit disingenuous, for at the end of the poem, after Dafydd's stout denials, the shadow says that if he told all he knew Dafydd would be sentenced and hanged in a trice. At that, Dafydd asks him to keep quiet. The shadow, unlike outsiders such as the gray friar or the magpie, *is* Dafydd–and the shadow knows!

Bibliography: Bromwich 1982; Parry 1952

The Poet's Shadow

Doe'r oeddwn dan oreuddail
Yn aros gwen, Elen ail

315

The best of leaves above me, yesterday,
Awaiting the likes of Elen, a beauty;
Safe from rain in a cloak of green,
4   Under a birch, a real madman.
Suddenly I saw a kind of sprite
Standing there, an ugly sight.
I stepped aside
8   To be polite,
And crossed myself with holy charms
To keep myself from mortal harm.

'Speak up! don't keep silent;
12   Who are you and what do you want?'

'Just to let you know,
I am your very own shadow;
For Mary's sake, don't interrupt us,
16   And let me tell you my business.
I have come, and a good thing too,
Naked to stand beside you,
And reveal to you what you are:
20   Lust has taken you too far!'

'Not so! I'm a noble sort, you ugly
Ghostly creature; I'm not what you say.
You weird humpbacked goat,
24   Awkward, sinister, unfortunate;
You're more like an eerie apparition,
Than a man in proper condition.
Beery, brawling bumpkin,
28   Hags' shanks on black stilts;
Shepherd of shitty demons,
Monkish sort of apparition.
Herdsman riding a hobby-horse,
32   A veritable heron grazing grass,
A crane flapping its wings,
Ghostly walls, over the grain;
Face of a doltish palmer,

36   Black friar with cloak in tatters;
       A corpse wrapped in threadbare cloth;
       Where have you been, you fence post?'

       'Many a day, I'll have you know,
40   I've been with you; O how I know you!'

       'What fault do you suspect,
       You with the milk-can neck,
       Other than what every person of wit
44   In the world knows; you devil's shit!
       I didn't slander my neighbors,
       I never struck a low blow, I know,
       I never shot hens with a slingshot,
48   Nor terrorized a tiny tot;
       I don't abuse my poetic gift,
       I haven't messed with a stranger's wife.'

       'If I were to tell what I know,
52   By Heaven, to those who don't,
       In a second, without hesitation,
       You'd be hanged, by Heaven!'

       'Yours is a painful trap, so beware
56   Of telling what you know ever,
       Any more than you could
       If there were stitches on your mouth!'

THE CELTIC POETS

A DEBATE WITH GRUFFUDD GRYG

Poetic debates or contentions are probably as old as the practice of poetry itself (Matonis 1982 adduces examples from around Europe in the Middle Ages). They are certainly old in Welsh and Irish and are a hallmark of the Celtic tradition of poetry (Bromwich 1986; Meroney 1949-50; Williams, J. E. C. 1970-71). We have seen references to this sort of contest in "The Story of Gwion Bach, Who Became Taliesin," when Taliesin challenges the bards in the court of Maelgwn Gwynedd. He says he'll silence them, and if they don't know what he knows then they have no right to be around him or bear the insignias of the bardic profession. There also seem to be references to poetic competition in "The Gododdin" (Ford 1987) and in the Welsh triads (Bromwich 1978). In early Ireland, texts such as *Immacallam in dá Thuarad* 'The Colloquy of the Two Sages' (Stokes 1905) suggest that poetic debates were used to determine the succession to the highest rank of poet. There may a reference to this practice among the continental Celts lurking behind Caesar's remark (*Gallic War* vi.13) that, upon the death of the chief druid, whoever is preeminent succeeds, or, if there are many worthy, the successor is chosen by vote (*suffragio*) of the body of druids, or even sometimes by arms (*armis*). Since Irish and Welsh poets sometimes refer to their poetic skills as weapons, it is possible that that was what Caesar was referring to as well.

There are allusions to poetic contentions in the poetry of the *gogynfeirdd*, Dafydd's immediate predecessors, but these seem to have to do with rivalries for the attention of the patron (see, for example, "A Threat to Dafydd ab Owain Gwynedd"). The contention between Dafydd and Gruffudd Gryg is entirely different. Gruffudd Gryg was a poet from Môn (in English, Anglesey) in Gwynedd, the north of Wales, whereas Dafydd was from the south. So there is an element of regionalism in their debate (see Bromwich 1986, p. 64). Gruffudd mocks Dafydd for the themes of his poetry, for indulging in courtly love themes and the popular *fabliaux*. In other words he questions the legitimacy of importing foreign themes into Welsh poetry; in that respect, his attacks constitute the earliest literary criticism we have in Wales. Dafydd, in turn, defends his themes and his metrical mastery (as he might have defended them to the friars and other critics in his poems), and attacks Gruffudd for his conservatism, for adhering to the older poetic themes. Interestingly enough, there's no debate about the *cywydd* as an appropriate vehicle for themes of any kind, even though that was an innovation and break with tradition in the fourteenth century.

318

There are eight poems surviving from the debate, and indications are that there may well have been more. The one that follows here is called by Parry (1952) the first in the series.

Bibliography: Clancy 1965; Matonis 1982; Meroney 1949-50; Parry 1952, no. 147; Williams, J. E. C 1970-71

Gruffudd Gryg's Complaint against Dafydd

Eres I Ddafydd oeryn
Fab Gwilym Gam, ddinam ddyn
Incredible thing for poor Dafydd,
Son of the good man Gwilym Gam,
A rash lad, afflicted soul,
4   Consumed by spears a hundredfold.
And yet this deranged lad
Indulges in song, a prisoner of poetry.
In long and tedious work he weeps,
8   Mother of God! he moans,
What wretched agony for a Welshman!
Incredible that he's still alive.
Mary hears from his blubbering jowls
12   How great are his wounds everywhere.

Spears numerous as the stars in heaven
Wreaking havoc in Dafydd's flesh.
Sad I'd say if indeed sharp spears
16   Stabbed inside this doyen of verse.
Not a spear of riotous battle,
Not spear of leprosy, but a feeble one;
Not spear in the back, as one would think,
20   Not a shooting pain, but shabby;
Not a spear hurled in anger, wrathful,
Not a stout spear, but shivering fear.

Weapons firmly planted in the belly,
24   Of this master of the weaving of poetry.

It's ten long years now, so he says,
Dafydd, so fine his verse,
That a hundred or so weapons,
28   Furious blows, have pierced him,
Arrows, awful to think on,
That caused him so much pain.
Men would think him terribly weak,
32   From all those spears that stab him.

But it's all a big lie, traitorous poet,
That Dafydd treats untruthfully.
If Arthur himself, stalwart wall,
36   Made a mad rush against a host,
The truth is, if all those spears
Produced a hundred wounds
(He did wage wild wars!)
40   The man himself wouldn't live a month!
Much less, then, our own skinny lad,
Lackey of love, for he's so puny.
I'll tell you this: if a Welshman from Môn
44   Holding his spearshaft firmly,
Stuck him through, wounded him
Beneath his broken, hurt breast,
He wouldn't last the morning, poor fellow,
48   Much less, perish the thought,
Only passing out from so much piercing.

His vows are the death of him,
His color killed by arms.
52   By Heaven, this wise and pleasant lad,
Despite his pride and refinement,
A clever foreigner has made him moan
With grief's arrow, a direct hit.
56   Peril awaits him along this sad course–
And that's death from the arms of Morfudd.

DAFYDD'S REPLY

Morgan Davies (1995b) has discussed the metaphor of carpentry as it applies to poetry, citing examples from antiquity through the Middle Ages. Dafydd makes good use of the conceit in his complex diatribe on Gruffudd. As he says, if good wood is hard to find, then it's easier to find a builder than material. In other words, Gruffudd can build, but his material isn't good. Dafydd says if he wants to make poetry, let him go into the forest to cut wood – rather than copy other poets, using their wood.

Rachel Bromwich (1986, pp. 47-8) has helped untangle two other arcane images in this difficult response by Dafydd. The first is the image of the harp. Dafydd says in effect that the worst harp imaginable, one with a ruined sounding-post, only three strings, and so ugly that a tinker in a rowdy pub would throw it out, would be welcomed by a young woman if it accompanied a *cywydd* of the sort Dafydd sings. The second is the image of the manuscript. The argument here is that an ill-treated manuscript, thrown onto the dung heap, would still be sought after for the love poetry written in it. A third image relates to the creation of poetry as an act of weaving. Gruffudd, Dafydd charges, uses worthless thread as he weaves the fabric of his song.

For the most part, Dafydd's *cywydd* poetry is relatively easy to understand. The complex nature of these responses to Gruffudd's charges suggest a seriousness of purpose, that the debate had heated up in both camps. It was, to a degree, a question of the future of Welsh poetry.

Bibliography: Bromwich 1986; Davies 1995b; Parry 1952

Dafydd's Reply

Gruffudd Gryg, wyg wag awen
Grynedig, boenedig ben
Gruffudd Gryg, vain, hollow *awen*,
Fearful, and full of torment,
A freshman at songs for women –
4   Worthless output of a simpleton;
A *cywydd* of playful praise
Is no less noble, though it be without pay.
Harmonious form, real pangs,

8   Alas for the lovely Ovidian song!
One abhors it, the other sang it,
In peevishness, one contested it.

A harp no two hands would play,
12   Its column deadened by rain,
No maid would begrudge it
If it was there with a *cywydd*;
If it has three strings it can swell,
16   With song – even in the hands of a minstrel,
Though in a rowdy, boozy tavern,
A tinker plays it beside his tankard,
Then throws it out, disgusting thing,
20   No better than dog shit, revolting.

A manuscript, tattered and dog-eared,
Tossed out upon a dung heap;
Dirtied though it be by its baptism,
24   Its verses, the handwriting in them,
And its withered pages will be sought
For no other reason than the love they tout.

We say anger and hatred blame song,
28   Where there never was any wrong.
Why is that songster up there
Determined to depose me –
Unconcealed effort by Gruffudd,
32   Cynwrig's son from Gwynedd?
A man without Gwynedd's manners,
He's ruined with his voice the song of choice.
There's no work amid flowing mead
36   For a reciter of songs in Gwynedd,
Only beating a path to some other place;
'Tis a heavy burden, spiteful malice.

Here a poet can't sing to fair weather,
40   Accompanied by his ten fingers,
Without Gruffudd , gloomy and bleak,

Huffing and puffing, trying to imitate.
Anyone could make a strong structure
44   If he had wood and good men;
Where the wood is bad or hard to find,
It's easier to find a wright than timber;
If he wants song, let him go to the forest,
48   And with a well-aimed blow cut the stuff!
Not too skilful, but fairly named,
It's a strange sort of poet
Who would need worthless thread
52   For the material of his false *cywydd*.
Holding on to a good strong railing,
An old buck moves on slowly.
Let the bard sing to some other pretty,
56   Use his own old wood for his silly ditty.

I give warning to Gruffudd the fool,
I'm drawing back the bow:
The strong will control the best of the fair,
60   You echo of poets, stammerer!
When the stammerer gets paid for a poem,
Let him pay the portion that's due me!

IRISH POEMS

IRISH BARDIC POETRY

Bardic poetry means poetry by bards, of course. The most common word for poet in early Ireland is *fili*, plural *filidh*. However, *bard* (plural *baird*) in the form of Greek *bárdos*, is one of the oldest Celtic words for a poet. It seems that in Ireland, in the earliest period, the function of the *bard* was praise poetry, whereas the *fili* or 'seer' was engaged in rather more mystical, almost priestly duties. But after the advent of the Normans in the second half of the twelfth century, society underwent changes, and there seems to have developed an antagonism or competition between *baird* and *filidh* in medieval Ireland. But whatever of the relationship between them, by the high middle ages, and in particular after the coming of the Normans, the principal function of poets was to compose songs of praise and satire, maintain pedigrees, and chronicle history. And so it became the principal function of the *filidh* as well, and the bardic meters were taken up by them. Most poets called themselves *fili* and the old distinction between the two groups more or less disappeared.

The principal features of bardic poetry are as follows:

i) It was composed in the strict meters (*dán díreach*, or *nua chrutha* 'new forms'), meters characterized by a regular number of syllables in each line. There are numerous requirements, such as that the last two stressed words in a stanza must alliterate, each line must end with a word bearing full accent, and the last words of a poem should repeat or echo its first words.

ii) The poems we refer to as bardic poetry were composed for the most part between the end of the twelfth century and the middle of the seventeenth century, but especially from around 1250 to 1650. During that four-hundred year period the poetry is so conservative and conventional (thanks to the Bardic Schools), that it is difficult to date any poem from the period on its language or form alone.

iii) The most frequent element in the poetry is praise of the living (eulogy) or of the dead (elegy). Such praise is often couched in general terms, and particulars relating to the subject's victories over certain individuals are often avoided. The poetry is also filled with references to the poet himself or poets and poetry in general, and the generosity of the patron or subject toward poets. The poets don't mind saying that such generosity is well deserved. There are clear and explicit parallels with the Welsh poetry of the princes.

While much of this poetry is conventional to the point of distraction for the modern reader, there are some conventions that have a rather modern appeal,

327

such as the four that are presented here. But whatever these poems may lack in content or in appeal for modern audiences, they are certainly not without artistic merit. The poet was the product of long training in the Bardic Schools. A good deal of this training was devoted to the study of language and meter. Bardic language was rigidly controlled by the schools, and it is remarkable that there is so little difference in the language of poems composed over a four-hundred year period. The poetry was intended for the ear, and so the language and its metrical ornamentation created a pleasing aural effect, a kind of music. Just as the verb *canu* 'singing' is used in Welsh for poetry, so does Irish use the verb *canaid* 'sing' to refer to the composition of poetry. In "Guaire's Greedy Guests," Dallán Forgaill's poems of praise and satire are unintelligible to the king and the meaning of the two poems must be explained to him. The sounds of the poetry and its musical accompaniment were, no doubt, meaning enough for many audiences.

The poet's profession was hereditary, a fact parodied in "Guaire's Greedy Guests." As one trained in pedigrees and history, as well as in praise and satire, his role in society was functional. What we often find in this poetry, then, is similar to what we find in the Welsh poetry of the princes: praise for the patron's generosity, beauty, noble lineage, valor in battle – often with an enumeration of his successes, his support of poets, and so on. As in Welsh, there are poems in which the poet complains against the patron for various offences, and poems in which the poet hopes to be forgiven for some trespass and reinstated to his proper position. Examples of these are to be found among the many bardic poems edited and translated by Professor Osborn Bergin over the years (see Greene 1970).

The present small selection concentrates on four poems from this period which, though somewhat unusual in their subjects, provide compelling evidence for the practice and function of poetry in medieval Ireland.

Bibliography: Carney 1967; Greene 1970; Knott 1960, 1966

GIOLLA BRIGHDE MAC CON MIDHE

Giolla Brighde was descended from a bardic family that claimed descent from Eogan son of Níall Noígiallach, and was, therefore, of noble ancestry. Little is known of his life, but evidence of his poems suggest that he flourished in the middle and second half of the thirteenth century. He belongs, then, to the beginning of the period of Irish Bardic Poetry. There are allusions to him in the work of later poets and examples of his work cited in the Irish bardic tracts, thus indicating that he was well thought of and admired. Approximately twenty of his poems have survived. They consist of eulogies and elegies as well as other genres, including a request poem asking God to give him children for those of his that have died, and a death-bed poem in which the poet renounces praise poetry. The two presented here are unique in their conceits.

A VISION OF EMAIN MACHA

The present poem is cast as a vision, experienced by the poet as he lay asleep on the grassy mound at Emain Macha, the seat of the legendary high-kingship of Ulster in the Irish heroic age, Conchobar's throne. It lay within the territory of Oriel (Airgialla), where Rolf's father, Eochaid, was king. It would appear that Rolf in fact never did succeed his father, but that his brother or half-brother Brian did. The circumstance of the present poem, then, suggests a time shortly after the death of the father, Eochaid, and an anticipation or hope on the part of the poet that Rolf would be inaugurated as his successor. Therefore, the poet chooses the *aisling* or 'dream-vision' as the vehicle to convey his aspirations and the pomp and circumstance of the glorious occasion of Rolf's inauguration. In the procession, Rolf is escorted by the poets of Ireland, likened to the mythical Túatha Dé Danann, a people of wisdom and wizardry. And it is the poets as well who enthrone him.

Meter: *deibhidhe*, rhyming couplets in stanzas of 4 lines (a quatrain). The rhyme is between words of unequal syllabic length; the shorter word is called *rinn*, the longer one *airdrinn*. In Irish, rhyme begins with the first stressed vowel of the word, and all subsequent consonants must be of the same consonant class and quality. There are six consonant classes: (*p, t, c*); (*b, d, g*); (*ph, th, ch*); (*bh, mh, dh, gh, l, n, r*); (*ll, mm, ng, nn, rr*); (*s*). Any consonant rhymes fully with itself or any other consonant in its group. There are additional

329

rules governing alliteration within each line and internal rhymes. See Knott 1966; Murphy 1961.

Bibliography: Murphy 1943; Williams, N. J. A. 1980

A Vision of Emain Macha

Iongnadh mh'aisling in Eamhain
I maidin chiúin Chéiteamhain:
Atá sí 'gá dhearbhadh damh
Ní nach dearnadh do dhéanamh.
I had a wonderful vision in Emain
one gentle May morning:
a sign that revealed to me
4   something that hadn't been was going to be.

I had gone one day to gaze on Emain,
on the grand business of poetry;
it was a specially happy and friendly occasion,
8   visiting this lofty site, so calm and serene.

I settled down on Emain's green,
fort of Macha, the red-haired queen,
Conchobar, king of Ulster,
12   Mugain his wife and all the rest.

When I had been there but a little while,
I began to feel drowsy and tire;
my lids were heavy as I fell asleep
16   on the cool, downy grass of the keep.

As I lay there deep in sleep,
a vision began to appear to me;
an angel of God appeared at my side –
20   he was my grip on reality, my guide.

On the northern side of the mound

a host of horsemen headed for Emain;
every path filled with horses
24   in a sea of red battle banners.

'What host is this I see?'
said I to my emissary;
'their faces on fire, cheeks hot,
28   from the mad clatter of their gallop.'

'You see there coming toward you
princes of the race of Eoghan Ailech;
every land rightfully theirs,
32   the host you see drawing near.'

'And what powerful host in front of me,
in Emain's plain heading this way?
They're geared for battle, armed with spears,
36   colorful shields on their shoulders.

A sheathed sword at each man's belt,
their sharp spears held aloft;
elegant ensigns on slender shafts
40   that rest against the horses shanks.'

'That great host you're seeing
are the champions of all of Erin;
Ulstermen and sons of the kings of Ulster,
44   descendants of the hero Conchobar.'

'Who are those lords coming from the south
toward Emain, home of poets?
The green turf torn by their horses,
48   like a field that's been ploughed afresh.

The flap of the bright red pennants
borne by the marshalled horsemen
sounds like the sea lapping the coast
52   or winds spanking groves of oaks.'

'Those proud and colorful hosts
are kings of Emain's Airther districts;
a people of Emain in the garden of the Gael
56   for whom aggressive courage is natural.'

'Who's the gleaming host in the west,
on their way to Emain of Airgialla?
Though they're not near, I see they're keen,
60   perhaps the best I've ever seen.

The greatest host one ever saw,
no weapons, just poets' wands;
magnificent appearance on all of them,
64   dressed in green and brown raiment.'

'The men there are a most noble clan,
out of the Túatha Dé Danann;
this lovely folk from another world
68   are scholars of the wise from Banba's pale land.

The man in their midst is noble and generous,
Rolf of Cluan, descendant of Durlas;
a mill, grinding out the defense of Banba,
72   MacMahon's line, dear and beloved.

Ravens, the poets of Inis Leary,
harbingers of luck for the king of the Duff;
the prince of Banba is dear to them,
76   and the signs of his success are welcome.'

'Twas the poets of the world enthroned him,
Rolf, in Conchobar's Emain;
the bustle as they crowned him king
80   was like waves filling the strand.

When he came to Emain, scion of Sligo,
his retinue of poets came there too;

when all were arrayed upon the hill
84   the royal site was ceded to Rolf.

The hosts from east, west, north and south
together converged on Emain's mound;
leaving behind a ploughed up plain
88   wherever their horses had pranced.

The butts of their spears were thrust in the ground,
there in the place where Rolf was crowned;
the four hosts gathered around him
92   in homage to the prince of Cechan.

Then the scions of Conchobar's fifth
crowned the prince of Fobhar king;
they rallied all around their Rolf
96   like vines winding about a post.

The poets of Inis Fáil, each in turn,
sang in praise of this champion of Iomghán;
not the least of them, I myself
100   seized the moment to eulogize Rolf.

I set about performing my poem
to the lord of Red-branch;
the worst a poet of praise can do
104   is deny to anyone that which is due.

From Carn Í Néid, deep in the south,
to Rock of Stacán in the far north,
From one end to another of Conn's land
108   Rolf is above all other men.

I've taken the measure of many a man;
nor do I ever give false judgement;
my choice is a man most estimable,
112   his stature a standard for nobles.

It doesn't pay for a poet to praise
any noble Gael I haven't assayed;
I've judged them all many a time,
116   sought out the many men of Ireland.

I've been on circuit out in Munster,
addressed Cashel's Clan Carthy;
I've been in Cliu of the kings before,
120   with the descendants of BrianBorú.

I've ranged among the Leinstermen,
examined the nobles of Meath;
chewed my hazels among the Connachta,
124   looked upon the heirs of Conchobar.

I know all of Ulster and Connaught,
and their fame is the better for it;
I've taken the measure of all in Conn's Half,
128   no one swerved me from my path.

Of those that I've examined,
of all the nobles in Ireland,
none could match my standard
132   but Rolf, champion of Ruidhe.

I traveled through all of Banba
to find the likes of MacMahon's son;
like a trip through wind and rain
136   to reach Rolf's sunny countenance.

Apart from his incredible lavishness,
the strangest thing of all is this:
even the poets of men he has killed
140   pray that Rolf will be successful.

Not a soul in the world will be blamed
for praising a man of his gifts and fame;
even his enemies have no quarrel

144   with my claim that Rolf is noble.

Nor has his fame failed to take root
among the poets of Connaught;
his bounty has eclipsed the sons of Créidhe
148   whom none had ever found fault with.

His fame has overspread their own,
his valor brought their own star down;
as he repels every challenge in every way,
152   his fortunes cause theirs to fade.

No man will rise against him –
it's wise to flee from fire!
no point in arming against him,
156   for Rolf has yet to be challenged.

Was any on earth ever blest
with such abundance of honor and prowess?
which of you, of any sort,
160   ever had his beauty and wit?

The more cattle graze the land,
the better grows the grass;
a cutting taken from the base of a tree
164   becomes a wood in maturity.

So the hawk of Fál will be richer
with everyone enjoying his purse;
just as a cairn doesn't lack rocks
168   so will his fortune never fail Rolf.

Lines will never mar his handsome face
from worry over raid or strife;
this Rolf's beauty and virulence
172   has bewitched Airgialla's maidens.

Many a maid would love to beguile

this man with pink cheeks and teeth of pearl;
few are the women allowed inside –
176   to protect the house from catching fire!

They plait his hair, pluck his brow;
women serving the son of Eochu;
now a woman about to wash
180   the hands of the son of Sláine.

In the north they've heard the roar
of the river of Rolf's generous nature;
the ceaseless thunder of his valor,
184   the dread he inspires, are currents of wonder.

A RESPONSE TO A THREAT AGAINST POETRY

This poem is a virtual manifesto for the practice of poetry in medieval Ireland. Poets were attacked by the Church for their pagan practices, and Patrick banned some of these (see "Imbas Forosnai"). They were attacked by the kings who rebelled against the extravagant behavior of the poets (e.g., "Guaire's Greedy Guests") and would eventually come under very grievous and deadly attack from the English crown, which passed legislation against them (Ford 1992a, chapter 4). The present poem is a defense of poets and the value to society of their poetry against an imagined messenger from Rome who has come with an edict to ban poetry. It is a remarkable piece, and the figure of Colum Cille lurks behind a key passage in it. According to the tradition, the kings of Ireland wished to banish the poets from the land. The saint, himself a poet as well, undertook the defense of the poets at the assembly of Druim Cetta, and in the end it was determined that the poetic orders would remain but would be reformed at the direction of the saint. The daring claim that even though poetry may lie, it is a lasting lie and not a transitory one, echoes Colum Cille's defense of the poets at Druim Cetta. Colum Cille said that as God bought thrice fifty psalms of praise from David, so is it proper that kings buy poems of praise from the poets of Ireland:

And sith all the world is but a fable, it were well for thee to buy the more abiding fable, rather than the fable that is less enduring.' And he made these quatrains:
'If poets' verses be but fables,
So be food and garments fables;
So is all the world a fable;
So is man of dust a fable.
For the fable more enduring
I shall give the one more transient' (O'Kelleher 1918, p. 353).

On Colum Cille and the importance of Thursday, the day he made his weekly trips to heaven, see O'Kelleher 1918, p. 167f.

As proof of the value of poets, Giolla Brighde points out that famous men of the past, the generous king Guaire, the hero Cú Chulainn, the leader Brian Ború, the god Lugh, and others, though they are all dead, live on through poetry. And as poets are the keepers of genealogies, without them none would be distinguished, rather all men would be equally common. Finally, and perhaps this is the ringer, the claim that patrons who have been praised will go straight to heaven!

Meter: *deibhidhe*; see preceding poem for details.

Bibliography: O'Kelleher 1918; Williams, N. J. A. 1980

A Response to a Threat Against Poetry

> *O theachtaire tig ón Róimh*
> *Lena síoltar gach seanmóir,*
> *Déana mar a-deir an peann:*
> *Ná geibh sgéala acht an sgríbheann.*
> O messenger sent from Rome,
> responsible for spreading the word,
> speak as the pen has directed,
> 4   no lies now, just read what's written!
>
> Out with the ban from Peter's heir,
> just as you received it from the chair;
> if he gave you a gloomy old bull,
> 8   unassailable, let's have it all.
>
> Look after all of the words,
> as they were spoken in Rome;
> no other voice carries such weight –
> 12   burden enough to endure it.
>
> You were not directed in Rome, cleric,
> to expel the poets from Erin;
> you got this directive's curse
> 16   by hap from some non-Rome source.
>
> Show us where it is written
> that the art of poetry needs revision;
> make good what you have declared to us
> 20   and reveal the contents of your document!

Never have any books insisted
that poetry in its many forms be dismissed;
and it's an ugly and alien idea
24   that Erin's poets be driven away.

Donum Dei is every sweet song,
rooted in traditional learning;
sing it and set forth its meaning –
28   that's God's gift, quite clearly.

To tell good men that songs cost nil,
if lords had poems without a bill,
then none would suffer satire,
32   cleric, and each would be a noble.

If it be for the sake of wealth
that poets will be denied their due,
doesn't every man have sufficient,
36   cleric, even after the poet has payment?

Why, when he came from Rome,
did Patrick of the holy religion
not banish our art and song
40   from the face of gentle Ireland?

And what made Colum Cille,
who knew nothing but truth,
pay for poems as he made his way
44   to converse with angels each Thursday?

Another decree would have expelled
the poets from the green sod of Fodla;
but in the same year this Colum
48   made a covenant that saved them.

Blessed Mo-Bhí Clárainech,
though his honor was entirely untarnished,

52   gave up his life to poets when asked –
a generous gesture, though rather excessive.

And a statue once gave her shoe away
for an eloquent and boisterous lay;
the request itself was inordinate
56   for it left her with an uncovered foot.

Holy Mary's Son will reward me
with compensation no man would pay;
in return for my songs I'll get heaven,
60   just like the bard O'Heffernan.

Another proof of the value
of the composers of verse men listen to –
the truth of this has long been told –
64   freedom for the patron from hell!

The praise of men is praise of Him,
the one who created and shaped them;
there is no praise at all in the world
68   save praise of His works and miracles.

The rhyme of a stanza, sense of a word,
all redound to the glory of the Lord;
the sound of every tide as it rushes in,
72   is but praise of the mighty King.

Though falsehood be found in poetry,
they're lasting lies, not transitory;
all is sham, and though shaped from clay,
76   man himself is a walking lie.

Were a man to act the miser,
his gold and herds would be no greater;
without respect for poetry in the world
80   there'd be no further need for cattle.

If the poetic art were killed,
no history, no ancient lays retold,
all but the father of each man
84   would pass away without mention.

If the well of knowledge went dry,
and we did not exist, none of the nobility
would hear of their famous forebears,
88   or know the descent of the Gaels.

A lasting, ill fate and dire
for tender young warriors,
a great loss, leaving them dumb
92   not knowing the stock from which they come.

Hiding assaults and battles
of the men of Ireland would be useless:
when they died, though courageous they'd been,
96   interest in prince or nobility gone.

Though he is dead, Guaire lives on;
and the Red-branch hero Cú Chulainn;
as a result of his fame both east and west,
100   Brian Ború is with us yet.

Since their praise continues to live,
Conall and Conchobar survive;
as his fame remains in place,
104   Fergus has not yet gone from us.

There's neither flesh nor bone of Lugh,
killed by the hand of Mac Cuill;
but his fame has gone throughout the world,
108   and thus Lugh lives, his memory preserved.

Had lays not preserved their deeds,
though they were noble men,
a cloak would long since have fallen

112   on Níall, Cormac, and Conn.

The line of kings of Cashel and Cruachan,
the House of Three Hostels' scions,
Tuathal of Tara and Dath Í:
116   poets are the roots of those pedigrees.

Were there no poetry sung
to sweet-strung harp or timpan,
none would know of noble passed,
120   nor his repute nor manly prowess.

Men of high station would never know
their noble past or historical lore;
put all that in poetic composition,
124   or say goodbye to all man has done.

If they ban the history of Conn's people,
along with songs about you, Donal,
then the children of your keeper of hounds
128   would enjoy the same status as your own.

If it's the will of the men of Ireland, messenger,
to banish the practice of poetry,
then no Gael's birth would merit fanfare,
132   for each would be but a commoner!

Tadhg Dall Ó hUiginn

Giolla Brighde appeared on the literary scene at the beginning of the period of bardic poetry; Tadhg Dall, 'Blind Tadhg,' came toward the end of that period. He was born about 1550 into an eminent literary family. One relative, Brian Mac Fearghal (died 1476), is called *cend scoile Érenn ocus Alban* 'head of the school [of poets] of Ireland and Scotland' in the Annals of Loch Cé. Brian's son is described as 'teacher in poetry of the men of Ireland.' Fearghal's brother, Tadhgh Óg (died 1448) is called 'head of the bardic order of Ireland' (Knott 1922, p. xxiii). The Ó hUiginns were, clearly, one of the most distinguished bardic families in Ireland

Though he is called Dall 'blind,' there is no evidence to determine whether he was totally blind, blind in one eye, or just hard of seeing. Blindness is a condition associated with the practice of poetry among the Celts. Dallán Forgaill is blind; Gwion Bach is assisted by a man called Dallmor Dallme (Welsh *dall*, like Irish *dall* means 'blind'); Irish and Scottish divination rituals required that the eyes be closed in sleep or trance; an early eighteenth-century account says that Irish poets composed their poems in utter darkness, light being kept out intentionally; and so on. Remembering that Irish *fili* means 'seer,' the designation 'blind' points to an understanding that the 'seer' sees in ways that ordinary persons do not; blindness is not an obstacle to 'seeing,' rather it reinforces in an obvious and physical way the specialness of poets (Ford 1990).

Tadhg Dall is said to have been poet to O'Conor of Sligo, and, perhaps indicative of his success, Tadhg held considerable land in Sligo. The forty or so surviving poems are on traditional themes, most of them conventional praise poems to persons, a couple in praise of places (houses of patrons), one to a weapon. There is an elegy, an appeal for reconciliation (through the wife of the patron), a complaint against a patron for refusing to protect the poet's kin on a raid, a versified pedigree, and two *aisling* or 'dream vision' poems.

Tadhg Dall died in 1591. According to tradition, he was murdered by some of the O'Haras, after he had composed a satire on six of them for having stolen milk from him. In the satire he describes the appearance of the six in most unflattering terms (one of them seems to be wearing the evidence of his own chronic dysentery); the poet concludes with a prayer to God, asking that no one be allowed to kill these six, because the wretched state of their existence is worse than death.

CHRISTMAS AT CREEVE

The present poem recounts a visit to Creeve, the residence of Turlough Luineach O'Neill, who died in 1595. Turlough invited the poets of Ireland to celebrate Christmas there, expecting that they, in turn, would celebrate him. The poets are well received, and eventually Turlough asks if they have a song that would celebrate his valor and his victories. They reply that they have not, but that they have his pedigree worked out in verse, the entitlements of the descendants of Níall, and the names of those who were kings. Turlough wants none of such pedestrian stuff and refuses to listen to their songs – even though he gives them the payment due them! The conceit of the poem yields the greatest praise imaginable for Turlough's martial abilities: the poets do not have the kind of poem Turlough wants, for to praise his many exploits would keep them all there till Doomsday. At the very end of the poem there are an additional three stanzas, now defective, and apparently dedicated to Turlough's wife.

Meter: *deibhidhe*; for details, see introductory note to "A Vision of Emain Macha."

Bibliography: Knott 1922

Christmas at Creeve

Nodlaig do-chuamair don Chraoibh
Ollamhain Fhódla d'éantaoibh
Ar slios réidh an bhrogha bhuig
I robha Ó Néill um Nodluig.
At Christmas time we went to Creeve,
We poets of *Fódla*, Ireland,
To the inviting hall, place of ease,
4   Where Ó Néill rested that season.

Creeve, bright and peaceful,
One of the castles of Ó Néill;
No better court than this on earth,
8   The joy of all Ireland in its hearth.

344

At that time, it was under protection
Of a king without opposition;
Noble scion of the Hill of Tara,
12   Fruitful heir, Turlough.

A full ten years it had been
Since the king's inauguration,
And since building his hall in Creeve,
16   This noble scion of Allen.

We converged on Creeve
The fresh face and bright smile to see;
Praise poets of the land of the fair,
20   Chief poets of all of Éire.

It appeared to us as we went in
That the sky above had fallen –
From the clatter of bright-bridled mounts
24   About the man of Raoiliu's plain.

And it appeared, too, at first,
From the brilliance of arms and dress,
That flames devoured the whole –
28   From top to bottom withal.

And the clamor and roar of the feast
In the scion of Níall Noígíallach's court –
The clash of crimson vats
32   Like waves, loud against the coast.

As we drew near the wall outside,
Though I stood close by his side,
I'd hear not a word from a soul then
36   From the sounds of the song within.

Coming ever nearer the place,
I thought they would completely suffice:

The glow of the bright drinking-horns,
40   And the smell of the finest of ales.

We sat on the edge of the lawn,
Poets from all of Ireland,
A host gathered before the house
44   On tufts of bright green grass.

After a while, came to us there
Servants of Conn Cédcathach's heir,
And offered warm reception
48   And greetings from the king.

But we did not on that occasion
Catch sight of Uisnech's king;
Brega's slender, soft-haired leader
52   Had us taken to our quarters.

From that point on till morning,
Proud servants of Ó Néill were pouring
A generous feast for all of us –
56   A procession that did not cease.

He sent a man to ask of us all
If any of our songs would tell
Tales of his bouts throughout Ireland
60   News of his victories or battles won.

'No,' replied the poets of Banba,
'But,' the learned folk went on,
'We have Conn's line worked out
64   Without an iota of doubt!

'We have the dues of the race of Níall,
And what they're entitled to do;
And which of them ruled Bregian Boyne,'
68   Said the poets of Ireland then.

'We have it that he's the one entitled
To Cruachan and its streams so gentle,
To the dewy precincts of Téa's House – Tara,
72   And that he is the sole heir of Éire.'

So this same man went to seek
The bright-cheeked daring chief,
Ó Néill of Mourne, the next day
76   To tell him what we had to say.

'If that,' said the son of Níall,
'Is the sort of praise they'll tell,
Then the greater blame to them –
80   For they're bearding Eoghan's kin!

'What a stain on the heroes of Tara
To even suggest,' roared Turlough,
'That Tara'd be taken from the seed of Art
84   And they not punish the act!'

He'd listen to none of our poems,
Said Ó Néill of Tara and Trim,
But would pay for every one –
88   A strange thought to think on!

And with that came Níall of Caille's kin,
Descendant of the race of Eoghan,
Lordly hazel of the plain of Ulster,
92   To rebuke us for our faulty art.

The son of Níall of Ó Néill's race
Lifted not his usually kind face,
Nor did those dancing, long-lashed eyes
96   Look at Eber's bardic companies.

Turlough shook with anger, frenzied,
His brilliant, bright face reddened,
From the soles of his nimble feet

100   To the full, flowing hair of his head.

Fear seized us all standing there
Before the king of clan Conchobar,
For the red-lipped prince of the Bóruma
104   Had become thoroughly angry with us.

We began to speak, softly and sweet,
Attempting to mollify and appease,
To assuage or abate his anger
108   But it didn't make things better.

Our own fee was paid to us
by the scion of Níall Nine-hostages,
Though the head of Monadh's host
112   Refused to hear a word of our art.

From that day to this without fail,
The king of the royal race of Fál
Has been sunk in a sea of wrath
116   And found no release from that.

If it's proper to ask just now,
From the king of Oileach I'd like to know
What caused such wrath to arise,
120   Such spell of anger in his eyes?

Why sits rage on the son of Níall
After paying the due wage to all?
Why are his cheeks still aflame –
124   Or is there, in fact, nothing to blame?

One might say to oneself alone
Of this rage that rules Níall's son:
To inflame it is all the easier –
128   And he without cause or matter!

He defends his folk with equal force

At the edge of the Erne's estuary
Finn's waters, shallow but lively,
132 And the bubbling beauty of Trághbaile.

His will is done throughout the district,
At Drowes and at the Ards of Ulster,
Done in the dewy-fresh headlands of Brega
136 And the green-banked Boyne of Tailtiu.

The curly-haired king of fair Derg
Has, I say, no cause for anger
Save lands that submit to his pleasure –
140 The kings and chieftains of Ulster.

I know full well what did inflame,
The silken brow and bring him shame:
That no one had enshrined his feats
144 In battle-song that praised his deeds.

But if Éire's poets composed a song
Of courageous exploits waged for so long,
Of Turlough's hostings and distant forays,
148 The task would keep us here till Doomsday.

Though the hosts of all of Erin
Stood marshalled against them as one,
It were no peril with him on their side,
152 For nowhere is he defied.

THE CELTIC POETS

ENNISKILLEN

Cú Chonnacht, the head of the Maguire clan, was lord of Fermanagh from 1566 to 1589. Greene (1972) calls him 'both fortunate and unscrupulous.' He was friendly to the English goverment and apparently appealed to them often for protection from Turlough Luineach and other Uí Néill hostile to him. His situation brought him considerable wealth, and, not surprisingly, he was much loved by the poets and the Church. The castle of Enniskillen was held by Cú Chonnacht throughout his reign, and when he died it passed to his son Hugh. There is a fine poem by the poet Eochaid Ó hEoghusa (Eochy O'Hussy) to Hugh Maguire, beautifully translated by Frank O'Connor (1989).

Tadhg Dall is one of not less than a dozen poets who composed praise poems for Cú Chonnacht. Twenty-four of these poems, representing the work of eleven different poets, were gathered together into a *duanaire* or 'song-book' after the fashion of the time. Such collections of poems in honor of a particular clan or family were probably quite common among the nobility; a dozen or so have survived. The unique thing about the *duanaire Mhéig Uidhir* 'the song-book of Maguire' (Greene 1972) is that all the poems are addressed to one person, Cú Chonnacht. Tadhg Dall's poem, presented here, is one of three surviving poems by him addressed to Cú Chonnacht, though none of them are in the *duanaire* edited by Greene.

Our poem recalls a visit to Enniskillen by Tadhg, after he had heard of the glories of the court. There is a strong sense of nostalgia that pervades the poem and is explicit in the opening and closing stanzas. The place holds such vivid memories for the poet that he can scarcely bear to look upon it. The mood is somewhat evocative of the regret Llywarch Hen feels looking at Urien's hall at Rheged.

Meter: *seadna*; the 1st and 3rd lines of each quatrain have 8 syllables; the 2nd and 4th have 7 syllables. The 2nd and 4th lines end in monosyllabic words, which rhyme. The final word of the 3rd line rhymes with the penultimate word in the 4th line. There are further requirements for internal rhyming and alliteration. See Knott 1966.

Bibliography: Knott 1922

Enniskillen

Mairg fhéagas ar Inis Ceithleann
    Na gcuan n-éadrocht, na n-eas mbinn;
Guais dúinn, 'snách féadair a fágbháil,
    Féagain an mhúir fhádbháin fhinn.
How sad, seeing Enniskillen –
    its silvery bays and tuneful falls;
Because we cannot let the image go,
4   It hurts to gaze on its splendid walls.

Long before I ever came
    to the gleaming hall and grassy knoll,
I knew that if ever I found it
8   I'd lack for nothing at all.

The fame had spread, sad to reflect,
    of this otherworld of flawless treasure;
I heard I'd be enchanted, beguiled,
12   Nothing would keep me from going there.

What everyone told me was
    That never in Banba was seen
A dwelling the likes of that one,
16   Hallowed hall of the lion of Erne.

They also said whoever saw
    the twining wood and dewy plain,
sandy beach and rich green fields,
20   would never venture forth again.

Once I'd heard this glowing report,
    Whenever I slept for a while,
No other vision visited me
24   But the beauty of that fair domicile.

Off I went, and gained the place –
    Enniskillen under gnarled oak,

across the field, through laden boughs,
28   the sight of it took me aback.

Even before I neared the place,
       the sounds were anything but tame:
lively yowls of dogs and hounds
32   in the woods flushing game.

The shore beside the court,
       On the still-watered, fairy bay,
scarcely could any of it be seen
36   so thick were the masts of ships arrayed.

And beside the court there I could see
       a beautiful, gilded plain,
the bright fort's dewy green,
40   Heaven's domain, or much the same.

This is how I saw the turf –
       overturned from horses' hoofs;
plants couldn't grow in the green there,
44   with herds competing in droves.

The steeds of the court were racing –
       I can see them now in their courses,
the hilly terrain completely obscured,
48   not by mist but by horses.

I kept to my course, straight on,
       to the arched fort of the Lia;
those I found inside the fair walls
52   were a wonderful sort of family.

I found the nobles of Colla's race
       in the crowded court giving gifts,
and men who could open the mysteries
56   of the origins of the Gaels of Greece.

I found, too, throughout the fort,
    its fill of minstrels and poets,
wall to wall one might say;
60   happy the house with such talents!

In another part I found maidens,
    fine-lipped and clad in silk,
embroidering fine, golden fringe,
64   there in the noble, sportive lodge.

A throng of warriors throughout the house,
    lining the walls within;
their pointed weapons just above them,
68   regiment of fruited Drumquin.

A great troop of youth, as if from the *sídh*,
    from Badb's *sídh* or the hostel of Ler,
so shining bright no eye could sight them,
72   manned the bright, branched rampart.

A group of artisans making goblets,
    another of smiths forging arms;
craftsmen from many lands about her,
76   precious gem of the soft, still water.

Swords being burnished, cloths dyed purple,
    spear heads hammered, horses exercising,
hostages pledged, terms arranged,
80   scholars examining lists of kings.

Hostages being taken, others let go,
    warriors recovering, others wounded,
wealth rolling in, gifts handed out
84   from this splendid palace, out of this world.

They passed the time part of the day
    recounting deeds and talking conflict;
then for a spate the men of Uisneach

88   would drink and dine and listen to music.

And so, till dinner, we passed the day,
        a lovely day that seemed but an hour,
in the shining, bright rampart,
92   fertile and grassy enclosure.

Each was set in his proper place,
        on smooth benches in the elegant hall;
rarely would a hostel have seen the likes
96   of the throng that filled the long table.

Cú Chonnacht Óg, Cú Chonnacht's son,
        passion's mist clings to him,
when all in the hall were in their seats
100   settled into his royal throne.

I sat on the right of the dragon of Tara
        till the drinking had run its course;
and the king did not ignore or snub me,
104   though plenty of nobles paid him court.

In a while, when the time came
        for the company to lie and rest,
downy coverlets were all arranged
108   for the well-mannered, the very best.

Before dawn broke in the house,
        a crew of them were fitting spears;
horses shod at break of day,
112   men rounding up horses.

Barely had I awakened
        there in the bright stone rampart,
when I saw around the hawk of Síoth Truim
116   fine warriors armed for conflict.

Before daylight they went from us,

hardened lads from the king's court;
    spear-bearing, solemn, a great brigade;
120   suing for peace was not their art.

Not long after, they returned;
    victorious wherever they roamed;
men of Colla with golden bands –
124   happy the land they call home!

Many a woman, that day at Loch Erne,
    whose husband did not survive;
and the aftermath of battle,
128   saw many a wounded hostage arrive.

There in the house, splendid wealth
    that hadn't been there in the morn,
and cattle grazing close at hand
132   that weren't there the night before.

Then came payments to poets
    by the Ó Eochaid who never shunned battle;
their costly verse did little damage,
136   though their rewards were more than was due.

I sought my leave of Maguire
    along with the other scholars,
parting from the bright, lofty fort –
140   alas that permission was granted!

As I turned to go, he said to me,
    tears coursing down his noble cheek,
that though I might be far away,
144   that would not cause our bond to break.

I remember the day I took my leave
    of the palace and all its retainers;
so heavy a pall lay upon them all
148   that none saw the grief of the others.

I'm the worse for the loss of the household;
    a pity my own time isn't here
rather than long life after them;
152   I fear that I shall long endure.

I never heard of a household so good
    as those in that fort, God bless them!
under any of those sprung from Colla –
156   and so every chief poet will claim.

None would leave, of his own free will,
    the bright plain of the hero's haven;
since it lured men from every quarter,
160   how sad, seeing Enniskillen.

GORMLAITH'S LAMENTS

Gormlaith, or Gormfhlaith, was the daughter of the high king Flann Sinna. She was married to three kings, the first of whom was Cormac mac Cuilennáin, king/bishop of Cashel and author of the *Sanas* or 'glossary' (see the introductory note to "The Spirit of Poetry"). Cormac was killed in the battle of Belach Mugna (Balagh Moon) in 908. There is an excellent poem, translated by Frank O'Connor (1989) in which the heads of three poets, brothers, lament his death and the fact that they cannot sing to him at the planned victory feast as they had intended to do. Gormlaith was next married to Cearbhall (Carroll) mac Muirecáin, king of Leinster, who died a year after Cormac. There is another fine poem addressed to the sword of this Cearbhall by the poet Dallán mac Móre (translated by O'Connor 1989). Cearbhall did not treat Gormlaith very well, and there is an as yet untranslated anecdote in the Book of Leinster that tells how Gormlaith left Cearbhall and then returned with her father to seek revenge on him for the shame he had caused her. The last of her husbands was Níall Glúndubh, king of Dublin, who was killed by the Norse in 919. She had a son by Níall, Donal, whose death she laments in poem VI. The entry concerning Gormlaith in the Annals of Clonmacnoise (original is lost, but the work was translated to English in 1627) is often quoted or referred to, and we present it again here:

> Neale Glunduffe was king three years and was married to the lady Gormphley, daughter to King Flann, who was a very faire, vertuous, and learned damozell, was first married to Cormack mc o'Cuillennann king of Mounster, secondly to king Neale,by whom she had issue a sonn called prince Donnell who was drowned, upon whse death she made many pittifull and learned dittyes in Irish, and lastly shee was married to Kervell mc Moregan king of Leinster, after all which royall marriages she begged from doore to doore, forsaken of all her friends and allies, and glad to be relieved by her inferiours.

The order of her marriages is incorrectly stated in this account, but it is consistent with the evidence of the poems (see last stanza of poem VII).

Serc Gormlaithe do Níall 'the love of Gormlaith for Níall' is one of the titles listed in the "A" list of tales (in the Book of Leinster) that poets were supposed to know; it has not survived. There are two other *serca* or 'love

stories,' one of which is *serc Caillige Berre do Fhothud Chanand* 'the love of
the *caillech* ('old woman' or 'nun') of Beare for Fothad Canann.' That tale has
not survived either, but there is extant a well-known poem, much anthologized,
usually called "The lament of the Old Woman of Beare." Thematically, it bears
a strong resemblance to the Gormlaith poems. In the poem, the *caillech* claims
to have had many lovers among the kings of Ireland, but now she is old,
decrepit, cold, in tattered clothes, and left alone. (There is no mention of Fothad
Canann in the poem; he is a figure presented elsewhere in the early literature as
a fenian chieftain and rival of Finn mac Cumhaill; see Nagy 1997, p. 299ff.)
According to its most recent editor (Ó hAodha 1989), "The Lament" was
composed ca. 900.

The date of the Gormlaith laments is unknown. Two of them appear in
the sixteenth-century Book of the Dean of Lismore, and Bergin (in Greene
1970) thought that in their original form they might well go back two or three
centuries before that. But he was unwilling to date them to Gormlaith's own
time because of serious anachronisms in the content and on linguistic grounds.
Still, the poems would indeed appear to belong to a *serc* or 'love story,' a prose
tale about Gormlaith, her loves, and her sad fate. Whatever of the changes to
the content and language through many tellings and reworkings of the poems,
they remain markedly similar in tone and circumstance to the lament of the hag,
or old woman, of Beare, with whom she is linked in the Book of Leinster tale
lists. The translation and numbering is based on the edition of Greene 1970.

Meter: Many of the lines do not conform to the meters as described here. That
may be due to the state of the manuscript or to the more 'popular' nature of the
poetry. The term *óglóchas* is applied to poems composed in loose imitation of
the *dán díreach* or 'strict' meters described here. Poems I, III, VI, VIII and X
are *rannaigheacht mhór,* 7 syllable lines ending in a monosyllable, with lines 2
and 4 rhyming; there is requisite internal rhyme and alliteration. Poems IV and
V are *rannaigheacht bheag,* like *rannaigheacht mhór* except that the final word
in each line is disyllabic. Poems II, VII, IX and XI are *deibhidhe*; for details,
see introductory note to "A Vision of Emain Macha."

Bibliography: Greene 1970, pp. 202-15; Knott 1966; Mac Cana 1980; Nagy
1997; Ó hAodha 1989

Gormlaith's Laments

I   *Dubhach sin, a dhúin na ríogh,*
      Ní hiongnadh dhuit do dhíth Néill;
    Dob annamh leat orchra ort;
      Dubhach sibh anocht dá éis.
    How sad you look, royal fort!
      No wonder, Níall is gone;
    Never decay on you before –
      But tonight, after him, you groan.

    Though tonight you seem so bleak,
      It was you where poets thronged;
    In the days of Níall Noigíallach
      You never stood alone.

    Every kingdom save God's alone,
      All, true, will soon depart;
    The world's no place of comfort –
      How sad you look, royal fort!

II   *Gáir bháinnsi san tigh si amuigh,*
    Gí bé dá ttabhair meanmuin,
    Atá neach dá ttabhair brón,
    Acc éisdeacht ris gach roghlór.
        A wedding feast in the house there,
    Though it brings joy to one,
    To another it brings but pain,
    Hearing such jubilation.

    Though the woman there rejoices
    As her marriage bonds are set,
    Woe to her whom the world wrongs;
    Who knows the fate I got?

    You deserve my accusation,
    O King of life everlasting,
    Why did you kill Hugh's son?

He was no ill-mannered buffoon!

Were he to be held for ransom,
He'd be worth gold and horses;
And if men should redeem him,
They'd just be returning favors.

Great were the favors I received,
'Tis I should redeem Ó Néill:
He gave me twelve score beeves,
Booty from one day's kill.

The feather-bed where Níall slept,
Where men of Oriel assembled,
I grieve that it sits untouched,
A bed without the beloved.

I can't bear to look on his shroud –
On him who was comely and good,
Gone my fine and short-lived Níall,
Dead now and lying in Kells.

Níall said a word as he rode
Westwards from Armagh:
'Whichever of us goes first,
Gormlaith, whither the path?'

'I would give you fair counsel,
O king of Eoghan's people,
Bring us to Ailech's cold soil,
And lay us in a single grave.'

'Gormlaith my love, were it you
Who were first to see earth,
No woman would I ever woo,
Only weep, and never know mirth.'

III   Kells! I grieve to see you,
      For I was wife to that Ó Néill;
    The beauty of Kells has faded,
      Since Níall now is dead.

    Cormac and Carroll were mine –
      I was their spouse – lucky them!
    But dearer than either was Níall;
      I grieve to see you, Kells.

    I don't see lovely Níall Glundubh,
      Don't see my man or my king;
    Only his land like a billowing wave;
      Kells! I grieve to see you.

    Neither Ailech nor Colt do I see,
      Bereft of a king who gave freely,
    For I am gone from Tara of Brega;
      Kells! I grieve to see you.

    When I reflect on what Níall would bestow,
      There by my side on the mound,
    And how he would scatter his gold,
      Kells! I grieve to see you.

    The grave of Níall, son of Hugh Finn,
      That's the place I'll go,
    And lie down beside him soon;
      Kells! I grieve to see you.

    And I, beloved daughter of Flann,
      Though I was wise, I was rash,
    And I am gone from Tara's land;
      Kells! I grieve to see you.

IV   *Folamh anocht Dún Chearma,*
      Do ráith Teamhra as cúis bháoghail;

361

Méad úaisgneasa an dúin dreachghlain,
  As beart do bheartaibh an tsáoghail.
Dún Cearmna's deserted tonight,
  Tara's walls have cause to fear:
How lonely lies the gleaming site,
  A trick the world plays.

Gentle kings who freely gave
  And feared no counter measures;
I mourn for them and grieve;
  Nothing now but loneliness.

They'll soon be utterly alone,
  Tuathal's walls and Tara's;
Isn't it warning enough for them?
  Deserted tonight is Dún Cearmna.

V   You, rag! look at all these patches!
       And how could it be other,
     for it's not the hands of a seamstress
       That artfully 'broidered you.

There was a time I was in Tara,
  With Níall on Emain's Green;
He strove to do me honor
  And together we shared his wine.

There was a time I was in Limerick,
  With Níall, beloved of Ailech;
Lovely was my colorful dress
  Among the princes of the west.

Spirited and swift, the family of Níall,
  Fond of watching horses run;
I drank wine beside them all,
  In sips from cups of horn.

A company of seven score women

Attending every assembly,
'Twas for us the riding was done
On the green of comely Níall.

I'm a woman of Meath and Leinster,
Yet they're not dearest to me;
Dearer by far is Ulster –
And I swear it on my honor.

Brambles tear at me often,
Probing my shift of rags;
To me the thorn is no friend,
And the briar a cruel felon.

VI   I weep, racked with pain,
I weep, parted from my lover;
Tonight, I might as well be slain,
For Ó Néill's son's gone under.

I weep without Dearbháil's son,
I weep for what I've become;
More generous than noble Guaire,
After him, Eire's an empty byre.

I weep, for Banba's king is gone;
Alive, his figure flourished;
But now, since he has perished,
My only song is a wail or groan.

                               I weep, I weep.

VII   Like a hound that sits untested,
And cannot prove itself,
So someone who's dear to no one,
'Tis she who soon comes to grief.

If I said the raven was black,
Leinster would say it was white;
They would also say that my walk,

363

Gimpy or true, was not right.

Out here, the back of my neck is bare;
The shoulder naked for one with no kin,
Without family, a hollow stare,
A tale whose truth I know well.

Bitterly I lament my existence,
Looking for a better deal;
But not for king nor prince
Are two nights one night's equal.

As a woman on her wedding-day
Finds but one man well-suited,
And no man ever found, he'd say,
But one woman worthy to mate,

So worthy of me was Ó Néill's son,
Beloved, gentle, and generous king,
worth comparing, one to one,
With the daughter of Erin's high-king.

It's long since then that I've been
In the house of rash mac Muirecáin;
My resolve is weak, I languish,
I can't remain in this prison!

VIII   Away with you, monk!
     Move from Níall's side;
You shovel the earth too thick
    On him with whom I'd lie.

You've been at it a good while,
    Throwing earth on noble Níall;
How long he's lain in that box,
    And the dirt not yet over the top

Son of Hugh, a man to feast and carouse,

I grieve that he's under the cross;
Lay the stone on his bed now,
  And then, monk, away with you.

Of Uisnech's famous offspring,
  Deirdre was as I am now –
The heart in her breast bursting;
  Monk, away with you.

And I, Gormlaith, make verses,
  Flann of Dún Rois's dear daughter,
I wish it were on me the stone rested;
  Away with you monk, forever!

IX   Oh, God! my sighs this night so heavy,
Heavier tonight than yesterday,
For Níall's radiant son I grieve,
Gladly I'd go alive into clay.

My kin grow generally fewer;
As I have lost Níall for keeps
Nothing reaches my keen, sharp ear
That brings a smile to my lips.

Dead is my father, and my mother;
My two brothers gone,
And my noble, lauded fosterfather,
As well as his two sons.

Dead, alas! stately Dub Chablaigh,
We drank together from a golden bowl,
He'd bring me meals with honey;
Dub Chablaigh, so beautiful.

Dead the son of the king of Innse Gall,
The son of Amlaíb of Arann;
Upon my knee I used to dandle
Him, as if he were my own dear son.

Though those have all now departed
From a world of conquest and doom,
Harder for me is Domhnall, my beloved,
Below, lying within his tomb.

Though keen every sorrow and pain
That comes to man here below,
The one that will remain
Is the one you've given birth to.

Had it been to the men of Meath
That I sent my beloved bairn,
That noble race of Colmán
Had provided his protection.

Alas! who trusts to a foolish woman
The protection of her tender offspring;
One needs for a life's protection,
An heir or son to a king.

Alas that the happy, sweet-voiced lad
Was left to the Uí Fíachrach –
To a land with too much water
And to men of shame and censure.

Domhnall son of fair Níall,
Son of Hugh Finnliath of Foyle;
Son of Níall Caill – sturdy as wood,
Son of distinguished Hugh Oirdnide.

Son of Níall Frasach of Ráth Mór,
Who showered poets with honor;
Son of Feargal, ruler of Femen,
Son of the honorable Mael Dúin.

Son of Mael Fithrich son of Hugh,
Son of Domhnall, comely and true,

Son of great Muircertach of the plain,
Son of Muiredach son of Eoghan.

Son of Níall Nóigiallach the provident,
Son of Eochu Mugmedon;
Alpin of Scotland's daughter,
She was Domhnall's grandmother.

That's the line of my son, my own,
He who brings darkess to the sun;
Lovely white from head to toe,
Never have I known greater woe.

X I've loved three times thirty and more,
    I've loved nine times nine;
  Though I've loved men by the score,
    It's not numbers a woman will mind.

I left them all for Níall,
  For I wanted to be at his call;
Why wouldn't I lose everyone
  To be with faultless Ó Néill's son?

Though Conn's Half breeds heroes aplenty,
  There's nothing Níall couldn't contain;
Given the misfortune that's come to me,
  'Twere better I'd married a poor swain.

Colorful cloaks had he, and golden rings,
  Fine, triumphant horses;
But time has taken all those things,
  All of it now in tatters.

All I have upon my back
  Is a pale smock and a dark cloak;
In Kells of the hundred kings,
  No one cares that I lack for things.

One Sunday there, at chapel,
  I and my prince by the bell,
At Kells, at the great cross,
  Decreeing Conn's Half's taxes,

My king spoke and said to me,
  Nudging me forward gently ,
'Go to the chapel with everyone,
  And join in the worship of God's Son.'

In truth, we did go in,
  Twelve score young maidens;
Mór went first – as was her due,
  And I gave her the bow from my pretty shoe.

I gave her a ball with a golden belt,
  Abbot Colum's fair wife,
And two score cows from the field
  On the chapel's north side.

I gave her a lovely, blue hood,
  A psalter-shrine made of horn,
And thirty ounces of gold to boot;
  Mór of Mag Sainb, hers to own.

Tonight she gave me in return –
  A fruitless friendship I scorn –
Two tithes of tough oats
  Two eggs straight from the nest.

By the King who gave light to the sun,
  If Níall Glúndubh had lived,
Abbot's wife of Tulach Léis,
  You could keep your eggs.

From Mór I received a comb,
  A cap and bits of homespun;
From me she got a red stallion,

And a bowl with golden apples.

Woe to one who overspends,
    And woe to the stingy, Mór;
I revelled in rewarding poets,
    Until the Lord lifted my treasure.

The man who'd give horses for poetry,
    May God repay him in eternity;
Though I speak so highly of Níall,
    The poets speak higher still.

XI   It's time I quit keening Hugh's son,
            Níall, of the fine swift stallions;
        God! it's sad where I've been left,
            Hanging between life and death.

        A year and thirty to the day,
            Since that good king passed away;
        I could weep forever and ever –
            Each night buckets of tears.

        Last night, when prayers were over,
            Níall himself appeared to me:
        'End your mourning fair Gormlaith,
            The king of angels grows weary.'

        I spoke and gave Níall answer,
            With a fury I had not felt ever,
        'Why should I anger Heaven's King
            And I here, ever atoning!'

        'Don't you know, dearest Gormlaith,
            That the one who made Heaven was He?
        That He it was made humankind,
            And so is loath to hear weeping?'

        Níall, illustrious son of Hugh,

Turned his back on me, through;
I screamed to see him turn,
    And rushed to cling to him.

I hit a post of elegant yew –
    There beside my couch it grew;
And struck my breast against it hard;
    Unyielding, it crushed my heart.

So now I ask the gift of death
    From the Son of God who made us;
And, wherever I find Níall,
    That he and I together travel.

Warlike Carroll endowed me well:
    Hundreds of cows and horses galore;
Cormac, however, and not without trouble,
    Gave me twice the gift of Carroll.

And why refuse from my king
    The wealth I got – all those things?
Yet all of that and thrice again
    I had from Níall in a month alone.
                    It's time I quit keening Hugh's son.

BIBLIOGRAPHY

Bibliography

Andrews, Rhian M. 1996a. Ed., with Catherine McKenna. "Gwaith Bleddyn Fardd." In *Gwaith Bleddyn Fardd a Beirdd Eraill Ail Hanner y Drydedd Ganrif ar Ddeg*, ed. Rhian M. Andrews et al., pp. 521-664. Cardiff: University of Wales Press.
1996b. Ed., with Catherine McKenna. "Gwaith Gruffudd ab yr Ynad Coch." In *Gwaith Bleddyn Fardd a Beirdd Eraill Ail Hanner y Drydedd Ganrif ar Ddeg*, ed. Rhian M. Andrews et al., pp. 409-520. Cardiff: University of Wales Press.

Bell, H. I. 1942. Trans. *Fifty Poems of Dafydd ap Gwilym*. London.

Best, R. I. Et al. 1954-83. Edd. *The Book of Leinster, formerly Lebor na Núachongbála*. 6 vols. Dublin: Institute for Advanced Studies.

Bloomfield, Morton and Charles Dunn. 1989. *The Role of the Poet in Early Societies*. Woodbridge: Boydell and Brewer.

Bowen, Charles. 1975-76. "A Historical Inventory of the *Dindshenchas*." *Studia Celtica* 10/11:113-37.

Bowen, D. J. 1966-67. "Agweddau ar Ganu's Bedwaredd Ganrif ar Ddeg a'r Bymthegfed." *Llên Cymru* 9:46-73.

Bramley, Kathleen. 1985-86. "Canu Hywel ab Owain Gwynedd." *Studia Celtica* 20/21:167-91.
1994. "Gwaith Hywel ab Owain Gwynedd." In *Gwaith Llywelyn Fardd I ac Eraill o Feirdd y Ddeuddegfed Ganrif*, ed. Kathleen Bramley et al., pp. 103-92. Cardiff: University of Wales Press.

Breatnach, Liam. 1981. "The Caldron of Poesy." *Ériu* 32:45-93.

Bromwich, Rachel. 1978. Ed. and trans. *Trioedd Ynys Prydein: The Welsh Triads*. 2nd ed. Cardiff: University of Wales Press.
1979. "Dafydd ap Gwilym." In *A Guide to Welsh Literature Vol. 2*, ed. A. O. H. Jarman and Gwilym Rees Hughes, pp. 112-43.

1980. Ed. *The Beginnings of Welsh Poetry: Studies by Sir Ifor Williams*. Cardiff: University of Wales Press.
1982. Ed. and trans. *Dafydd ap Gwilym: Poems*. Llandysul: Gomer Press.
1986. *Aspects of the Poetry of Dafydd ap Gwilym*. Cardiff: University of Wales Press.

Byrne, Francis John. 1973. *Irish Kings and High-Kings*. London: B. T. Batsford Ltd.

Calin, William. 1994. *The French Tradition and the Literature of Medieval England*. Toronto: University of Toronto Press.

Carney, James. 1955. *Studies in Irish Literature and History*. Dublin: Institute for Advanced Studies.
1967. *The Irish Bardic Poet: A Study in the Relationship of Poet and Patron*. Dublin: Dolmen Press.

Chadwick, Nora. 1935. "Imbas Forosnai." *Scottish Gaelic Studies* 4:97-135.

Charles-Edwards, T. M. 1978. "The Authenticity of the *Gododdin*: An Historian's View.". In *Astudiaethau ar yr Hengerdd*, ed. Rachel Bromwich and R. Brinley Jones, pp. 44-71. Cardiff: University of Wales Press.

Chotzen, Th. M. 1927. *Recherches sur la poesie de Dafydd ap Gwilym*. Amsterdam.

Clancy, Joseph H. 1965. Trans. *Medieval Welsh Lyrics*. New York: St. Martin's Press.
1970. Trans. *The Earliest Welsh Poetry*. New York: St. Martin's Press.

Connellan, Owen. 1860. Ed. and trans. "*Imtheacht na Tromdhaimhe* or: The Proceedings of the Great Bardic Institution." *Transactions of the Ossianic Society* 5:1-129.

Conran, Tony. 1986. Trans. *Welsh Verse*. Bridgend: Poetry Wales Press.

Davies, Morgan T. 1995a. "Dafydd ap Gwilym and the Friars: The Poetics of Mendicancy." *Studia Celtica* 29:237-56.
    1995b. "'Aed i'r coed i dorri cof': Dafydd ap Gwilym and the Metaphorics of Carpentry." *Cambrian Medieval Celtic Studies* 30:67-85.

Dimock, James F. 1868. Ed., *Descriptio Kambriae*. (Rolls Series). London.

Dunn, Charles W. Ed., with Introduction. *The Romance of the Rose by Guillaume de Lorris and Jean de Meun, Translated into English Verse by Harold W. Robbins*. New York: E. P. Dutton.

Edwards, H. J. 1968. Ed. and trans. *Caesar: De Bello Gallico*. Harvard University Press.

Edwards, Huw M. 1996. *Dafydd ap Gwilym: Influences and Analogues*. Oxford: Clarendon Press.

Eoyang, Eugene Chen. 1993. *The Transparent Eye*. Honolulu.

Evans, D. Ellis. 1978. "Rhagarweiniad I Astudiaeth o Fydryddiaeth Y Gododdin." In *Astudiaethau ar yr Hengerdd*, ed. Rachel Bromwich and R. Brinley Jones, pp. 89-122. Cardiff: University of Wales Press.

Flower, Robin. 1947. *The Irish Tradition*. Oxford: Clarendon Press.

Ford, Patrick K. 1974a. "The Well of Nechtan and 'La Gloire Lumineuse.'" In *Myth in Indo-European Antiquity*, ed. Gerald James Larson, pp. 67-74. Berkeley: University of California Press.
    1974b. *The Poetry of Llywarch Hen*. Berkeley: University of California Press.

1975. "A Fragment of the Hanes Taliesin by Llywelyn Sion." *Études Celtiques* 14:451-60.

1976. "The Death of Merlin in the Chronicle of Elis Gruffudd." *Viator* 7:379-90.

1977. *The Mabinogi and Other Medieval Welsh Tales*. Berkeley: University of California Press.

1979. "Meredith Lloyd, Dr. Davies, and the *Hanes Taliesin*." *National Library of Wales Journal* 21:27-37.

1987. "The Death of Aneirin." *Bulletin of the Board of Celtic Studies* 34:41-50.

1990. "The Blind, The Dumb, and The Ugly." *Cambridge Medieval Celtic Studies* 19:27-40.

1992a. With J. E. C. Williams. *The Irish Literary Tradition*. Belmont, MA: Ford & Bailie.

1992b. Ed. *Ystoria Taliesin*. Board of Celtic Studies. Cardiff: University of Wales Press.

1996a. "Re-Reading Dafydd ap Gwilym." In *A Celtic Florilegium: Studies in Memory of Brendan O Hehir*, ed. Kathryn a. Klar et al., pp. 20-31. Lawrence, MA: Celtic Studies Publications.

1996b. "Medieval Irish Manuscript Culture." In *Field Work: Sites in Literary and Cultural Studies*, ed. Marjorie Garber et al., pp. 164-68. New York: Routledge.

Frank, Roberta. 1981. "Snorri and the Mead of Poetry." In *Speculum Norroenum: Norse Studies in Memory of Gabriel Turville-Petre*, ed. Ursula Dronke et al., pp. 155-70. Odense: Odense University Press.

Fulton, Helen. 1991. "Medieval Welsh Poems to Nuns." *Cambrian Medieval Celtic Studies* 21:87-112.
1996. Ed. and trans. *Selections from the Dafydd ap Gwilym Apocrypha*. Llandysul: Gomer Press.

Gardner, Helen. 1957. *The Metaphysical Poets*. Harmondsworth: Penguin.

Gray, Elizabeth. 1982. *Cath Maige Tuired: The Second Battle of Mag Tuired*. London: Irish Texts Society 52.

Greene, David. 1970. Ed, with Fergus Kelly. *Irish Bardic Poetry: Texts and Translations, Together with an Introductory Lecture by Osborn Bergin.* Dublin: Institute for Advanced Studies.
    1972. Ed. and trans. *Duanaire Mhéig Uidhir: The Poembook of Cú Chonnacht Mág Uidhir, Lord of Fermanagh 1566-1589.* Dublin: Institute for Advanced Studies.

Gresham, Colin. 1942. "The Book of Aneirin." *Antiquity* 16:237-57.

Gruffydd, Geraint. 1969. "Cyntefin Ceinaf Amser o Lyfr Du Caerfyrddin." *Ysgrifau Beirniadol* 4:12-26.
    1978. "Sylwadau ar Gywydd 'Offeren y Llwyn.'" *Ysgrifau Beirniadol* 10:181-89.
    1979. "Sylwadau ar Gywydd 'Yr Adfail' gan Ddafydd ap Gwilym." *Ysgrifau Beirniadol* 11:109-15.
    1986. In *1282: Casgliad o Ddogfennau/A Collection of Documents*, ed. Rhidian Griffiths, p. 27. Aberystwyth.

Gulick, C. B. 1927. Ed. and trans. *Athenaeus: The Deipnosophists.* Cambridge: Harvard University Press.

Gwynn, Edward. 1913. *The Metrical Dindshenchas*, pt. III. Dublin: Royal Irish Academy. Rpt. Dublin: Institute for Advanced Studies, 1991.

Hamp, Eric P. 1978. "Gwion and Fer Fí." *Ériu* 29:152-53.

Haycock, Marged. 1983-84. "'Preiddeu Annwn' and the Figure of Taliesin." *Studia Celtica* 18/19:52-78.
    1988. "Metrical Models for the Poems in the Book of Taliesin." In Brynley F. Roberts, ed., *Early Welsh Poetry*. Aberystwyth: National Library of Wales.

Henry, P. L. 1979-80. "The Caldron of Poesy." *Studia Celtica* 14/15:114-28.

Higley, S. L. 1988. "Forcing a Gap: the Stylistics of 'Amputation' in *Marwnad Llywelyn* by Gruffudd ab yr Ynad Coch." *Viator* 19:247-72.

Huws, Daniel. 1989. *Llyfr Aneirin: A Facsimile*. South Glamorgan County Council and Aberystwyth: National Library of Wales.

Jackson, Kenneth H. 1935. *Studies in Early Celtic Nature Poetry*. Cambridge: University Press.
    1969. Trans. *The Gododdin: The Oldest Scottish Poem*. Edinburgh: University Press.
    1990. Ed. *Aislinge Meic Con Glinne*. Dublin: School of Celtic Studies.

Jarman, A. O. H. 1967. "The Heroic Ideal in Early Welsh Poetry." In *Beiträge zur Indogermanistik und Keltologie: Julius Pokorny zum 80. Geburtstag gewidmet*, ed. Wolfgang Meid. Innsbruck.
    1981. *The Cynfeirdd: Early Welsh Poets and Poetry*. Cardiff: University of Wales Press.
    1982. Ed. *Llyfr Du Caerfyrddin: gyda Rhagymadrodd, Nodiadau Testunol a Geirfa*. Cardiff: University of Wales Press.
    1988. Ed. and trans. *Aneirin: Y Gododdin: Britain's Oldest Heroic Poem*. Llandysul: Gomer Press.
    1992a. "Taliesin." In *A Guide to Welsh Literature Vol 1*, ed. A. O. H. Jarman and Gwilym Rees Hughes, pp. 51-67. Rev. ed. Cardiff: University of Wales Press.
    1992b. "Aneirin: The Gododdin." In *A Guide to Welsh Literature Vol 1*, pp. 68-80. Rev. ed. Cardiff: University of Wales Press.
    1992c. "Saga Poetry – The Cycle of Llywarch Hen." *In A Guide to Welsh Literature Vol 1*, pp. 81-97. Rev. ed. Cardiff: University of Wales Press.

Johnston, David. 1983. "The Serenade and the Image of the House in the Poems of Dafydd ap Gwilym." *Cambridge Medieval Celtic Studies* 5:1-20.

Jones, Elin M. 1991. Ed., with Nerys Ann Jones. *Gwaith Llywarch ap Llywelyn: 'Prydydd y Moch'* Cardiff: University of Wales Press.

Jones, H. L. 1939. Ed. and trans. *The Geography of Strabo*.
Cambridge: Harvard University Press.

Jones, Nerys Ann. 1992. "Prydydd y Moch: Dwy Gerdd 'Wahanol'."
Ysgrifau Beirniadol 18:55-72.

Jones, T. Gwynn. 1915. *Rhieingerddi'r Gogynfeirdd*. Dinbych, North
Wales.

Joynt, Maud. 1941. Ed. *Tromdámh Guaire*. Dublin: Institute for
Advanced Studies.

Kelly, Fergus. 1988. *A Guide to Early Irish Law*. Dublin: Institute for
Advanced Studies.

Knott, Eleanor. 1922. Ed. and trans. *The Bardic Poems of Tadhg Dall
Ó hUiginn (1550-1591)*. 2 vols. London: Irish Texts Society 22
(1922), 23 (1926).
    1960. *Irish Classical Poetry, Commonly Called Bardic Poetry*.
    Dublin: At the Sign of the Three Candles.
    1966. Ed. *Irish Syllabic Poetry: 1200-1600*. Dublin: Institute for
    Advanced Studies.

Koch, John T. 1997. Ed. and trans. *The Gododdin of Aneirin: Text and
Context from Dark-Age North Britain*. Andover, MA: Celtic
Studies Publications; Cardiff: University of Wales Press.

Lefevere, Andre. 1975. *Translating Poetry*. (= Approaches to
Translation Studies, Nr. 3). Amsterdam.

Lewis, Ceri. 1992. "The Court Poets: Their Function, Status, and
Craft." ." *In A Guide to Welsh Literature Vol 1*, ed. A. O. H.
Jarman and Gwilym Rees Hughes, pp. 123-56. Rev. ed. Cardiff:
University of Wales Press.

Lewis, Henry et al. 1937. *Cywyddau Iolo Goch ac Eraill*. Rev. ed.
Cardiff: University of Wales Press.

Lloyd, D. Myrddin. 1932. "Barddoniaeth Cynddelw Brydydd Mawr."
Y Llenor 11, no. 3:172-87.
1990. "The Poets of the Princes." In *A Guide to Welsh Literature Vol
1*, pp. 157-88. Rev. ed. Cardiff: University of Wales Press.

Loomis, Richard Morgan. 1982. Trans. *Dafydd ap Gwilym: The
Poems*. Binghamton, NY: Center for Medieval and Early
Renaissance Studies.
1992. Trans., with Dafydd Johnston. *Medieval Welsh Poems*.
Binghamton, N.Y.

Loth, Joseph. 1907. "Le Surnom de *Prydydd y Moch*." *Zeitschrift für
Celtische Philologie* 5:177.

Mac Cana, Proinsias. 1980. *The Learned Tales of Medieval Ireland*.
Dublin: Institute for Advanced Studies.
1988. "The Poet as Spouse of His Patron." *Ériu* 39:79-85.

McGahern, John. 1993. *The Collected Stories*. New York: Alfred A.
Knopf.

MacNeill, Eoin. 1908. Ed. and trans. *Duainaire Finn: The Book of the
Lays of Fionn 1*. London: Irish Texts Society 7.

Matonis, A. T. E. 1979-80. "The Rhetorical Patterns in *Marwnad
Llywelyn ap Gruffudd* by Gruffudd ab yr Ynad Coch." *Studia
Celtica* 14/15:188-93.
1981. "Later Medieval Poetics and some Welsh Bardic Debates."
Studia Celtica 29:635-65.

Meroney, Howard. 1949-50. "Studies in Early Irish Satire." *Journal of
Celtic Studies* 1:199-226.

Meyer, Kuno. 1882. Ed. "Macgnimartha Find." *Revue Celtique* 5:195-
204.
1892. Ed. and trans. *Aislinge Meic Conglinne: The Vision of
MacConglinne*. London.

1896. Ed. and trans. "The Death of Finn mac Cumaill." *Zeitschrift für Celtische Philologie* 1:462-65.

1901. Ed. and trans. *King and Hermit: A Colloquy Between King Guaire and His Brother Marbán.* London.

1904. Trans. "The Boyish Exploits of Finn." *Ériu* 1:180-90.

1910. Ed. and trans. *Fianaigecht.* School of Celtic Studies: Dublin Institute for Advanced Studies, 1993.

1912. Ed. *Sanas Cormaic: An Old Irish Glossary. Anecdota from Irish Manuscripts* IV. Halle.

Morris-Jones, John. 1918. *Taliesin* (= *Y Cymmrodor* 18). London.

Murphy, Gerard. 1933. Ed. and trans. *Duanaire Finn: The Book of the Lays of Fionn 2.* London: Irish Texts Society 28.

1953. *Duanaire Finn: The Book of the Lays of Fionn 3* [introduction and notes to vols. 1 and 2.]. London: Irish Texts Society 43.

1955. Ed. and trans. "Finn's Poem on May-Day." *Ériu* 17:86-99.

1961. *Early Irish Metrics.* Dublin: Royal Irish Academy.

1971. *The Ossianic Lore and Romantic Tales of Medieval Ireland* [rev. by Brian Ó Cuív]. Cork.

1943. "A Vision Concerning Rolf MacMahon: Giolla Brighde Mac Con Midhe .cc." *Éigse* 4:79-111.

Nagy, Gregory. 1990. *Greek Mythology and Poetics.* Ithaca: Cornell University Press.

Nagy, Joseph Falaky. 1985. *The Wisdom of the Outlaw: the Boyhood Deeds of Finn in Gaelic Narrative Tradition.* Berkeley and Los Angeles: University of California Press.

1997. *Conversing with Angels and Ancients: Literary Myths of Medieval Ireland.* Ithaca: Cornell University Press.

Ó Cathasaigh, Tomás. 1986. "Curse and Satire." *Éigse* 21:10-15.

1989. "The Eponym of Cnogba." *Éigse* 23:27-38.

Ó Coileáin, Seán. 1977. "The Making of *Tromdám Guaire.*" *Ériu* 28:32-67.

Ó Concheanainn, Tomas. 1981-2. "Dinnshenchas Erenn." *Journal of Celtic Studies* 3:88-131.
  1982. "A Pious Redactor of Dinnshenchas Erenn." *Ériu* 33:85-98.

O'Connor, Frank. 1989. *Kings, Lords, & Commons: An Anthology from the Irish*. Van Nuys, CA: Ford & Bailie.

O Daly, Máirín. 1965. "The Metrical Dindshenchas." In *Early Irish Poetry*, ed. James Carney, pp. 59-72. Cork.

O'Grady, Standish Hayes. 1892. Ed. and trans. "The Boramha." In *Silva Gadelica*. 2 vols. London: Williams and Norgate.

Ó hAodha, Donncha. 1989. Ed. and trans. "The Lament of the Old Woman of Beare." In *Sages, Saints, and Storytellers: Celtic Studies in Honour of Professor James Carney*, ed. Donnchadh Ó Corráin et al., pp. 308-31. Maynooth Monographs 2. Maynooth: An Sagart.

O'Kelleher, A. 1918. Ed. and trans., with Gertrude Schoepperle. *Betha Colaim Chille: Life of Columcille*. Rpt. 1994. Dublin: Institute for Advanced Studies.

Oldfather, C. H. 1939. Ed. and trans. *Diodorus of Sicily*. Cambridge: Harvard University Press.

Ong, Walter. 1982. *Orality and Literacy: The Technologizing of the Word*. London: Routledge.

Owen, Morfydd E. 1978. "Hwn yw e Gododin. Aneirin ae Cant." In *Astudiaethau ar yr Hengerdd*, ed. Rachel Bromwich and R. Brinley Jones, pp. 123-50. Cardiff: University of Wales Press.

O'Rahilly, Thomas F. 1946. *Early Irish History and Mythology*. Dublin: Institute for Advanced Studies.

Ó Riain, Pádraig. 1978. Ed. *Cath Almaine*. Dublin: Institute for Advanced Studies.

Parry, Thomas. 1944. "Pethau nas Cyhoeddwyd 5: Hanes Llywelyn ap Iorwerth a Chynwrig Goch o Drefriw: Dau Fersion o Chwedl Werin." *National Library of Wales Journal* 3:151-57.

1952. Ed. *Gwaith Dafydd ap Gwilym*. Cardiff: University of Wales Press.

1970. *A History of Welsh Literature*. Trans. H. I. Bell. Oxford: Clarendon Press.

Rees, Alwyn and Brinley Rees. 1961. *Celtic Heritage*. London: Thames and Hudson.

Richards, Melville. 1948. Ed. *Breudwyt Ronabwy*. Cardiff: University of Wales Press.

Roberts, Brynley F. 1988. *Early Welsh Poetry: Studies in the Book of Aneirin*. Aberystwyth: National Library of Wales.

Roberts, Tomos. 1982. *Marwnadau Llywelyn ap Gruffudd*. Gwasg y Wern, 1982

Robinson, F. N. 1912. "Satirists and Enchanters in Early IrishLiterature." In *Studies in the History of Religions*, ed. David Gordon Lyon and George Foote Moore, pp. 95-130. New York.

Ross, Anne. 1967. *Pagan Celtic Britain: Studies in Iconography and Tradition*. London: Routledge and Kegan Paul.

Rowland, Jenny. 1990. *Early Welsh Saga Poetry: A Study and Edition of the Englynion*. Cambridge: University Press.

Rowlands, Eurys I. 1958. "Cywydd Dafydd ap Gwilym I Fis Mai." *Llên Cymru* 5:1-25.

1976. *Poems of the Cywyddwyr*. Dublin: Institute for Advanced Studies.

Rowlands, John. 1971. "Morfudd fel yr Haul." *Ysgrifau Beirniadol* 6:16-44.

Schmitt, Rudiger. 1967. *Dichtung und Dichtersprache in indogermanische Zeit.* Wiesbaden.

Scott, Robert D. 1930. *The Thumb of Knowledge in Legends of Finn, Sigurd, and Taliesin.* New York.

Simms, Katharine. 1989. "The Poet as Chieftain's Widow: Bardic Elegies." *In Sages, Saints, and Storytellers*, ed. Donnchadh Ó Corráin et al., pp. 400-11. Maynooth: An Sagart.

Sjöblom, Tom. 1994. "On the Threshold: The Sacredness of Borders in Early Irish Literature." *Ulidia: Proceedings of the First International Conference on the Ulster Cycle of Tales.* Belfast.

Slotkin, Edgar M. 1978-9. "Medieval Irish Scribes and Fixed Texts." *Éigse* 17:437-50.

Stephens, Meic. 1986. Ed. *The Oxford Companion to the Literature of Wales.* Oxford University Press.

Stokes, Whitley. 1887. Ed. and trans. "The Siege of Howth." *Revue Celtique* 8:48-63.
1892. Ed. and trans. "The Borama." *Revue Celtique* 13:32-124, 299.
1894. Ed. and trans. The Rennes Dindshenchas." *Revue Celtique* 15:273-336; 418-84.
1895. Ed. and trans. "The Rennes Dindshenchas." *Revue Celtique* 16:31-83; 134-67; 269-312.
1905. Ed. and trans. "The Colloquy of the Two Sages." *Revue Celtique* 26:4-64.

Thurneysen, Rudolph. 1918. Ed. and trans. (German). "Zu Irischen Texten I: Athirne von seiner Ungastlichkeit geheilt." *Zeitschrift für Celtische Philologie* 12:398-99.

Tymoczko, Maria. 1983. "'Cétamon': Vision in Early Irish Seasonal Poetry." *Éire-Ireland* 18:17-39.

1996. "A Poetry of Masks: The Poet's Persona in Early Celtic Poetry." In *A Celtic Florilegium: Studies in Memory of Brendan O Hehir*, pp. 187-209. Lawrence, MA: Celtic Studies Publications.

Watkins, Calvert. 1963. "Indo-European Metrics and Archaic Irish Verse." *Celtica* 6:194-249.

Williams, Gwyn. 1956. *The Burning Tree*. London.

Williams, J. E. C. 1968. *The Poems of Taliesin*. (English version of *Canu Taliesin*. Ed. Ifor Williams. Cardiff: University of Wales Press. 1960.) Dublin: Institute for Advanced Studies.
1970-71. "Beirdd y Tywysogion: Arolwg." *Llên Cymru* 11:3-94.
1971. "The Court Poet in Medieval Ireland." *Proceedings of the British Academy* 57:1-51.
1976. *The Poets of the Welsh Princes*. Cardiff: University of Wales Press.
1994. Ed., with Peredur I. Lynch. "Gwaith Meilyr Brydydd." In *Gwaith Meilyr Brydydd a'i Ddisgynyddion*, pp. 49-128. Cardiff: University of Wales Press.
1996. "The Celtic Bard." In *A Celtic Florilegium: Studies in Memory of Brendan O Hehir*, pp. 216-26. Lawrence, MA: Celtic Studies Publications.

Williams, Ifor. 1957. *Chwedl Taliesin*. Cardiff.
1961. *Canu Aneirin*. 2nd ed. Cardiff: University of Wales Press.
1980. (see Bromwich 1980)

Williams, N. J. A. 1980. Ed. and trans. *The Poems of Giolla Brighde Mac Con Midhe*. London: Irish Texts Society 51.

Wood, Juliette. 1982. "The Folklore Background of the Gwion Bach Section of *Hanes Taliesin*." *Bulletin of the Board of Celtic Studies* 29:621-34.
1983. "Virgil and Taliesin: the Concept of the Magician in Medieval Folklore." *Folklore* 94:91-104.